SPRINGER SERIES IN PHOTONICS 7

Dear MyCopy Customer,

This Springer book is a monochrome print version of the eBook to which your library gives you access via SpringerLink. It is available to you at a subsidized price since your library subscribes to at least one Springer eBook subject collection.

Please note that MyCopy books are only offered to library patrons with access to at least one Springer eBook subject collection. MyCopy books are strictly for individual use only.

You may cite this book by referencing the bibliographic data and/or the DOI (Digital Object Identifier) found in the front matter. This book is an exact but monochrome copy of the print version of the eBook on SpringerLink.

Springer-Verlag Berlin Heidelberg GmbH

http://www.springer.de/phys/

SPRINGER SERIES IN PHOTONICS

Series Editors: T. Kamiya   B. Monemar   H. Venghaus

The Springer Series in Photonics covers the entire field of photonics, including theory, experiment, and the technology of photonic devices. The books published in this series give a careful survey of the state-of-the-art in photonic science and technology for all the relevant classes of active and passive photonic components and materials. This series will appeal to researchers, engineers, and advanced students.

1 **Advanced Optoelectronic Devices**
By D. Dragoman and M. Dragoman

2 **Femtosecond Technology**
Editors: T. Kamiya, F. Saito, O. Wada, H. Yajima

3 **Integrated Silicon Optoelectronics**
By H. Zimmermann

4 **Fibre Optic Communication Devices**
Editors: N. Grote and H. Venghaus

5 **Nonclassical Light from Semiconductor Lasers and LEDs**
By J. Kim, S. Lathi, and Y. Yamamoto

6 **Vertical-Cavity Surface-Emitting Laser Devices**
By H. Li and K. Iga

7 **Active Glass for Photonic Devices**
Photoinduced Structures and Their Application
Editors: K. Hirao, T. Mitsuyu, J. Si, and J. Qiu

Series homepage – http://www.springer.de/phys/books/ssp/

K. Hirao T. Mitsuyu J. Si J. Qiu (Eds.)

Active Glass for Photonic Devices

Photoinduced Structures and Their Application

With 165 Figures

Springer

Professor Kazuyuki Hirao
Division of Material Chemistry,
Faculty of Engineering, Kyoto University,
Sakyo-ku, 606-8501 Kyoto, Japan
e-mail: hirao@bisco1.kuic.kyoto-u.ac.jp

Dr. Jinhai Si
Dr. Jianrong Qiu
ICORP, JST, Photon Craft Project,
Super-Lab. 2-5, Keihanna-Plaza,
1-7 Hikaridai, Seika-cho, 619-0237 Kyoto,
Japan - e-mail: jrz@photon.jst.go.jp

Dr. Tsuneo Mitsuyu
Advanced Technology Research
Laboratories,
Matsushita Electrical Industrial Co., Ltd.,
3-4 Hikaridai, Seika, 619-0237 Soraku,
Japan - e-mail: mitsuyu@ctmo.mei.co.jp

Series Editors:

Professor Takeshi Kamiya
Dept. of Electronic Engineering,
Faculty of Engineering,
University of Tokyo,
7-3-1 Hongo, Bunkyo-ku, Tokyo, 113, Japan

Dr. Herbert Venghaus
Heinrich-Hertz-Institut
für Nachrichtentechnik Berlin GmbH,
Einsteinufer 37,
10587 Berlin, Germany

Professor Bo Monemar
Dept. of Physics and Measurement
Technology, Materials Science Division,
Linköping University,
58183 Linköping, Sweden

ISSN 1437-0379

Library of Congress Cataloging-in-Publication Data

Hirao, K. (Kazuyuki), 1951 -
Active glass for photonic devices : photoinduced structures and their application / K. Hirao, T. Mitsuyu, J. Si, J. Qiu. – p. cm. – (Springer series in photonics, ISSN 1437-0379 ; 7) – Includes bibliographical references and index. – – 1. Photonics–Materials. 2. Glass. I. Mitsuyu, T. (Tsuneo), 1949- II. Si, J. (Jinhai), 1960- III. Qiu, J. (Jianrong) - IV. Title. V. Springer series in photonics ; v. 7. – TA1522 .H57 2000
621.36–dc21 00-046336

This work is subject to copyright. All rights are reserved, whether the whole or part of the material is concerned, specifically the rights of translation, reprinting, reuse of illustrations, recitation, broadcasting, reproduction on microfilm or in any other way, and storage in data banks. Duplication of this publication or parts thereof is permitted only under the provisions of the German Copyright Law of September 9, 1965, in its current version, and permission for use must always be obtained from Springer-Verlag. Violations are liable for prosecution under the German Copyright Law.

DOI 10.1007/978-3-662-04603-6

© Springer-Verlag Berlin Heidelberg 2001

Originally published by Springer-Verlag Berlin Heidelberg New York in 2001.
MyCopy version of the original edition 2001

The use of general descriptive names, registered names, trademarks, etc. in this publication does not imply, even in the absence of a specific statement, that such names are exempt from the relevant protective laws and regulations and therefore free for general use.

Typesetting: PTP, Heidelberg Berlin
Cover concept: eStudio Calamar Steinen
Cover production: *design & production* GmbH, Heidelberg

Printed on acid-free paper SPIN: 10779627 57/3141 5 4 3 2 1 0
www.springer.com/mycopy

Preface

The information revolution of this century was brought about by photonics based on simple and common materials, such as glasses and semiconductors. Although semiconductors will continue to be of central importance in the present century, glasses will also be of great importance in future photonic devices since they have various advantages over other materials in homogeneity, transparency, easy fabrication and excellent solvent properties.

This book focuses on selected topics which are new and of fundamental importance in the applications of active glasses in photonic devices based on our research concept called "induced structure." The book originates from a final report of the Hirao Active Glass Project (HAP), Exploratory Research for Advanced Technology (ERATO), Japan Science and Technology Corporation (JST). Most of the reports in the book concern glasses under the action of very strong electromagnetic fields such as that induced by femtosecond lasers. They include creation of induced structures in glasses, analysis of induced structure, and some functional devices using active glasses. This book is designed to provide graduate students and new researchers with an introductory review of the recent developments in the field of photonic materials. The reader will benefit from an overview of the latest results in the applications of active glasses in photonic devices and from a wealth of knowledge covering most basic solid-state physics, chemical physics, and electronic engineering.

Many people have offered their support and assistance in the publishing of this book. I would like, firstly, to express my appreciation to ERATO, JST, for providing their support, without which this book could not have been written. I am deeply indebted to all of the researchers of the HAP, ERATO, JST, for their outstanding contributions. I also wish to thank Dr. Kouichiro Tanaka of Faculty of Science, Kyoto University, Japan for his valuable suggestions and Mrs. R. Fujimoto for her assistance. Finally, I am indebted to Dr. Claus E. Ascheron of Springer-Verlag for his excellent management of the publication of this book and his constant encouragement.

Kyoto, December 2000 K. Hirao

Contents

List of Contributors

Chutinan, A.
Department of Electronic Science and Engineering,
Kyoto University, Sakyo–ku,
Kyoto 606–8501, Japan

Davis, K. M.
IBM, B/630, Zip EM1,
1580 Route 52,
Hopewell Junction, NY 12533, USA

Fujiwara, S.
Fine Chemical Business Development Department (Ube)
Optical Device Group,
Central Glass Co., Ltd.,
Ube 755–0001, Japan

Hayashi, M.
Technology Researsh Group,
R&D Operation, IBIDEN Co., Ltd.
1–1, Kitagata, Ibigawa–cho, Ibi–gun,
Gifu 501–0695, Japan

Hirao, K.
Dept. of Material Chemistry,
Graduate School of Engineering,
Kyoto University, Sakyo–ku,
Kyoto 606–8501, Japan

Inouye, H.
Institute of Applied Physics,
University of Tsukuba,
1–1–1 Tennodai, Tsukuba,
Ibaraki 305–8573, Japan

Kanbara, H.
NTT Photonics Loboratories,
3–1, Morinosato Wakamiya, Atsugi,
Kanagawa 243–0198, Japan

Kanzansky, P. G.
Optoelectronics Research Centre,
University of Southampton,
Southampton SO17 1BJ, UK

Kishimoto, S.
Kansai Research Center,
Technical Research Laboratory,
Nippon Sheet Glass Co. Ltd.,
1, Kaidoshita, Konoike, Itami,
Hyogo 664–8520, Japan

Kitaoka, K.
Optical System Operations,
Itami Plant, Minolta Co., Ltd.,
Itami, Hyogo 664–8511, Japan

Kondo, Y.
Research Center,
Asahi Glass Co., Ltd.,
1150 Hazawa–cho, Kanagawa–ku,
Yokohama 221–8755, Japan

Makino, Y.
R&D Planning Department,
Daikin Industries, Ltd.,
1304, Kanaoka, Sakai City,
Osaka 591–8511, Japan

Mitsuyu, T.
The Nakao Laboratory, Matsushita Electric Industrial Co., Ltd.,
3–1–1, Yagumo–Nakamachi,
Moriguchi, Osaka 570–8501, Japan

Miura, K.
Fine Chemical Business Development Department (Ube)
Optical Device Group,
Central Glass Co., Ltd.,
Ube 755–0001, Japan

Nouchi, K.
Showa Electric Wire & Cable Co., Ltd.,
1–1, Minami-Hashimoto 4–Chome, Sagamihara,
Kanagawa 229–1133, Japan

Qiu, J.
Photon Craft Project, ICORP, JST,
Keihanna-Plaza,
Super-Laboratory 2–5,
1–7, Hikaridai, Seika–cho,
Kyoto 619–0237, Japan

Shimizugawa, Y.
Osaka National Research Institute (ONRI), AIST,
1–8–31, Midorigaoka, Ikeda,
Osaka 563–8577, Japan

Si, J.
Photon Craft Project, ICORP, JST,
Keihanna-Plaza,
Super-Laboratory 2–5,
1–7, Hikaridai, Seika–cho,
Kyoto 619–0237, Japan

Sugimoto, N.
Research Center,
Asahi Glass Co., Ltd.,
1150 Hazawa-cho, Kanagawa-ku,
Yokohama 221–8755, Japan

Suzuki, T.
Nippon Roper, D–10E,
Makuhari Technogarden Bldg. 1–3,
Makase, Mihama–ku,
Chiba-shi 261–8501, Japan

Acknowledgements

The authors are indebted to the following publishers and societies for granting permission to use figures and certain pages from the cited references in the present edition:

American Institute of Physics (J. Appl. Phys. and Appl. Phys. Lett.); The American Physical Society (Phys. Rev. and Phys. Rev. Lett.); Elsevier Science Ltd. (J. Non-Cryst. Solids, Opt. Commun.), The Japan Society of Applied Physics (Jpn. J. Appl. Phys.); Ceramics Society of Japan (J. Ceram. Soc. Jpn.); The Optical Society of America (Opt. Lett.); Pergamon Press (J. Phys. Chem. Solids); The Chemical Society of America (J. Phys. Chem.).

Introduction

Glass was found more than 5000 years ago. Since then, it has been widely used in daily life. We could even say that today's highly civilized society would not be what it is without glass.

It is well known that glass is one of the most important materials in optics, being used in optical fibers, lenses, mirror substrates, and prisms. In all of these applications, however, glass is almost always used as a passive medium. Since the development of integrated optics, glass is able to be used in active functions as well, such as in light amplification, optical storage, ultrafast optical switching, and various modulations of light.

As a general rule, glass has very low optical nonlinearity, and the application of an electric field does little to the optical wave traveling in the material. It has recently been found that when a high voltage is applied across a rare-earth-doped SiO_2 plate at a high temperature, and after the material is subsequently cooled to room temperature, the poled glass can frequency-double incoming infrared light up to visible light [1]. In addition, as early as the beginning of the 1960s, glasses doped with rare-earth ions, such as Nd-doped glass and Er-doped glass, were used as gain media for lasers [2]. These are typical examples of the success in using glass to perform active optical functions.

We know that glass is homogeneous, transparent and can be easily fabricated into various forms. Moreover, a high level of active ions can be stuffed into glass. We pay special attention to the fact that glass is metastable from the viewpoint of thermal dynamics [3]. A metastable state of glass can easily be changed to other states after the injection of an external electromagnetic field. Novel optical functions can be achieved if the external electromagnetic field induced electron structure is controlled in an active manner. In particular, we have used a femtosecond laser with an ultrahigh-strength electric field as one of our tools to make microscopic modifications in glasses and to realize the novel functions of glasses [4–13]. We found various types of interactions with glass can be produced by using a femtosecond laser operating at a nonresonance wavelength. A short pulse width means that an extremely high peak power can be obtained, and high-intensity light can easily be achieved by focusing the laser beam. The development of high-energy-density, femtosecond-pulse lasers has prompted us to investigate the unexplored potential for inducing multiphoton photochemical reactions. Photoinduced effects and the creation of induced structures in glasses in the context of photonic devices have been the subject of many publications, including photoinduced refractive-index gratings in glass waveguides and fibers, photoinduced second-harmonic generation (SHG), optical storage based on photoinduced refractive-index alteration, fast modulation and switching of light, photowritten optical waveguides, microcrystallization by femtosecond lasers, photostimulated luminescence, photoinduced long-lasting fluorescence and valence state manipulation of rare-earth ions in rare-earth-ion-doped glasses.

This book focuses on selected topics which are new and of fundamental importance in the applications of active glasses in photonic devices. It originates from a final report of the Hirao Active Glass Project (HAP), Exploratory Research for Advanced Technology (ERATO), Japan Science and Technology Corporation (JST). This project has conducted research on glasses under the action of very strong electromagnetic fields such as that induced by a femtosecond laser; studies have ranged from the most basic physics and chemistry to experiments applicable to optical communications.

In the interest of the reader, an introductory review of some important photoinduced effects of glasses is given in the following.

- Photoinduced refractive-index gratings [14]: Intense light propagating inside the core of a germanium-doped silicate glass fiber can modify the core refractive index sufficiently to form a measurable permanent hologram. Fiber Bragg gratings form excellent narrow-band optical filters with a multitude of application: sensors, fiber laser mirrors, wavelength multiplexers, and dispersion control devices.
- Optical storage based on photoinduced refractive-index alteration [15]: Two kinds of optical storage, volume holographic storage and three-dimensional optical data storage, can be achieved in some glasses such as germanium-doped silicate glass by using a femtosecond laser.
- Poling of glasses [1,16,17]: There are three kinds of poling techniques for glasses at present – optical poling, thermal poling, and UV poling. When infrared fundamental light is introduced into a fiber along with its second-harmonic light, optical poling can be performed in the fiber. Intense light containing frequencies ω and 2ω can produce a semipermanent, spatially periodic dc electric field in glass. This strong dc field then enables phase-matched SHG in the glass. In addition, the optical poling technique can be used in hybrid glasses, such as dye-doped silica glass [18].
- Fast modulation and switching of light [19]: Poled glass exhibits the linear electro-optic effect that can be used for the modulation and switching of light. Ultrafast all-optical switching in glass can be realized using optical Kerr shutter operation of glasses with large third-order optical susceptibility, $\chi^{(3)}$, and ultrafast response. In such all-optical devices, a probe light beam can be switched on or off by a pump beam, which changes the refrac-

tive index of the glass. All-optical switching in glass nonlinear directional couplers is of use in integrated optics.

- Photowritten optical waveguides [5]: Permanent optical waveguides can be written in various glasses by using a femtosecond laser, where refractive-index changes are continuously induced along a path traversed by the focal point. Producing waveguide-like channels using this technique is much faster, easier and cheaper than constructing a waveguide by standard chemical vapor-deposition techniques.
- Photoinduced microcrystallization in photosensitive glasses [7]: Selective three-dimensional crystallization can be induced in some photosensitive glasses by focusing a femtosecond laser beam on a nonresonant wavelength region. The crystallization reaction is due to multiphoton absorption.
- Spectral hole-burning [20]: Spectral hole-burning of Sm^{2+}-doped glass can be achieved at room temperature and can be used for high-density optical storage. Spectral hole-burning in glass fiber is expected to be useful for the development of demultiplexers in wavelength mutiplexing optical communication systems.
- Photoinduced long-lasting fluorescence [6]: After irradiating rare-earth-ion-doped glasses with a femtosecond laser or ultraviolet light, the site at which the laser was focused emits long-lasting phosphorescence. By selecting appropriate glass compositions and species of rare-earth ions, long-lasting phosphorescence in various colors, including blue, green, and red, can be induced.
- Photostimulated luminescence in rare-earth-ion-doped glasses [21]: In photostimulated luminescence, a glass material excited by light of frequency ω_1 after irradiation with X-rays emits light of frequency ω_2 ($\omega_1 < \omega_2$). Photostimulated luminescence is due to the photostimulated recombination of holes and electrons at traps which leaves electrons in a long-lasting excited state. Photostimulable luminescence glasses are expected to be novel materials for 2-dimensional X-ray sensors.
- Optical memory based on photoinduced valence state manipulation of rare-earth-ions in glasses [9, 10]: The valence state of rare-earth ions, such as Sm, in glasses can be modified by exposure to femtosecond laser irradiation. This effect is expected to be useful in the fabrication of optical memory devices.
- Frequency upconversion of rare-earth-ion-doped glasses [22]: Frequency upconversion of rare-earth-ion-doped glasses can convert the wavelength of incident light to a shorter one via a multiphoton excitation process. At present, there is great interest in such phenomena because of the possibility of infrared-pumped visible lasers and visible to ultraviolet light amplifiers.
- Crystal growth by femtosecond laser irradiation [13]: Small single crystals can be produced by focusing a femtosecond laser beam on a tiny region of a specially designed glass composition containing barium and boron. By moving the focal point, fibrous BaB_2O_4 (BBO) crystals can be grown.

This book is divided into three parts on the basis of the creation of induced structures in glasses, the analysis of induced structures, and some functional devices using active glasses. The first, and largest, part deals with creations of induced structures in glasses and consists of three chapters. Chapters 1 and 2 discuss ultrafast induction of electronic structures and induction of permanent structures, respectively, by ultrashort laser pulses. The most typical of the many findings of this project, the photowritten optical waveguide, is also presented in Chap. 2. Discussion regarding the generation of induced structures using rare-earth ions is presented in Chap. 3, including photoinduced luminescence and long-lasting fluorescence. Part 2 deals with analyses of induced structures in glasses; both the development of analytical methods for induced structures (Chap. 4) and the computer simulation of induced structures (Chap. 5) are presented. In Part 3, Chaps. 6 and 7 deal with several functional devices using active glasses and ultrafast optical switches, respectively.

We believe that the research results presented in this book open up new possibilities in the production of novel functional optical materials and photonic devices, and we expect that most of them can be applied in optical communications. However, it is important to point out that the purpose of this book is to inspire further research and development of active glasses in photonic devices. In this field, new results and discoveries are reported frequently at meetings and in journals. The research results presented in this book are only a part of the extensive research work being done in this field. Further information can be obtained from the references given.

Part 1

Creation of Induced Structures in Glasses

1. Ultrafast Induction of Electronic Structures by Ultrashort Laser Pulses

1.1 Introduction

The availability of ultrashort laser pulses has recently stimulated much interest in both fast photonic devices and materials that can be applied in optical communication and optical computing. Third-order optical nonlinearity is the most important property for realization of photonic devices, such as all-optical switching, all-optical bistability, and optical limiting devices. Because of their large third-order nonlinearity, there has been significant interest in semiconductors (quantum-well structures). This resonant-type material, however, show large optical absorption and a slower response time in the limited wavelength range where large third-order nonlinearity is obtained.

Nonresonant-type materials such as organic polymers with conjugated π-electron and inorganic homogeneous glasses, on the other hand, have the potential to respond in less than 1 ps. Of these materials, inorganic homogeneous glasses seem to be preferable for optical devices because they have the advantages of ease of fabrication of the fiber or film waveguide, high transparency, high chemical and thermal durability, and a high threshold to optical damage. Glasses doped with nanocrystallites of semiconductors or metals also possess a large and fast third-order optical nonlinear response as a result of the quantum confinement effect on excitons in them.

In this chapter, the nonlinear optical properties of several nonlinear optical materials such as glasses, glasses doped with metallic nanoparticles, and organic materials are described. In these materials, nonlinear optical response arises mainly from ultrafast induction of electronic structures by femtosecond laser pulses. Third-order nonlinear optical properties of glasses containing Bi_2O_3 [18] and chalcogenide glasses [22] are presented in Sects. 2 and 3, respectively. In Sect. 4, the results measured for ultrafast dynamics of nonequilibrium electrons in a gold nanoparticle system using femtosecond pump–probe method are discussed and analyzed [23]. Sects. 5 and 6 introduce the high-speed nonlinear optical response measured in organic solutions [24] and the anomalous anisotropic light scattering observed in Ge-doped silica glass [25], respectively.

1.2 Ultrafast Refractive Index Alteration in Glasses Containing Bi_2O_3

Several studies of glass composition have been performed and yielded large third-order optical susceptibility, $\chi^{(3)}$, because a glass having a high refractive index exhibits a large $\chi^{(3)}$ [26–31]. The maximum $\chi^{(3)}$ estimated so far by third-harmonic generation (THG) measurements was reported to be 1.4×10^{-11} esu in chalcogenide glasses [30] and 3.7×10^{-12} esu in oxide glasses [29]. Also, optical Kerr shutter (OKS) switching with a response time of several picoseconds was observed when a chalcogenide glass fiber was used [32]. However, more information on response properties of nonresonant-type glass is needed for realization of all-optical switching with response times below picoseconds.

Here, a new nonresonant-type glass containing Bi_2O_3 is presented and some results from nanosecond THG measurements and degenerate four-wave mixing (DFWM) experiments performed on the glasses using 200-fs laser pulses are shown.

Table 1.1 shows the composition of the glasses containing Bi_2O_3. Reagent grades of Bi_2O_3, SiO_2, B_2O_3, TiO_2, Li_2CO_3, Na_2CO_3, $BaCO_3$, and CeO_2 were used as the raw materials. CeO_2 was used in BI-3 to suppress the precipitation of Bi metal under melting. The mixtures of raw materials were melted in a Pt crucible in a SiC furnace in air at 1300°C for 1 h. The melt was poured onto a stainless-steel plate and was annealed. The glass plate obtained was polished to a thickness of 0.6 mm for THG measurement and to 2.3 mm for response measurement.

Transparent glass samples were obtained in all compositions. A glass block of 100 mm × 50 mm × 5 mm was fabricated easily. Figure 1.1 shows transmission spectra of these glasses of 2.3-mm thickness. There is no clear absorption above the absorption edge of 450 nm.

$\chi^{(3)}$ values of the glasses were determined by THG measurements at 1.9-μm pump wavelength. The pump pulse duration was 6 ns, and the repetition rate was 10 Hz. The peak power density was near 50 MW/cm^2. We estimated experimental $\chi^{(3)}$ values by using the following equation:

$$\chi^{(3)} = \left(\frac{n+1}{n_s+1}\right)^4 \left(\frac{I_{3\omega}}{I_{3\omega,s}}\right)^{1/2} \chi_s^{(3)} \frac{l_{c,s}}{l_c}\,, \tag{1.1}$$

Table 1.1. Composition of glasses

	Component (mol. %)							
Glass	Bi_2O_3	SiO_2	TiO_2	B_2O_3	Li_2O	Na_2O	BaO	CeO_2
BI-1	18.7	56.2	8.3	–	8.4	8.4	–	–
BI-2	25.5	51.0	–	15.7	–	–	7.8	–
BI-3	42.5	28.4	–	28.4	–	–	–	0.7

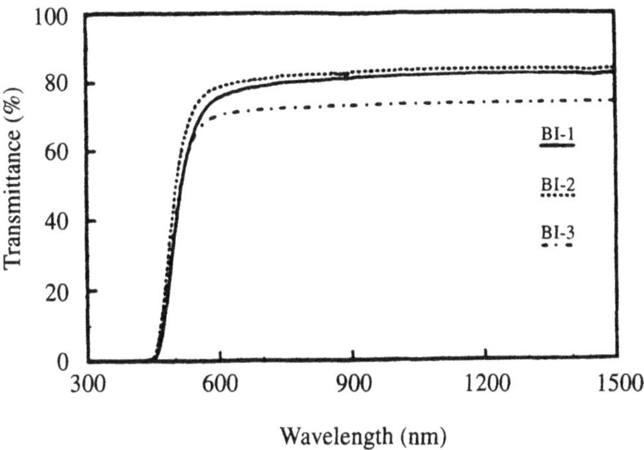

Fig. 1.1. Transmission spectra of glasses containing Bi_2O_3

Table 1.2. Measured refractive indices and third-order nonlinear susceptibilities ($\chi^{(3)}$) of glasses containing Bi_2O_3 and values related to the estimation of molar refraction ([R]). M: molecular weight; d: density; M_c: molar concentration

Glass	n	$\chi^{(3)}$ (10^{-12} esu)	M(g)	d (g/cm^3)	[R] (cm^3/mol)	M_c (mol/cm^3)	[R]M_c
BI-1	1.87	5.8	135.4	4.90	12.5	0.036	0.45
BI-2	1.87	5.8	172.3	5.47	14.3	0.032	0.46
BI-3	2.05	9.3	236.2	6.64	18.4	0.028	0.52
SiO_2	1.46	0.028	60.1	2.2	7.5	0.036	0.27
$As_{40}S_{57}Se_3$	2.5	14	50.6	3.28	9.8	0.064	0.64

where l_c is the coherence length of the sample and $I_{3\omega}$ and $I_{3\omega,s}$ are the measured peak intensity values in the THG intensity patterns of the sample and of standard fused silica, respectively, n and n_s are the refractive indices of the specimens employed and of standard fused silica (1.46 at 633 nm), respectively, and $\chi_s^{(3)}$ and $l_{c,s}$ are the third-order susceptibility and the coherence length of standard fused silica. For the calculation, a $\chi_s^{(3)}$ of 2.8×10^{-14} esu and an $l_{c,s}$ of 18.1 μm at 1.9 μm wavelength were used, as reported by Meredith et al. [33]. The refractive indices of the samples were measured at a 656.3-nm wavelength with a KPR-2 refractive-index meter (Kalnew Optical Industry).

The $\chi^{(3)}$ of As_2S_3 chalcogenide glass was also measured to confirm the reliability of our experiment. The value obtained was 1.0×10^{-11} esu, which agreed sufficiently with the value previously reported for the THG method [30,34,35]. The error of this experiment is estimated to be $< 10\%$. Table 1.2 shows the refractive indices and $\chi^{(3)}$ of glasses containing Bi_2O_3. It was found that glasses containing Bi_2O_3 exhibited large third-order optical nonlinearities. The maximum $\chi^{(3)}$ value was estimated to be 9.3×10^{-12} esu, which is almost as large as that of chalcogenide glasses and three times larger than the maximum value known to the authors for oxide glasses. Here, the molar refractions of materials are expressed by the following equation, which uses the Lorenz–Lorentz equation:

$$\left(\frac{n^2-1}{n^2+2}\right)\frac{M}{d} = \frac{4\pi}{3}N_{\mathrm{A}}\alpha = [R]\,, \tag{1.2}$$

where $[R]$ is the molar refraction, n is the refractive index, d is the density, M is the molecular weight, N_{A} is Avogadro's constant, and α is the polarizability of a molecule. Third-order nonlinear polarization of a molecule depends on α; therefore the larger the $[R]$, the larger the $\chi^{(3)}$ of a molecule. The third-order nonlinear property of a bulk sample, moreover, depends on the number of molecules in the unit volume, i.e., on the molar concentration. The molar concentration of a material is given by

$$M_{\mathrm{c}} = d/M\,, \tag{1.3}$$

where M_{c} is the molar concentration. Consequently, it can be concluded that third-order optical nonlinearities depend on the product of $[R]$ and M_{c}.

Table 1.2 shows M, d, $[R]$, M_{c}, and $[R]M_{\mathrm{c}}$ of glasses containing Bi_2O_3. The values for both chalcogenide glass ($As_{40}S_{57}Se_3$) and SiO_2 glass are shown as references. The average molecular weights of glasses containing Bi_2O_3 are calculated from the compositions shown in Table 1.1. $[R]$ is larger in glasses containing Bi_2O_3 than in chalcogenide glass. BI-3 glass exhibits the largest value, 18.4, which is much larger than the estimated value of ~15 for PbO–TiO_2–TeO_2 glass, which has a $\chi^{(3)}$ of 3.7×10^{-12} esu. Hence it can be understood that the value of BI-3 is very large. On the other hand, the estimated M_{c} is smaller in glasses containing Bi_2O_3 because of the large molecular weight. The products $[R]M_{\mathrm{c}}$ of glasses containing Bi_2O_3 and the chalcogenide glass were much larger than that of SiO_2 glass, which has a small $\chi^{(3)}$. These estimations lead to the conclusion that $\chi^{(3)}$ of glasses containing Bi_2O_3 depend mainly on the molar refraction and that $\chi^{(3)}$ of the chalcogenide glass depend mainly on the molar concentration. The origin of large $\chi^{(3)}$ in glasses containing Bi_2O_3, therefore, can be attributed to the large molar refraction of the glass.

In oxide glasses the molar refraction depends mainly on O^{2-} ions, and O^{2-} ions are also affected by neighboring cations. Increasing the ionic radius of the neighboring cations enlarges the molar refraction of glasses, because the ionic refraction of the cation itself increases and the asymmetry of the electric field around the O^{2-} ion becomes large. The bismuth ion is a case in point, because it has a large coordination number of 5 or 6 in glasses [36] and its ionic radius is large. Thus, glasses containing Bi_2O_3 exhibit large molar refraction. Hall et al. [26] reported that a lead bismuth gallate glass exhibits a larger nonlinearity than do other oxide glasses.

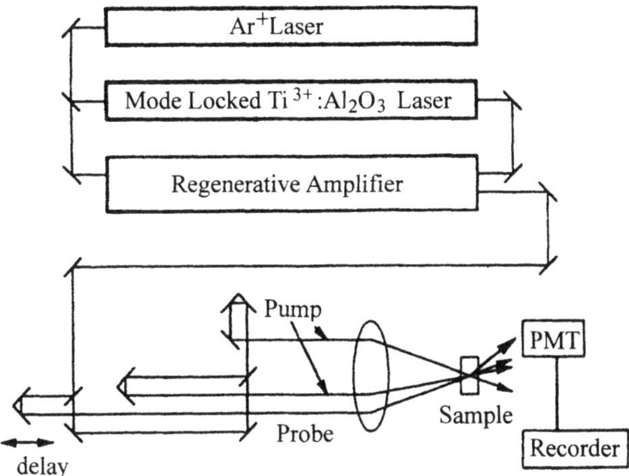

Fig. 1.2. Experimental setup for degenerate four-wave mixing (DFWM) measurement. PMT: photomultiplier tube

DFWM measurements at a wavelength of 810 nm were also performed in the boxcar configuration, using 200-fs laser pulses derived from a regenerated amplified Ti:sapphire laser operating at 200 kHz. The experimental setup is shown in Fig. 1.2. The output beam of the Ti:sapphire laser was split into three partial beams. Two of the three beams were used as pump beams, and the other was used as a probe beam. The three beams were focused onto the same sample spot by a lens of 160-mm focal length, leading to a focal diameter and an interaction length of $\sim$100 and $\sim$500 μm, respectively. The pump power density was varied from $\sim$1 to $\sim$10 GW/cm^2. The diffracted beam, i.e., the DFWM signal, was detected by a photomultiplier. The probe beam was delayed with respect to the two pump beams to measure the response time of the third-order optical nonlinearity. CS_2 in a quartz cuvette of 1-mm thickness was used as a reference.

For all measurements the signal intensity was observed to vary in proportion to the cube of the pump beam intensity. Decay properties of BI-3 glass and CS_2 are shown in Fig. 1.3. CS_2 had a decay component of $\sim$1 ps, the main origin of which is molecular orientation relaxation [37]. DFWM signals in the glass containing Bi_2O_3, however, were detected only when the probe beam overlapped the pump beams. BI-1 and BI-2 glass showed same decay properties. Hence the response times of third-order optical nonlinearity in glasses containing Bi_2O_3 were considered to be below 200 fs, indicating that third-order optical nonlinearity in these glasses mainly originated from pure electronic polarization. Even with a pump power density of 10 GW/cm^2 no damage was found in the samples, nor was any slow decay component detected. This finding leads to the conclusions that the thermal effect or the slow process that originated from the two-photon absorption did not occur,

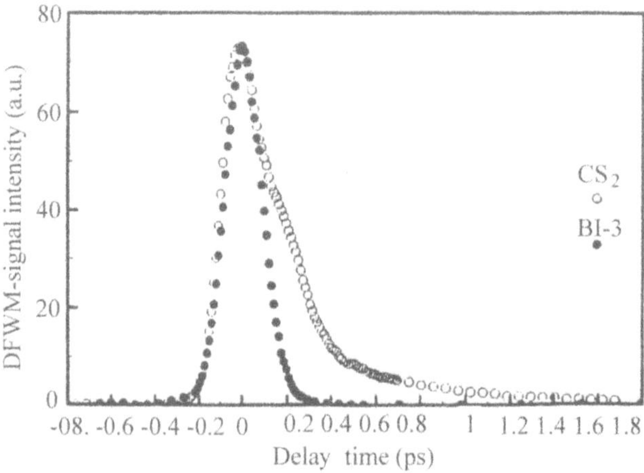

Fig. 1.3. Decay curve of the DFWM signal for BI-3 glass and CS_2

even under such a high pump power density, and that this glass has a high damage threshold.

1.3 Third-Order Nonlinear Optical Properties of Chalcogenide Glasses

The previous section described the third-order nonlinear optical properties of glasses containing Bi_2O_3 observed using THG and DFWM. In this section THG, OKS, and DFWM measurements are introduced for the third-order nonlinear optical response of chalcogenide glass. The reason for the selection of chalcogenide glass was that chalcogenide glasses exhibit higher refractive indices than oxide glasses, and very good third-order nonlinear optical properties were expected.

The THG measurement was carried out using a pump light with wavelengths from 1.9 to 2.2 μm. The pump pulse duration was 6 ns and the repetition rate was 10 Hz. The third-harmonic (TH) wave was detected with a photomultiplier tube and a boxcar averager. The pump power density varied from 50 to 100 MW/cm^2. The THG susceptibility $\chi^{(3)}$(THG) value was determined by comparing the TH intensity with the standard of fused silica [38] using (1.1), where we used the $\chi_s^{(3)}$(THG) value reported by Meredith et al. [33].

In the OKS experiment, an Nd:YAG nanosecond laser (1.064-μm wavelength; 6-ns duration; 10-Hz repetition) and an Nd:YAG laser-pumped nanosecond dye laser (0.70-μm wavelength; 6-ns duration; 10-Hz repetition) were used to generate a gate beam. A laser diode pulse (50-ns duration) with a wavelength of 0.81 μm was used as the probe beam. The photomultiplier tube was

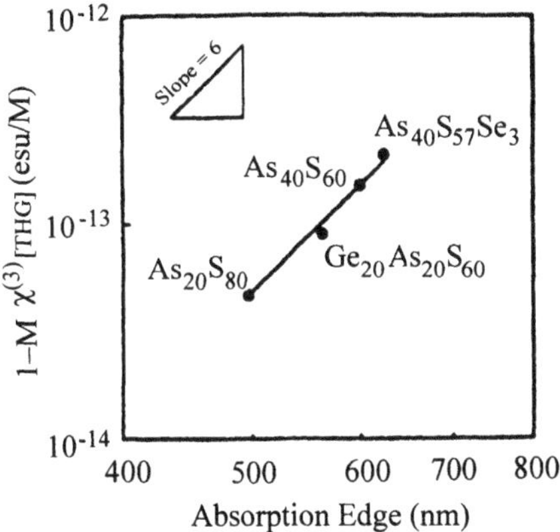

Fig. 1.4. Dependence of the measured $\chi^{(3)}$(THG) value on the absorption edge of the chalcogenide glass. Chalcogenide glass with a more red-shifted absorption edge can produce a larger third-order nonlinearity

employed as the detector. The polarization of the gate beam was set at $\pi/4$ with respect to that of the probe beam. The gate power density was around 50 MW/cm^2. We calculated the OKS susceptibility $\chi^{(3)}$(OKS) by comparing the probe transmittance intensity with the standard of carbon disulfide under the same gate power [35, 39]. The $\chi^{(3)}$(OKS) value is given by

$$\chi^{(3)}(\mathrm{OKS}) = \left(\frac{n}{n_{\mathrm{s}}}\right)^2 \left(\frac{T}{T_{\mathrm{s}}}\right)^{1/2} \chi_{\mathrm{s}}^{(3)}(\mathrm{OKS}) , \tag{1.4}$$

where n is the refractive index, T is the probe transmittance, and the subscript indicates the standard medium.

The boxcar configuration was made when conducting the DFWM measurement. The beam wavelength of 0.81 μm was produced by the combination of a Ti:Al_2O_3 regenerative amplifier system and an optical parametric amplifier. The pulse duration was 200 fs, and the repetition rate was 200 kHz. The pump power density was around 50 MW/cm^2. The photomultiplier tube was used to detect the DFWM signal. The probe beam was delayed with respect to the two pump beams to investigate the response time.

Figure 1.4 shows the dependence of the measured $\chi^{(3)}$(THG) value on the absorption edge of the chalcogenide glass. Various absorption edges were obtained by changing the component atoms of the chalcogenide glass. Both the THG susceptibility and the absorption edge were estimated using a 0.5-mm-thick medium. Since chalcogenide glasses have wide-ranging densities (from 2.5 to 3.3), all the $\chi^{(3)}$(THG) values were calculated at a concentration of 1 M, in order to evaluate the nonlinearity at the same concentration throughout. In Fig. 1.4, the 1 M $\chi^{(3)}$(THG) value exponentially increased as the absorption edge was red shifted; the exponential slope was found to be approximately six, which sufficiently coincided with the theoretical predic-

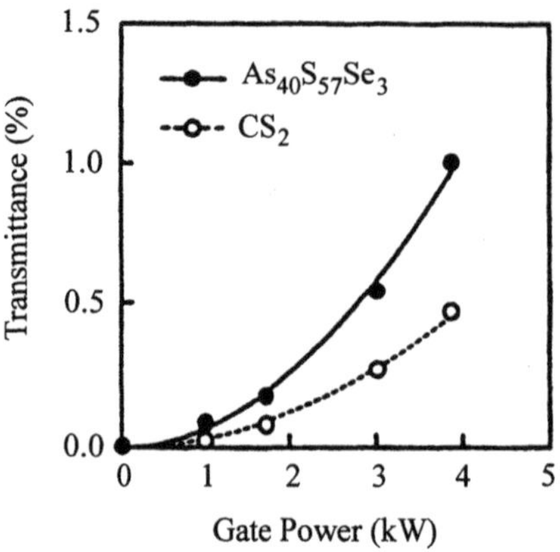

Fig. 1.5. Probe transmittance as a function of gate power for $As_{40}S_{57}Se_3$ and CS_2. When the gate power is adequately small, the probe transmittance increases in proportion to the square of the gate power

tion [40]. Larger nonlinearity was obtained by using As and Se atoms instead of Ge and S atoms, respectively. The maximum $\chi^{(3)}$(THG) value reached 1.4×10^{-11} esu in the case of the $As_{40}S_{57}Se_3$ bulk. For chalcogenide glasses, increasing the Se atomic fraction is one of the effective keys to yielding larger nonlinearity.

The OKS property of the $As_{40}S_{57}Se_3$ bulk, which exhibits the largest THG susceptibility, is shown in Fig. 1.5. The transmittance of the probe light was plotted as a function of the gate power. The result for carbon disulfide was also shown in Fig. 1.5 for comparison. The $As_{40}S_{57}Se_3$ bulk had a thickness of 3 mm. The probe transmittance of the OKS measurement is given by

$$T \propto \sin^2[\chi^{(3)}(\mathrm{OKS})P_\mathrm{g}]\,, \tag{1.5}$$

where P_g is the gate power. The probe transmittance of the $As_{40}S_{57}Se_3$ bulk was observed to follow (1.5), thus confirming OKS operation. It was also found that the probe transmittance of the $As_{40}S_{57}Se_3$ bulk was almost twice as large as that of carbon disulfide. The influence of two-photon absorption (TPA) was not seen in this experiment. The chalcogenide glass having a more red-shifted absorption edge reasonably reduces the gate power, which provides a compact optical switching device. In the OKS configuration, $\chi^{(3)}$(OKS) is written as

$$\chi^{(3)}(\mathrm{OKS}) = \chi_{\parallel}^{(3)}(\mathrm{OKS}) - \chi_{\perp}^{(3)}(\mathrm{OKS})\,. \tag{1.6}$$

Here the designations $\parallel$ and $\perp$ refer to the directions parallel and perpendicular to a linearly polarized gate light. $\chi_{\perp}^{(3)}$(OKS) is equal to $\frac{1}{3}\chi_{\parallel}^{(3)}$(OKS) for the case of solid media [41], and the OKS susceptibility tensors are considered to be twice those values defined in self-phase modulation (SPM), so the following relationship can be obtained [35]:

Table 1.3. Measured susceptibility ratios of OKS to THG. The OKS nonlinearity of $As_{20}S_{80}$ bulk was not obtained because its probe transmittance was under the detection limit of our measurement system

Bulk	$\chi^{(3)}_{\mathrm{SPM}}(\mathrm{OKS})/\chi^{(3)}_{\mathrm{SPM}}(\mathrm{THG})$
$Ge_{20}As_{20}S_{60}$	0.24
$As_{40}S_{60}$	0.27
$As_{40}S_{57}Se_3$	0.24

$$\chi^{(3)}(\mathrm{OKS}) = \frac{4}{3}\chi^{(3)}_{\mathrm{SPM}}(\mathrm{OKS}) , \tag{1.7}$$

where the degeneracy factor is included in the third-order susceptibility. Note that this is not the Maker–Terhune definition for the third-order susceptibility. Similarly, the nonlinearity of THG can be related to that of SPM by supposing that the THG susceptibility tensors are one-third of the SPM ones. That is,

$$\chi^{(3)}(\mathrm{THG}) = \frac{1}{3}\chi^{(3)}_{\mathrm{SPM}}(\mathrm{THG}) . \tag{1.8}$$

By considering (1.7) and (1.8), it is clear that the OKS and THG susceptibilities are both represented by the SPM susceptibility, and because of this it can be concluded that the OKS susceptibilities can be calculated from the data of the more simple THG measurement. The experimental results in Table 1.3 support this conclusion. The measured susceptibility ratios of OKS to THG, $\chi^{(3)}_{\mathrm{SPM}}(\mathrm{OKS})/\chi^{(3)}_{\mathrm{SPM}}(\mathrm{THG})$, were found to almost coincide within the range of experimental error. Table 1.3 also shows that all of these ratios are less than 0.3, although the SPM susceptibilities for the OKS and THG measurements should be equal. This might, as in the case of organic low-molecular-weight compounds [41], support previous works indicating that the nonlinearity of silica glass is overestimated, being two or three times larger than the actual value [43, 44].

The response behavior of the chalcogenide glass bulk is shown in Fig. 1.6. A 0.5-mm-thick $As_{20}S_{80}$ bulk was used in the DFWM investigation. The DFWM intensity was plotted as a function of the delay time. The $As_{20}S_{80}$bulk was found to have a response time as fast as the pump pulse. The signal increased in proportion to the cube of the pump beam intensity, and slow decay was not observed. Hence, the electric polarization effect, the relaxation time of which is less than a picosecond, is plausibly the main third-order nonlinear mechanism of chalcogenide glass. Neither the thermal effect or the TPA effect was considered to be the origin of the third-order nonlinearity. If a faster pump pulse is employed, the chalcogenide glass can achieve high-speed switching operation.

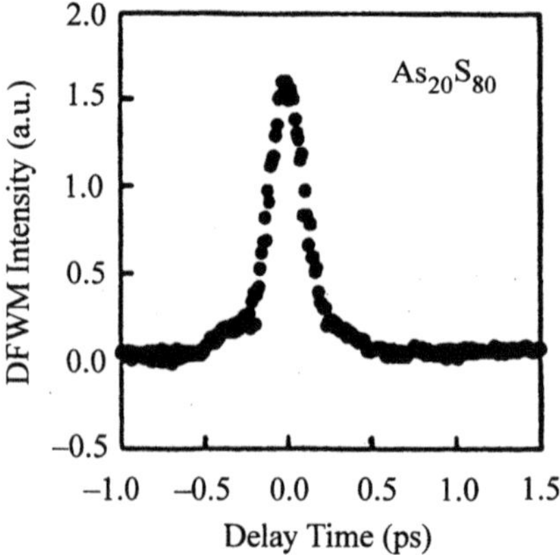

Fig. 1.6. DFWM intensity as a function of the delay time for $As_{20}S_{80}$ bulk. This fast response behavior without any slow relaxation is characteristic of the electric polarization effect

1.4 Refractive Index Change Induced by Femtosecond Laser Pulses in a Metallic Nanoparticle System

In this section, first several important research results with regard to the nonlinear optical response of a gold nanoparticle system are reviewed, then our results observed using the femtosecond pump–probe method in this system are introduced and discussed. Transient absorption spectra were measured using a white-light pump–probe method, and the temporal behavior of the electron temperature and the damping constants in the dielectric function are discussed using Mie scattering theory. Considering the smearing effect on the Fermi–Dirac distribution and the simultaneous changes of damping constants, the electron temperature is demonstrated to be the most characteristic parameter for describing the nonlinear optical response. The temporal behavior of the electron and the lattice temperatures are also discussed, taking into account the thermal diffusion processes from a gold nanoparticle to the host matrix. It was found that the thermal diffusion process is considerable even in the ultrafast region. It is suggested that the transient change of the effective damping constant in $\varepsilon_{\text{intra}}(\omega)$ mainly comes not from electron–electron scattering but from the electron–proton scattering process.

1.4.1 Historical Background

In a noble-metal nanoparticle system, such as gold or copper, an absorption peak due to a surface plasmon is frequently observed in the visible region. Particularly, in an SiO_2 matrix, the absorption peak appears near the edge of the band-to-band transition from the valence d band to the Fermi surface.

This system has been actively investigated in both basic and applicable research fields, because the strong enhancement of the third-order nonlinear optical susceptibility, $\chi^{(3)}$, has been observed around the peak of the surface-plasmon resonance [45–47]. The mechanism causing the large $\chi^{(3)}$, however, has not yet been clarified.

The particle-size dependence and host-matrix dependence of the absorption spectrum have been discussed in copper systems with Mie scattering theory [48]. The study took into account two contributions to the dielectric function $\varepsilon(\omega)$, a Drude term, $\varepsilon_{\text{intra}}(\omega)$, originating from free electrons, and an interband term, $\varepsilon_{\text{inter}}(\omega)$, reflecting the band-to-band transition. As for the time response of nonlinear optical properties, the transient reflectivity measurement and the transient absorption measurement clarified that transient changes of reflectivity and absorption recovered in a few picoseconds [49,50]. The time constant of the recovery strongly depended on the pump-pulse energy density [49]. The origin of the time response was ascribed to the cooling process of nonequilibrium electrons through electron–phonon coupling [51].

The following is the widely accepted model for the whole relaxation process in a metal nanoparticle system with ultrafast light excitation. First, surface plasmons are excited when a pump pulse strikes nanoparticles. Plasmons lose their coherence instantaneously through an electron–electron (e–e) scattering process and change into a quasi-equilibriated hot electron system within 100 fs [52]. As the hot electron system loses its energy through an electron–phonon (e–p) coupling process, the phonon system becomes hot. After 5–10 ps, a quasi-equilibrium state is formed between the electron system and the phonon system in a nanoparticle. Over a long time (>100 ps) the heat transfer from the nanoparticle to the host matrix should be a dominant process. Recently, several studies have tried to justify the nonlinear response using this model [49–51]. In these studies, electron temperatures are calculated as a function of time from the macroscopic energy balance equation for 1-dimensional heat flow with the incident pulse energy. However, the relation between the nonlinear response and the electron temperature has not been clarified directly.

In the gold nanoparticle system, Hache and co-workers conducted an optical Kerr experiment in the picosecond region and discussed the origin of large $\chi^{(3)}$ [47]. It was suggested that the large $\chi^{(3)}$ originates from the hot electron which smears the Fermi–Dirac distribution and modifies the absorption coefficient. Assuming that the pulse duration is much longer than the time constant of the cooling of hot electrons, they theoretically estimated the value of $\text{Im}\{\chi^{(3)}\}$ caused by the hot electron as 1.1×10^{-7} esu, which is almost as large as the result obtained from the optical Kerr experiment (7.5×10^{-8} esu) [47].

Recently, Perner and co-workers reported a temporal change of the effective damping constant in a gold nanoparticle system [53]. They estimated the damping constant by fitting the surface-plasmon resonance peak to a simple

Lorentzian line shape. They suggested that the nonlinear response originates from the broadening of the surface–plasmon band, which reflects the increase of the effective damping constant through the rise of the electron temperature. This suggestion is quite different from the discussion by Hache and co-workers, where the smearing effect of the Fermi–Dirac distribution plays an important role in the nonlinear response [47].

1.4.2 White-Light Pump–Probe Method and Transient Absorption Spectra

Gold nanoparticles embedded in an SiO_2 glass matrix were prepared by a sputtering method. The SiO_2 and gold layers were constructed alternately on an SiO_2 glass base plate. After an annealing treatment, gold nanoparticles were precipitated and dispersed in the SiO_2 glass matrix. More details are reported elsewhere [46]. The mean diameter of the particles was 7.6 nm, with a deviation of 2.4 nm. The sample was 480 nm thick and the volume fraction was 0.027. This high volume fraction was a special feature of this method.

In the femtosecond pump–probe experiment, the output pulse from an optical parametric amplifier (OPA) was used as the pump pulse. The OPA was pumped by a Ti:Al_2O_3 regenerative amplifier. The typical pulse energy of the OPA was 1 μJ. The pulse duration was less than 200 fs. Since the OPA had a wide tunability for a wavelength of the pump pulse, the wavelength was set to the surface-plasmon resonance. The typical energy density of the excitation pulse was 1.4 mJ/cm^2, corresponding to a total energy input of 3×10^{-4} pJ per particle. To probe the change in the optical density (ΔOD) caused by the pump pulse, the white-light pulse generated through the self-phase modulation process in the water flow cell by the amplified pulse was used. The white light included wavelengths from 450 nm to over 1.2 μm. The absorption spectra of the sample was measued using a 27.5-cm single monochromator with dual-diode arrays. To improve the signal-to-noise ratio, the spectrum of the white-light pulse itself was monitored simultaneously as a reference. The ΔOD spectrum was obtained by subtracting the absorption spectrum with no pump pulse from that with the pump pulse at each delay time τ, where τ is the time separating the probe pulse from the pump pulse. The chirping effect of the probe pulse, which is caused by group-velocity dispersion, was estimated with a cross-correlation method, and ΔOD spectra were corrected by a simple calculation. All experiments were executed at room temperature (301.5 K).

Figure 1.7 shows an optical density (OD) spectrum of an Au/SiO_2 composite thin film at 301.5 K (solid curve). An absorption peak at 2.33 eV can be seen clearly along with a slightly increasing background. The origin of the peak is the surface-plasmon resonance. The background originates from the optical transition of valence electrons in the d band to the Fermi surface, as shown in the inset. The arrow indicates the photon energy of the pump pulse used in the pump–probe experiments.

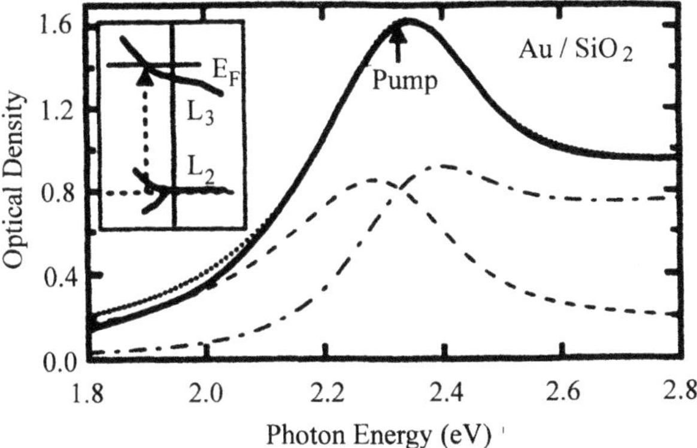

Fig. 1.7. Absorption spectrum (*solid curve*) of the Au nanoparticles in the SiO_2 matrix. The curve fitted using Mie scattering theory is also depicted (*dotted curve*). The related band structure of gold is depicted in the inset. The *arrow* corresponds to the pump photon energy. The *dashed* and *dot-dashed curves* show the contributions of the surface plasmon and the band-to-band transition in the absorption spectrum, respectively

Typical time-resolved differential optical density spectra (ΔOD) obtained by the white-light pump-probe method are shown in Fig. 1.8 at several delay times, i.e., different values of τ. At $\tau = -1.0$ ps, the spectrum clings closely to the zero line. At $\tau = 0.4$ ps, the OD decreases significantly around the peak of the surface plasmon and increases on both sides of the peak. As the delay time increases, the magnitude of ΔOD becomes small. In all cases, the ΔOD spectrum crosses the zero line at two points. In the figure, vertical lines emphasize the movements of the crossing points. At $\tau = 0.4$ ps, the crossing point on the low-energy side is at 2.16 eV. This point moves to the high-energy side as τ increases. After $\tau > 7$ ps, the position remains unchanged at 2.25 eV. In contrast, the crossing point on the high-energy side hardly moves from the initial point. A close look at the movement of the points reveals that the transient change of the absorption spectrum is not a simple symmetrical broadening of the absorption peak.

Figure 1.9 shows the temporal change of ΔOD at the peak of the surface-plasmon band. The inset shows the long-time-scale behavior. The temporal behavior is decomposed into two decay components, a fast decay component (less than 3 ps) and a slow decay component (more than 100 ps). It is suggested that the fast decay constant reflects the thermal equilibrium process between the electron system and lattice system in the metallic nanoparticle and the slow decay constant comes from the cooling process by thermal diffusion from the metallic nanoparticle to the host matrix [49, 54]. The decay constants of the fast and slow components are estimated to be 2.8 and 120 ps by fitting. The result of the fitting is shown as a dotted curve in Fig. 1.9.

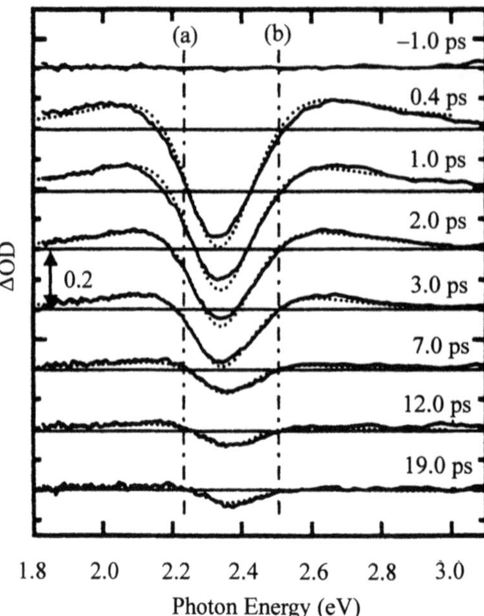

Fig. 1.8. Transient differential absorption spectra for various delay times (*solid curves*). Curves fitted using Mie scattering theory (*dotted curves*) are also shown. *Vertical lines* a and b have been inserted to emphasize the movement of the crossing points, as mentioned in the text

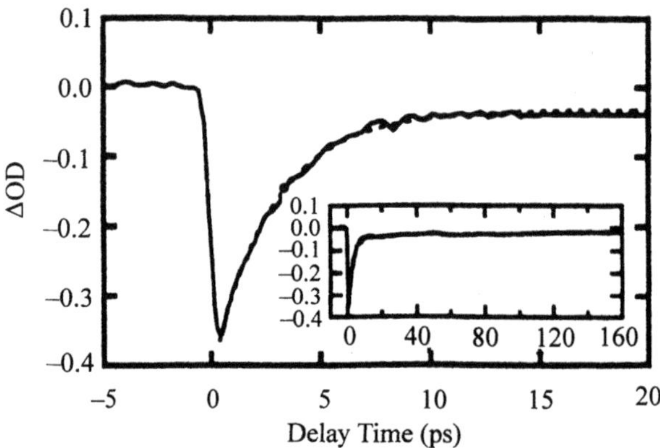

Fig. 1.9. Time evolution of ΔOD measured at the absorption peak of the surface-plasmon band. A fitted curve is also shown (*dotted curve*). In the inset, the long-time-scale behavior is shown

1.4.3 The Origin of the Nonlinear Response

It is reported that the absorption spectrum of a nanoparticle can be reproduced in terms of the Mie scattering theory [45, 48]. In the analysis of the optical nonlinear response of a nanoparticle, the theory is applicable and successfully describes temporal behaviors of transient absorption spectra [55].

The dielectric function of gold can be written in the form

$$\varepsilon(\omega) = \varepsilon_{\text{intra}}(\omega) + \varepsilon_{\text{inter}}(\omega) \,, \tag{1.9}$$

where $\varepsilon_{\text{intra}}(\omega)$ is the Drude part originating from the free electron,

$$\varepsilon_{\text{intra}}(\omega) = 1 - \frac{\omega_{\text{p}}^2}{\omega(\omega - \text{i}\gamma_{\text{eff}})} \,, \tag{1.10}$$

and $\varepsilon_{\text{inter}}(\omega)$ is the interband part originating from the band-to-band transition,

$$\begin{aligned} \varepsilon_{\text{inter}}(\omega) = K \int_{\omega_{\text{g}}}^{\infty} \text{d}x \frac{\sqrt{x - \omega_{\text{g}}}}{x} [1 - F(x, \Theta_{\text{e}})] \\ \times \frac{(x^2 - \omega^2 + \gamma_{\text{ee}}^2 - 2i\omega\gamma_{\text{ee}})}{(x^2 - \omega^2 + \gamma_{\text{ee}}^2)2 + 4\omega^2\gamma_{\text{ee}}^2} \,, \end{aligned} \tag{1.11}$$

where ω_{p} is an effective plasma frequency, γ_{eff} is an effective plasma damping constant, $F(x, \Theta_{\text{e}})$ is an energy distribution function of conduction electrons whose energy is $\hbar x$ at temperature Θ_{e}, and γ_{ee} represents the damping constant in the band-to-band transition. A dispersionless d band and a parabolic conduction band with a gap energy $\hbar\omega_{\text{g}}$ were assumed.

By using Mie scattering theory, the absorption spectrum $\alpha(\omega)$ of nanoparticles embedded in the glass matrix can be calculated as [45]

$$\alpha(\omega) = \frac{2\pi R_0^2 N}{\chi_0^2} \sum_{l=1}^{\infty} (2l + 1) \text{Re}[a_l(\chi_0, \chi_{\text{i}}) + b_l(\chi_0, \chi_{\text{i}})] \tag{1.12}$$

where

$$\chi_0 = \frac{R_0 \omega}{c} \sqrt{\varepsilon_{\text{glass}}} \,, \quad \chi_{\text{i}} = \frac{R_0 \omega}{c} \sqrt{\varepsilon(\omega)} \,, \tag{1.13}$$

and a_l and b_l are Mie scattering coefficients [45]. Here, R_0 is the diameter of the nanoparticle, N is the number density of nanoparticles in the sample, c is the velocity of the light, and $\varepsilon_{\text{glass}}$ is the dielectric constant of the glass matrix. In Fig. 1.7, the best-fit absorption spectrum calculated using (1.12) is shown as a dotted curve. Fixed parameters used in the calculation are listed in Table 1.4. The electron temperature Θ_{e} was also fixed at 301.5 K. The remaining parameters, the two damping constants, were determined by the least-squares method to be $\hbar\gamma_{\text{eff}} = 0.450$ eV and $\hbar\gamma_{\text{ee}} = 0.158$ eV. The

Table 1.4. Fixed parameters of the gold nanoparticle sample

Parameter	Value	Source
Particle diameter, R_0 (nm)	7.6	[46]
Sample thickness, d (nm)	480	[46]
Number density, N	1.17×10^{23}	[46]
Dielectric constant, $\varepsilon_{\text{glass}}$	2.25	[55]
Plasma frequency, $\hbar\omega_{\text{p}}$ (eV)	8.2	[33]
Gap energy, $\hbar\omega_{\text{g}}$ (eV)	1.7	[47]

dotted curve reproduces the absorption spectrum excellently. In the following analysis, (1.12) is used to analyze the transient absorption spectra. Contributions of the Drude part and the interband part are also depicted in Fig. 1.7 as dashed and dot-dashed curves, respectively. From these curves, it can be seen that the Drude part mainly contributes to the absorption in the low-energy region; on the other hand, the interband part is dominant in the high-energy region. It is noteworthy that the contributions of the Drude and interband parts are comparable at the peak of the surface-plasmon band.

Time-resolved differential absorption spectra were analyzed using (1.12) with three running parameters – Θ_{e}, γ_{eff}, and γ_{ee}. Best-fit curves at each delay time are depicted in Fig. 1.8 as dotted curves. These curves excellently reproduce the bleaching around the absorption peak of the surface plasmon and the absorption increase on both sides of the absorption peak.

Figure 1.10a–c shows the temporal changes in the fitting parameters. The inset in Fig. 1.10a shows the temporal change in Θ_{e} over a long time scale. It can be seen that the electron system cools down with two characteristic time constants of a few picoseconds and approximately one hundred picoseconds. After the rapid increase in Θ_{e} to 1700 K, the electron temperature decreases to 400 K with a decay constant of 2.8 ps. The electron temperature gradually cools down with a time constant of 120 ps. It is suggested that the fast decay constant reflects the thermal equilibrium process between the electron system and the lattice system in the metallic nanoparticle and the slow decay constant comes from the cooling process by thermal diffusion from the gold nanoparticle to the host matrix [49, 54].

In Fig. 1.10b, a rapid increase in $\hbar\gamma_{\text{eff}}$ from 0.450 to 0.505 eV around $\tau = 0$ and a decrease thereafter with a decay constant of 1.7 ps can be seen. The temporal change in γ_{ee} is shown in Fig. 1.10c. The magnitude of the change is almost as large as its standard deviation. Therefore, the change in γ_{ee} barely affects the transient change of the absorption spectrum. In the following discussion, the change in γ_{ee} is ignored.

To clarify the most effective parameter in transient absorption spectra, normalized magnitudes of changes in parameters are introduced, defined as $\Delta\Theta_{\text{e}}(t) = [\Theta_{\text{e}}(t) - \Theta_0]/\delta\Theta_{\text{e}}(t)$ and $\Delta\gamma_{\text{eff}}(t) = [\gamma_{\text{eff}}(t) - \gamma_0]/\delta\gamma_{\text{eff}}(t)$, where Θ_0 is the initial temperature of the electron and γ_0 is the initial effective

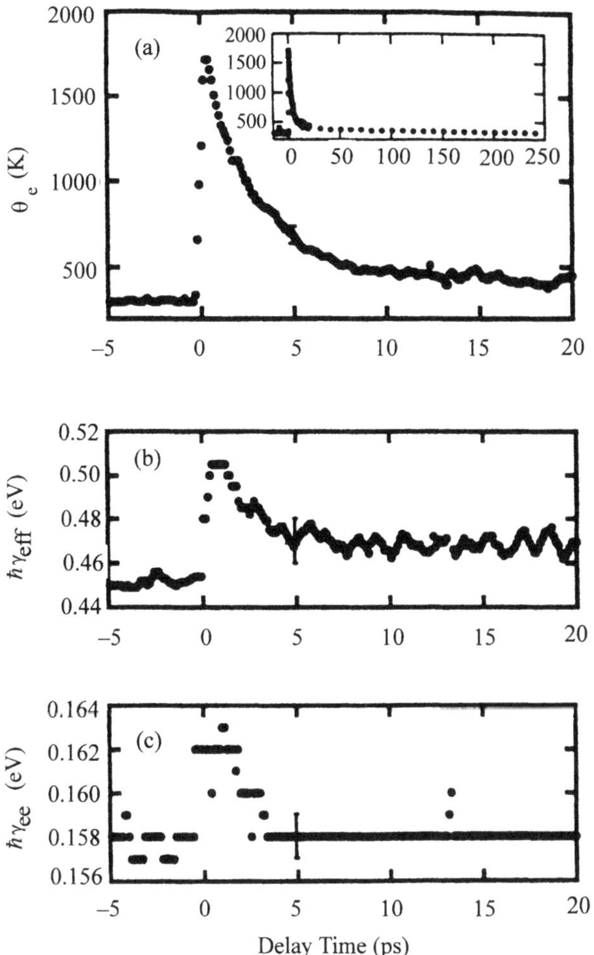

Fig. 1.10. (**a**) Fitting results of the electron temperature at each delay time. The inset shows the temporal change of the electron temperature on a long time-scale. (**b**) Temporal change of the effective plasma damping constant, $\hbar\gamma_{\text{eff}}$. (**c**) Temporal change of the damping constant in the band-to-band transition, $\hbar\gamma_{ee}$. The degrees of error allow a 5% change in the mean-square error for each running parameter

damping constant ($\Theta_0 = 301.5$ K, $\hbar\gamma_0 = 0.450$ eV). $\delta\Theta_e(t)$ and $\delta\gamma_{\text{eff}}(t)$ are degrees of error to allow a 5% change in the mean-square error for each running parameter. A typical value is plotted for each spectrum at $\tau = 5.0$ ps. The temporal changes in $\Delta\Theta_e$ and $\Delta\gamma_{\text{eff}}$ are shown in Fig. 1.11. The dotted line indicates a value of 1, which would indicate that the change in the parameter and the error are comparable. It can be reasonably concluded that the electron temperature Θ_e is the most effective parameter for the nonlinear optical response up to $\tau < 5.0$ ps. The parameter Θ_e is five times more

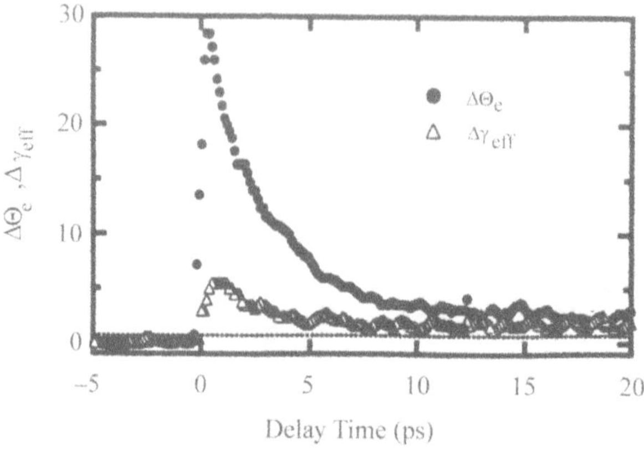

Fig. 1.11. Temporal changes of $\Delta\Theta_e$ and $\Delta\gamma_{eff}$, which are defined in the text. *Dotted line*: corresponds to the value of 1

efficient than γ_{eff} around $\tau = 0$. Other parameters only affect details of the transient absorption spectrum.

In the region $\tau > 10$ ps, both Θ_e and γ_{eff} contribute to the transient absorption spectrum. This means that γ_{eff} becomes more important in the quasi-equilibrium state between the electron and phonon systems. In the time region $\tau > 10$ ps, therefore, both contributions to the nonlinear optical response should be considered. As will be discussed later, an increase in the phonon temperature plays an important role in γ_{eff} over a long time scale.

In contrast with the results found here, Perner et al. reported that γ_{eff} in the Drude term is most effective for the nonlinear optical response in the gold nanoparticle system [53]. Damping constants were estimated in their study by fitting the surface-plasmon absorption band as a single Lorentzian line shape. In the analysis, the electron temperature only affects the transient absorption spectrum through the change in the damping constants. The results of the present study demonstrate that the change in the electron temperature mainly affects the transient absorption through the smearing effects on the electron distribution function, especially in the region $\tau < 5$ ps. This means that the ΔOD spectrum should not be considered as a simple broadening of the spectral band shape in the gold nanoparticle system.

In the analysis by Hache et al. [47], it is suggested that the large $\chi^{(3)}$ is caused by the rise of the electron temperature, which induces a change in the electron distribution function. The results presented here indicate that the temporal change in Θ_e is the main cause for the nonlinear response and the large $\chi^{(3)}$ in a gold nanoparticle system.

1.4.4 Nonequilibrium Thermodynamics in the Metallic Nanoparticle System

In the previous section, the temporal change of the electron temperature Θ_e was obtained. To discuss the cooling process of the hot electron system, nonequilibrium thermodynamics in a metal nanoparticle system with a host matrix should be considered. In this section, an estimate of the temporal change of the lattice temperature with the e–p coupling model is attempted, taking into account the thermal diffusion to the glass matrix.

It has been reported that the relaxation dynamics of the electron temperature in a metallic nanoparticle can be described by the usual e–p coupling model [49–51, 56]. In the model, the metal system is described as a couple of subsystems, an electron subsystem and a phonon subsystem. The electron subsystem is characterized by an electron temperature Θ_e and the phonon subsystem is characterized by a lattice temperature Θ_l, where each subsystem is assumed to be in local equilibrium. The energy transfer between the subsystems occurs through the e–p coupling. The time evolution of the temperatures are obtained with the following heat equations:

$$C_e(\Theta_e)\frac{\partial \Theta_c}{\partial t} = -G(\Theta_e - \Theta_l) + p(t) \tag{1.14}$$

and

$$C_l\frac{\partial \Theta_l}{\partial t} = G(\Theta_e - \Theta_l) \, , \tag{1.15}$$

where G is the e–p coupling constant, $C_e(\Theta_e)$ and C_l are the electronic and lattice heat capacities, and $p(t)$ represents a direct heat input to the electron system by the pump pulse. For gold, $C_e(\Theta_e) = \gamma\Theta_e$, with $\gamma = 67.3\ \mathrm{J\ m^{-3}\ K^{-2}}$, $C_l = 2.49 \times 10^6\ \mathrm{J\ m^{-3}\ K^{-1}}$ at room temperature. The electron temperature is increased by the absorption of the pump pulse. The initial heat input can be calculated from the initial rise in the electron temperature. A simple calculation indicates that the input energy is about 2.3×10^{-5} pJ per particle, which corresponds to 1/13 of the total energy input mentioned in Sect 1.4.2. In addition, from (1.14) and (1.15), it can be estimated that the rise in the lattice temperature should be about 40 K in the quasi-equilibrium state, which is quite different from the experimental results. The equilibrium temperature is about 400 K and corresponds to a 100 K rise of the lattice temperature from room temperature. These facts strongly suggest that the initial energy of hot electrons flows via pathways other than the e–p coupling. Nonequilibrium thermodynamics including an energy transfer to the lattice system through scattering processes or a thermal diffusion to the glass matrix should be considered.

To investigate the nonequilibrium thermodynamics of the whole system, at first, a thermal diffusion from a metal nanoparticle to the glass matrix by a simple diffusion equation is considered,

$$\frac{\partial \Theta_{\text{glass}}}{\partial t} = D_{\text{glass}} \nabla^2 \Theta_{\text{glass}} , \tag{1.16}$$

where D_{glass} is the diffusivity of heat in the glass matrix. For the silicate glass, $D_{\text{glass}} = 8.4 \times 10^{-3}$ cm^2 s^{-1} at room temperature [57]. From (1.16), the thermal distribution function outside of the metallic nanoparticle can be obtained as a function of the distance r and time t. Thermal diffusion inside the metallic nanoparticle should be neglected, because diffusivity of gold, D_{gold}, is nearly 10^3 times larger than D_{glass}. This means that the inside of the metallic nanoparticle has an uniform thermal distribution. When thermal continuity at the interface between the nanoparticle ($r = R_0/2$) and the glass and uniformity of the lattice temperature in the nanoparticle are assumed, the following energy-balance equation is obtained [54]:

$$C_l V_0 \Theta_{l0} = C_l V_0 \Theta_l(t) + C_{\text{glass}} \int_{r=R_0/2}^{\infty} 4\pi r^2 \Delta\Theta_{\text{glass}}(t,r) \mathrm{d}r , \tag{1.17}$$

where Θ_{l0} is an initial lattice temperature of the gold nanoparticle in the aftermath of the pump pulse, C_{glass} is a heat capacity of the glass taken as $C_{\text{glass}} = 1.63 \times 10^6$ J m^{-3} K^{-1}, $\Delta\Theta_{\text{glass}}(t,r) = \Theta_{\text{glass}}(t,r) - \Theta_0$ ($\Theta_0 = 301.5$), and $V_0 = \frac{4}{3}\pi (R_0/2)^3$ [47, 57]. By using the analytic solution of (1.16), the temporal change of the lattice temperature inside the metal nanoparticle can be derived from (1.17) as

$$\begin{aligned}\Theta_l(t) = \Big[\Theta_{l0} - \Theta_0\Big] \Big/ \Big[1 + 3\frac{C_{\text{glass}}}{C_l} \Big\{ &[(2D_{\text{glass}}t)^{3/2}/\sqrt{2\pi}(R_0/2)^3] \\ &\exp[(R_0/2)^2/4D_{\text{glass}}t] \\ &\operatorname{erfc}(R_0/2)/\sqrt{4D_{\text{glass}}t} + 2D_{\text{glass}}t/(R_0/2)^2 \Big\}\Big] + \Theta_0 \,.\end{aligned} \tag{1.18}$$

From (1.14) and (1.15), with $G = (3.0 \pm 0.5) \times 10^{16}$ W m^{-3} K^{-1}, reported by Fann and co-workers for a gold film [56], it can be reasonably assumed that the electron system and the lattice system are sufficiently equilibrated after $\tau > 10$ ps. In the region, it can be assumed that the lattice temperature is the same as the electron temperature. By using the electron temperature at $\tau = 10$ ps represented in Fig. 1.10a, the temporal change of the lattice temperature can be estimated from (1.18). The calculated temporal change of the lattice temperature is shown in Fig. 1.12 by a dashed curve. The dashed curve traces the temporal change of the electron temperature well in the region $\tau > 7$ ps, justifying the assumption of equilibrium between the electron and lattice systems over time.

The result shows that the initial temperature of the lattice system directly following incidence of the pump pulse is nearly 950 K. The total input energy can be estimated to be 3.9×10^{-4} pJ per particle from the initial increases in the electron and lattice system temperatures. This value is nearly the same as the value estimated experimentally from the energy density of the incident

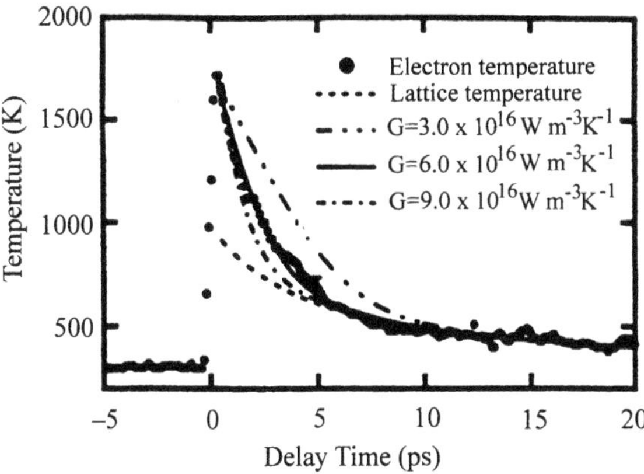

Fig. 1.12. Temporal change of the lattice temperature (*dashed curve*). Curves fitted to the electron temperature using the lattice temperature and (1.15) and (1.16) with the following three values of G are also shown: 3.0×10^{16} W m^{-3} K^{-1} (*dot-dot-dashed curve*), 6.0×10^{16} W m^{-3} K^{-1} (*solid curve*), and 9.0×10^{16} W m^{-3} K^{-1} (*dot-dashed curve*)

laser pulse. The results mean that a large proportion of the incident energy is spent in heating up the lattice system in the first step of the relaxation process of hot carriers.

To understand the direct energy input to the lattice system, the absorption process of the pump pulse in a gold nanoparticle system must first be understood. In the case of excitation at the peak wavelength of the surface-plasmon band, the incident pump pulse is absorbed by both the surface-plasmon band and the band-to-band transition, as described earlier. It is natural to consider that the electron system is heated by the excitation of surface plasmons. On the other hand, generation of electron and hole pairs through the band-to-band transition should lead to nonradiative surface recombination of electron and hole pairs. The surface recombination will input heat to the lattice system. As discussed in the next section, a typical surface scattering rate estimated from an effective plasma-damping constant is 1×10^{14} s^{-1}. This value corresponds to a time constant of 10 fs. Thus, it is likely that the nonradiative surface recombination of electron–hole pairs generates phonons in the aftermath of the pump pulse. Similarly, the possibility of heat input to the lattice system through a scattering process between plasmons and phonons at the surface should be taken into account. As a result, it is concluded that all the energies absorbed by the band-to-band transition and 86% of the energies absorbed by the surface plasmon are spent heating up the lattice system.

The initial temperature of the lattice system seems to be very high. If the surface scattering processes heat up the lattice system, thermal distribution in the metal nanoparticle at the initial stage of excitation may well occur. Such a thermal distribution possibly generates a coherent strain wave. Strain wave generation is reported in the case of gallium and tin nanoparticle systems [58]. In the experimental ΔOD data of the present study, however, no oscillation due to strain waves was observed, indicating that a coherent strain wave did not occur. Therefore, the generation of a coherent strain wave is not considered in our discussion.

The cooling process of the electron system is of interest here. In the previous section, it was pointed out that the fast decay constant reflects the thermal equilibrium process between the electron and lattice systems in the metallic nanoparticle [49,54]. The thermal equilibrium process is usually described by (1.14) and (1.15). From the equations, it can be seen that the e–p coupling constant, G, governs the thermal equilibrium process. In Fig. 1.12, the temporal changes in the electron temperature are shown, calculated using (1.14) and (1.15), with several values of G and the lattice temperature obtained above. The result with $G = 6.0 \times 10^{16}$ W m^{-3} K^{-1} reproduces quite excellently the temporal change of the electron temperature. This value is about two times larger than the value found for the gold film [56]. The reason for this is not clear at present, although a mesoscopic effect would play an important role in increasing the e–p coupling constant of the nanoparticle system.

In summary, the temporal change in the lattice temperature was obtained taking into account the thermal diffusion to the glass matrix, by using (1.14)–(1.17). The total energy flow in the metallic nanoparticle system can be understood quantitatively, indicating that the lattice temperature still plays an important role in the first stage of the nonequilibrium state.

1.4.5 The Origin of the Damping Constant in the Drude Term

There are still open questions on the damping mechanism of free electrons in the metallic nanoparticle system. In this section, to investigate the electron dynamics in the nonequilibrium state, the temporal change of the damping constant is discussed, since it reflects the electron dynamics such as the e–e and e–p scattering processes.

As shown in Fig. 1.10b, $\hbar\gamma_{\text{eff}}$ increases rapidly around the delay time $\tau = 0$ from 0.450 to 0.505 eV. First, consider the e–p scattering process, which is linearly dependent on the lattice temperature. The following is obtained:

$$\hbar\gamma_{\text{eff}}(\Theta_{\text{l}}) = \Gamma_{\text{sur}} + \Gamma_{\text{e-p}}\Theta_{\text{l}} \,, \tag{1.19}$$

where Γ_{sur} is a constant which mainly reflects the impurity scattering process, and the second term represents the e–p scattering process. The calculated result of (1.19) is shown as a solid curve in Fig. 1.13. The best-fit parameters are $\Gamma_{\text{sur}} = 0.427$ eV and $\Gamma_{\text{e-p}} = 8.28 \times 10^{-5}$ eV K^{-1}. The curve very nearly reproduces the temporal change in γ_{eff}.

The result leads to the following important conclusion: the transient response of γ_{eff} is mainly governed by the e–p scattering term. It can also be

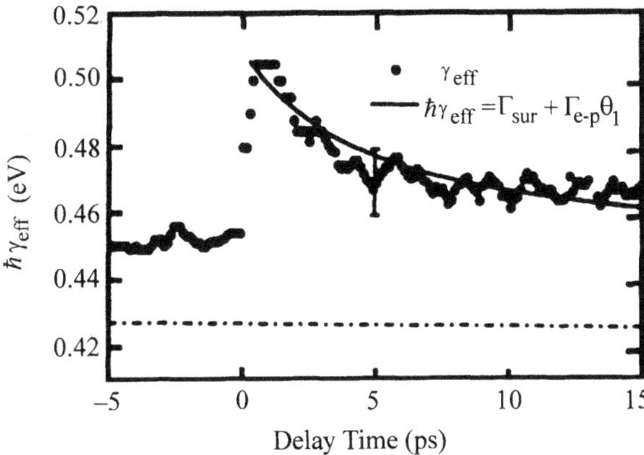

Fig. 1.13. Damping constant $\hbar\gamma_{\rm eff}$ at each delay time (*solid circles*) and fitted curves; the *solid curve* is the result of a fit using (1.19). *Dot-dashed line* indicates the value of $\Gamma_{\rm sur}$ in (1.19)

deduced from Fig. 1.11 that the lattice temperature could be used as a parameter to describe the nonlinear response in the temporal change in $\gamma_{\rm eff}$ as well as the temporal change in $\Theta_{\rm e}$ over a time scale of 10 ps. In an e–e scattering process, it is expected that the damping constant shows quadratic dependence on $\Theta_{\rm e}$ [53,59]. From the temporal behavior of $\Theta_{\rm e}$, a more drastic change in $\gamma_{\rm eff}$ in the first step of the excitation can easily be imagined. Such behavior, however, cannot be extracted from the temporal change in $\gamma_{\rm eff}$. Thus, it can be concluded that only the e–p scattering process contributes significantly to the temporal change in $\gamma_{\rm eff}$.

Comparing the magnitudes of each term in (1.19), it was found that even around $\tau = 0$ the ratio of $\Gamma_{\rm sur}$ to $\Gamma^{\rm e-p}\Theta_{\rm l}$ is about 6. The value of $\Gamma_{\rm sur}$ (0.427 eV) is much larger than the value reported in bulk ($\Gamma_{\rm bulk} = 0.170$ eV) [60]. In the present case, it is suggested that scattering by a structural fluctuation on the metal–glass interface induces the dephasing process of plasmons. If it is assumed that the electron dephases within a trip from one point to another on the surface, the damping energy due to the process is described as $hV_{\rm F}/(2R_0)$. For the gold nanoparticle, the value is estimated to be 0.272 eV. If $\Gamma'_{\rm sur} = \Gamma_{\rm bulk} + hV_{\rm F}/(2R_0)$ is calculated, $\Gamma'_{\rm sur} = 0.442$ eV is obtained. This value is nearly the same as the value of $\Gamma_{\rm sur}$ obtained experimentally. This means that the surface of the nanoparticle plays an important role in the damping process of electrons through the collision at the metal–glass interface. Zhou et al. and Yang et al. also used a similar expression to explain the effective damping constant [60,61]. To confirm this point, the size dependence of $\Gamma'_{\rm sur}$ should be studied quantitatively.

1.5 Optical Switches Using Organic Solutions

Conjugated organic nonlinear optical materials are of interest due to the delocalized π-electron systems which give rise to large values of $\chi^{(3)}$, with extremely fast response times, in wavelength regimes where there is minimal background absorption [61–65]. However, the response mechanism of such materials, if they are used in solution, is often governed by the molecular contribution, such as the molecular orientation effect; for this reason organic solutions tend to exhibit a relatively slow response time.

In this section, by changing the molecular length of the π-conjugated low-molecular-weight compounds, it is shown that the slow molecular contribution of the organic solutions can be lessened, leading to a high-speed third-order nonlinear optical response. The following structures were used: carbon disulfide, nitrobenzene, and the saturated 4-N,N-dimethylformamide (DMF) solutions of 4-(N,N-diethylamino)-β-nitrostyrene (DEANST) and terephthal-bis-(4-N,N-dihexylaminoaniline) (HH-SBA); their molecular structures are shown in Fig. 1.14. To investigate the response characteristics in these organic solutions, their third-order nonlinear coefficients are estimated by OKS and THG measurements. Moreover, a DFWM experiment is conducted to prove the high-speed response.

The OKS measurement was performed using a gate beam generated from an Nd:YAG laser (1.064-μm wavelength; 6-ns duration; 10-Hz repetition) and an Nd:YAG laser-pumped dye laser (0.70-μm wavelength; 6-ns duration; 10-Hz repetition). An AlGaAs laser diode pulse (0.81-μm wavelength; 50-ns duration), synchronized with the gate pulse, was used as a probe beam. The detector was a photomultiplier tube. The gate and probe power densities were around 50 MW/cm^2 and 100 W/cm^2, respectively. In calculating the

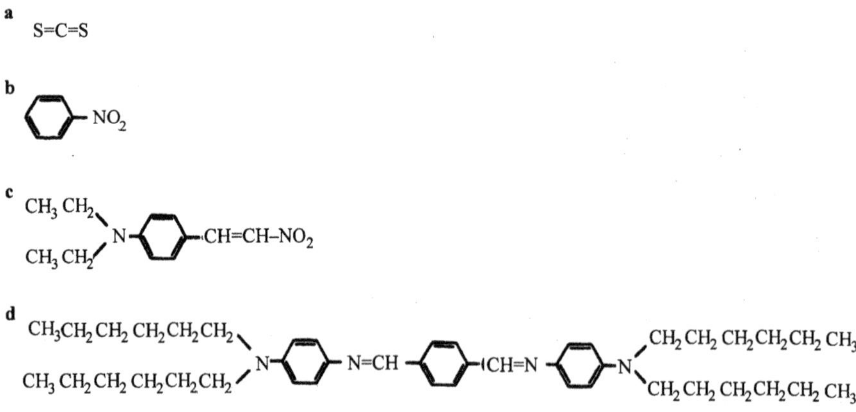

Fig. 1.14. Molecular structures of (**a**) carbon disulfide, (**b**) nitrobenzene, (**c**) DEANST, and (**d**) HH-SBA. The molecular length changes by degrees. Each solution was poured into a 1-mm-thick glass cell

OKS nonlinear refractive index n_{2B}(OKS), the probe transmittance intensity, T, was compared with the standard of carbon disulfide under the same gate power and medium length [35, 39]. The Kerr nonlinearity n_{2B}(OKS) is obtained from (1.4).

The nonlinear refractive index n_2(THG), which is defined in terms of self-phase modulation (SPM) [35, 65], was derived from the THG measurement. The difference-frequency generator, consisting of a $LiNbO_3$ crystal, provided a pump beam with a wavelength from 1.5 to 2.2 μm. A pump beam with a duration of 6 ns and a repetition rate of 10 Hz was used. The TH wave was detected with a photomultiplier tube and a boxcar averager. The pump power density was varied from 50 to 100 MW/cm^2. The THG nonlinearity n_2(THG) was calculated by comparing the TH intensity with the standard of fused silica glass [33, 41]. The n_2(THG) value is given by (1.1)

The DFWM properties were examined at a wavelength of 0.81 μm. The beam was produced by the combination of a $Ti{:}Al_2O_3$ regenerative amplifier and an optical parametric amplifier. The pulse duration was 200 fs, and the repetition rate was 200 kHz. The pump power density ranged from 10 to 50 MW/cm^2. The DFWM signal was detected using a photomultiplier tube. The probe beam was delayed with respect to the two pump beams in order to estimate the response time.

In the OKS measurement using solution media, the Kerr nonlinearity n_{2B}(OKS) is mainly given by the sum of the electronic and molecular contributions

$$n_{2B}(\mathrm{OKS}) = n_{2B}^{e}(\mathrm{OKS}) + n_{2B}^{m}(\mathrm{OKS}) \,, \tag{1.20}$$

where the first and second terms are the electronic and molecular contributions, respectively. In contrast, in the THG measurement, since only the nonlinearity due to the electronic contribution can be detected, the THG nonlinearity n_2(THG) is represented by the electronic part of the SPM nonlinear refractive index n_2^e as follows [41]:

$$n_2(\mathrm{THG}) = n_2^{e} \tag{1.21}$$

Therefore, using the relationship $n_{2B}^{e}(\mathrm{OKS}) = \frac{4}{3}n_2^{e}$ [35], from (1.20) and (1.21), the ratio of the electronic contribution in all-Kerr nonlinearity, $n_{2B}^{e}(\mathrm{OKS})/n_{2B}(\mathrm{OKS})$, is obtained, assuming that the wavelength dispersion of the nonlinearity can be ignored. The electronic contribution $n_{2B}^{e}(\mathrm{OKS})/n_{2B}(\mathrm{OKS})$ is written as

$$\frac{n_{2B}^{e}(\mathrm{OKS})}{n_{2B}(\mathrm{OKS})} = \frac{4n_2(\mathrm{THG})}{3n_{2B}(\mathrm{OKS})} \,. \tag{1.22}$$

Table 1.5 shows the concentrations and the OKS and THG nonlinearities for carbon disulfide, nitrobenzene, and the DMF solutions of DEANST and HH-SBA. The $n_{2B}^{e}(\mathrm{OKS})/n_{2B}(\mathrm{OKS})$ value was found to increase with increasing

Table 1.5. Concentrations of the organic solutions and the OKS and THG nonlinearities. The nonlinearities were calculated for 1 M concentration. The long molecules of DEANST and HH-SBA provided higher 1 M nonlinearity, in addition to large $n_{2B}^{e}(\mathrm{OKS})/n_{2B}(\mathrm{OKS})$ value

Solution	Concentration (mol/L)	$n_{2B}(\mathrm{OKS})$ ($\mathrm{cm^2/W}$)	$n_2(\mathrm{THG})$ ($\mathrm{cm^2/W}$)	$n_{2B}^{e}(\mathrm{OKS})/$ $n_{2B}(\mathrm{OKS})$
Carbon disulfide	16	4.9×10^{-15}	6.7×10^{-16}	0.18
Nitrobenzene	9.8	3.6×10^{-15}	5.4×10^{-16}	0.20
DEANST	2.8	5.2×10^{-14}	1.2×10^{-14}	0.31
HH-SBA	4.5×10^{-2}	5.7×10^{-13}	2.5×10^{-13}	0.58

molecular length. In the case of carbon disulfide, the electronic contribution accounts for only $\frac{1}{5}$ of the Kerr nonlinearity; however, in the solution of the long HH-SBA molecule, the electronic contribution is almost $\frac{3}{5}$. Increasing molecular length yields larger $n_{2B}^{e}(\mathrm{OKS})/n_{2B}(\mathrm{OKS})$ values.

The molecular length dependence of the nonlinear property was further investigated in the DFWM experiment. Figure 1.15 shows the DFWM intensity as a function of the delay time. The magnitude of the DFWM intensity is normalized in this figure. The DFWM intensity was, for all the solutions, observed to change in proportion to the cube of the pump intensity. A notable molecular length dependence was found: the large molecules of DEANST and HH-SBA have a fast response time, that is, the component having a slow relaxation time is reduced for these large molecules. This molecular length dependence is explained in the following.

The optically induced refractive index change, $\Delta n(t)$, in the DFWM experiment using solution media is phenomenologically described as [63]

$$\Delta n(t) = n_{2B}^{e}(\mathrm{DFWM})I(t) + \sum_i (n_{2B,i}^{m}(\mathrm{DFWM})/\tau_i) \int_{-\infty}^{t} I(t') \exp[-(t-t')/\tau_i]\mathrm{d}t' . \tag{1.23}$$

Here, $n_{2B}^{e}(\mathrm{DFWM})$ is the DFWM nonlinear refractive index. The first and second terms are the electronic and molecular contributions, respectively. The summation index i indicates the ith component of the molecular contribution. Although the response time for the electronic contribution is less than a picosecond, the molecular contribution, like the molecular orientation effect, has a relatively slow response time of more than a picosecond. The response time τ_s for the molecular orientation effect is qualitatively represented by one third the Debye relaxation time,

$$\tau_s = \frac{\eta \nu}{k_B T} , \tag{1.24}$$

where η is the viscosity of the solution, ν is the molecular volume, k_B is the Boltzmann constant, and T is the temperature of the solution. From (1.24), it

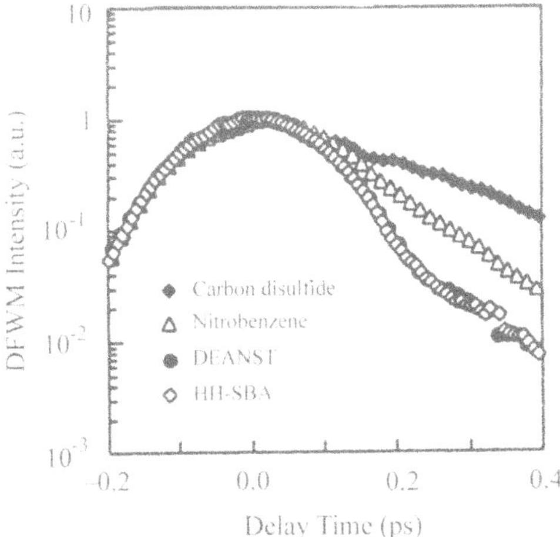

Fig. 1.15. DFWM intensity as a function of the delay time for carbon disulfide, nitrobenzene, and the DMF solutions of DEANST and HH-SBA. The DFWM intensity decays quickly in the solution consisting of long molecules. The DFWM signal of the DMF solvent is very weak compared with that of the DEANST and HH-SBA molecules

is shown that, as the molecular length increases, the response time τ_s for the molecular orientation effect becomes slower. However, (1.23) points out that the contribution of the molecular orientation effect for the long molecules of DEANST and HH-SBA is negligible because of their large τ_s.

For our DFWM experimental setup, the DFWM signal is given by

$$I(t_d) \propto \int_{-\infty}^{\infty} I_p(t - t_d)[\Delta n(t)]^2 \mathrm{d}t \,, \tag{1.25}$$

where t_d is the delay time. Using (1.23) and (1.25), the experimental data in Fig. 1.15 can be fitted theoretically. The fitting results for the molecular contribution are summarized in Table 1.6. The ratio in the whole nonlinearity is shown for each nonlinear coefficient, and for the calculation, the electronic part was regarded to be equal to the $n_{2B}^{e}(\mathrm{OKS})/n_{2B}(\mathrm{OKS})$ values listed in Table 1.5. It was assumed that all the solutions have an electronic contribution as well as a molecular contribution consisting of two components, one fast and the other slow. The fast component of the molecular contribution is thought to be mainly due to intermolecular interaction and intramolecular vibration [67]. The slow component originates from the molecular orientation effect. In Table 1.6, it can be seen that the long molecule has both the smallest nonlinearity ratio and the largest τ_s value for the slow component of the molecular contribution (the molecular orientation effect). It can be inferred from this finding that, as understood from (1.23), the DEANST and HH-SBA solutions sufficiently decrease the influence of the molecular orientation effect, and thereby exhibit a fast response. There is no noticeable difference

Table 1.6. Nonlinearity ratios and response times τ for the fast and slow components of the molecular contribution. These results were obtained by fitting the DFWM data

Solution	Fast-component ratio [τ_f (ps)]	Slow-component ratio [τ_s (ps)]
Carbon disulfide	0.20 [0.25]	0.62 [1.5]
Nitrobenzene	0.20 [0.25]	0.60 [30]
DEANST	0.20 [0.60]	0.49 [100]
HH-SBA	0.30 [0.60]	0.12 [500]

between the DEANST and HH-SBA curves in Fig. 1.15, which might suggest that DEANST has a molecular length long enough to yield a solution which has a high-speed response time. Table 1.6 also shows that the response times for the molecular orientation effect for carbon disulfide and nitrobenzene agree with the typical reported values [37, 68, 69]. In addition, it can be seen that a long molecule has a larger τ_f value for the fast component of the molecular contribution; however, the τ_f value of DEANST and HH-SBA is less than a picosecond even for the long molecules. A slower decay than that originating from the molecular orientation effect was not seen in the DFWM experiment. As in the OKS and THG measurements, the pump powers in the DFWM experiment using the DEANST and HH-SBA solutions were found to be several times smaller compared with that for carbon disulfide.

1.6 Anomalous Anisotropic Light Scattering in Ge-Doped Silica Glass

In the previous sections of this chapter, mainly nonlinear optical response properties of several glass materials were described. Here, the observation of a new phenomenon in glass pumped by intense laser radiation is introduced – the scattering of light, in particular luminescence, which peaks in the plane of light polarization (anomalous anisotropic light scattering). The phenomenon is interpreted in terms of the angular distribution of photoelectrons in isotropic solid-state materials.

Applications of glass span from high power lasers for laser fusion [70] to optical waveguides for optical communication [71]. Light scattering, a phenomenon that occurs widely in nature, is also very common when an intense laser beam propagates in optical glass materials [72]. It is well known that the scattering of polarized light in the plane of light polarization in an isotropic medium, such as glass, is always weaker compared to that in the orthogonal plane, since a dipole does not radiate in the direction of its axis.

In the experiments Ge-doped silica glass (Ge:SiO_2) was used, which is the main constituent material of optical fibers for optical communication and which has an interesting property, strong photosensitivity, associated with defects in glass such as germanium oxygen-deficient centers (Ge-ODC or Ge–Si wrong bonds) [73, 74]. These centers produce a strong absorption band at 5 eV (240 nm, singlet–singlet transition), a weak absorption band at 3.7 eV (330 nm, forbidden singlet–triplet transition) and blue triplet luminescence at 3.1 eV with a decay time of about 100 μs [75, 76]. Many studies of blue luminescence in silica glass under the excitation with ultraviolet light have been carried out [77–79]. These studies were motivated by the important role of defects responsible for the blue luminescence in two kinds of phenomena. The first one includes refractive-index changes and gratings induced via one- or two-photon absorption of ultraviolet or visible light [74, 80]. The second one involves gratings of second-order optical nonlinearity [15, 81, 82] induced via coherent photocurrent in glass [83] (modulation of the angular distribution of photoelectrons [84–86]) or coherent photoconductivity in glass under an applied dc electric field [87] (modulation of the total cross section of ionization) as a result of quantum interference between coherent light fields at two different frequencies. More recently, strong refractive-index changes were induced in glass by femtosecond laser pulses via multiphoton absorption of infrared light [5]; this is introduced in Sect. 2.1. On the other hand, the luminescence of silica glass under excitation with intense (10^{11}–10^{12} W/cm^2) ultrashort (100 fs) infrared radiation has received little attention. It should be pointed out that the high optical damage threshold of silica pumped with ultrashort pulses offers unique possibilities for the study of optical excitations at high light intensities.

The laser radiation in Gaussian mode produced by a regeneratively amplified mode-locked (120-fs pulse duration, 200-kHz repetition rate) Ti:sapphire laser operating at a wavelength of 800 nm was used in the experiments. Glass samples of ~3-mm thickness were placed on a stage under the optical microscope (Fig. 1.16). The infrared laser radiation reflected by a dichroic mirror inside the microscope was focused via a 20× objective onto the sample. The pump spot size in the focus of the beam was 4.6 μm. Simultaneously, the irradiated spot was imaged in the visible spectral range via the microscope using a color CCD (charge-coupled device) camera.

During the experiments on Ge-doped (GeO_2 ~ 8 mol%) silica glass, strong blue luminescence (with a center wavelength at 410 nm) of defect states (Ge-ODC) was observed (Fig. 1.17). Using a cross-sectional area for Ge-ODC of 5×10^{-18} cm^2 [88], the absorption value at 240 nm for our sample of ~15 cm^{-1} gives a Ge-ODC concentration of about 10^{19} cm^{-3}. This luminescence (triplet luminescence) can be excited via the singlet–singlet transition by absorption of three pump photons or one UV photon of the third harmonic of the pump followed by quick nonradiative decay (with a decay time of 1 ns) to the long-lived triplet level (Fig. 1.18).

When the pump (10-mW average power, 0.4-MW peak power, 2.5×10^{12} W/cm^2 intensity in the focus of a beam) was focused slightly (~50 μm)

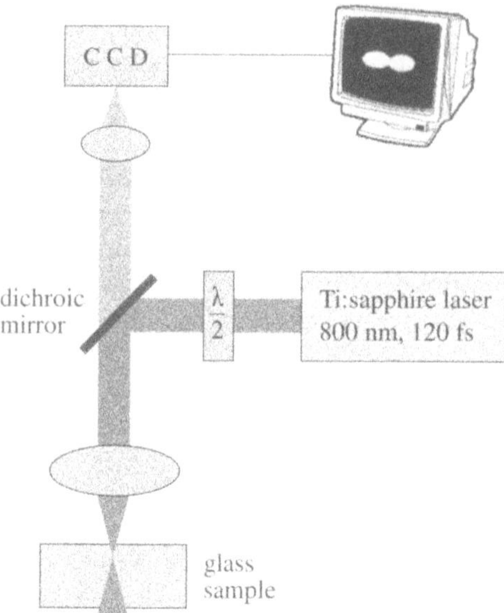

Fig. 1.16. Schematic of the experimental setup. CCD: color charge-coupled device camera

above the surface of the sample, the shape of the spot of the blue luminescence imaged via the microscope and CCD camera was circular (Fig. 1.19a). Unexpectedly, it was discovered that when the pump was focused inside the sample the spatial isotropy of the blue luminescence could be broken (Fig. 1.19b). The luminescence scattering increased along the direction of pump polarization, while the circular shape of pump beam remained unchanged. When the direction of the pump polarization was rotated by using a half-wave plate, the elongated pattern of the blue luminescence followed this rotation (Fig. 1.19c–e). It should be noted that the blue luminescence was not polarized and self-focusing was not observed at peak powers used in the experiments. This phenomenon was named the "propeller effect," due to the propeller-like shape of the luminescence spot in the focus of the pump beam. *The observed phenomenon represents the first evidence of anisotropic light scattering which peaks in the plane of light polarization in isotropic media.*

How can this phenomenon be explained? First, an estimate is taken of the size of the light spot ($1/e^2$ intensity diameter) produced by the isotropically emitted luminescence in the focal plane of the microscope objective. Assuming that the luminescence is excited by the three-photon absorption of the pump at wavelength $\lambda = 800$ nm in a Gaussian beam with radius $r_0 = 2.3$ μm or by the one-photon absorption of the UV (267 nm) third harmonic of the pump and that it is emitted isotropically along the length of the beam waist, the size of the light spot a can be estimated to be $a \leq \pi r_0^2 n/\lambda = 30$ μm, where $n = 1.45$ is the refractive index of silica glass. This estimate is in a

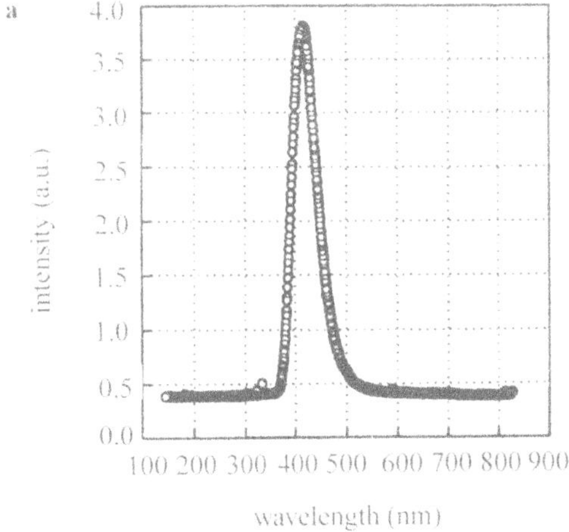

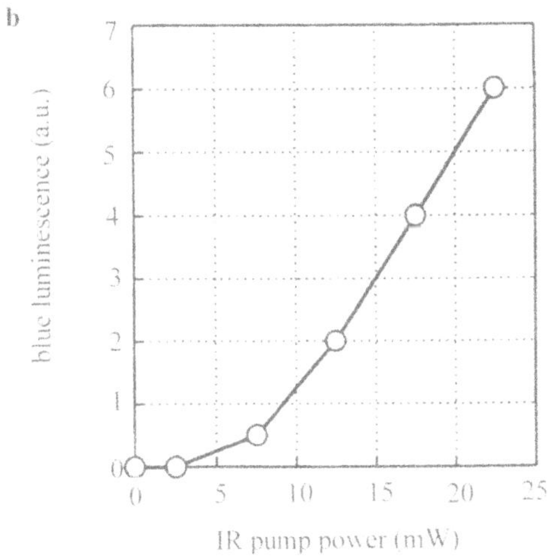

Fig. 1.17. (**a**) Spectrum and (**b**) pump-power dependence of the blue luminescence

good agreement with the transverse section of the blue propeller (Fig. 1.19b–e), which could be justified by ordinary (isotropic) luminescence. However, the longitudinal size of the blue propeller (~100 μm) is about 4.5 times larger than the transverse size of the propeller (Fig. 1.20). The fact that the blue luminescence is elongated along the direction of pump polarization indicates that some additional momentum is acquired by the photons in this direction. Such a transformation of the momentum could be caused by photoelectrons moving in the direction of pump polarization. Photoelectrons with an anisotropic momentum distribution can be created via the multiphoton ionization of defects (two-photon ionization of Ge-ODC from the long-lived

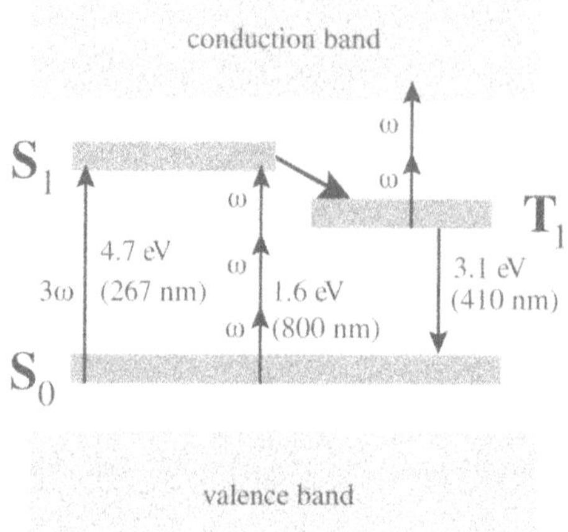

Fig. 1.18. Energy-level diagram of a Ge–Si defect in silica glass with the possible channels of excitation

triplet state) by the linearly polarized light of high intensity (Fig. 1.18). Indeed, it is well known that the angular distribution of photoelectrons can be elongated along the direction of the light polarization: $\mathrm{d}\sigma/\mathrm{d}\Omega \propto 1 + \cos^2\theta$, where $\mathrm{d}\sigma/\mathrm{d}\Omega$ is the differential scattering cross section of electrons and θ is the angle between the field-amplitude vector, $\boldsymbol{E}$, and the electron-momentum vector, $\boldsymbol{k}_\mathrm{e}$ [89, 90]. Assuming that the momentum relaxation time is about 100 fs and the speed of photoelectrons is 10^7 cm/s (which can be easily reached in the process of photoionization), the distance of a photoelectron path along the direction of the light polarization is about 10 nm. The distance between defects responsible for the blue luminescence (Ge-ODC at concentration of 10^{19} cm^{-3}) in the glass samples is ~10 nm, which is of the same order as the free path length estimated above. It is clear that the photoelectrons can be involved in a microscopic movement (with a displacement of the order of 10 nm) in the direction of the light polarization. Microscopic (much less than a wavelength of light) displacements of the photoelectrons in the direction of light polarization can lead to the anisotropic fluctuations of the dielectric constant. Such fluctuations are obviously stronger in the direction of light polarization (in the direction of electron movement) compared to the perpendicular direction. The fluctuations of the dielectric constant along the direction of light polarization induce index inhomogeneities which are elongated in the direction perpendicular to the pump polarization and which have $\boldsymbol{k}$ vectors of spatial harmonics parallel to the direction of polarization. The anisotropic inhomogeneities scatter photons (e.g., the ultraviolet photons of the third harmonic of the pump) in the plane of light polarization. Considering the angle of scattering $\varphi = 80°$ ($\tan\varphi = 3b/2z_0$, where $b = 100$ µm is the longitudinal size of the "blue propeller," $2z_0 = 2\pi r_0^2 n / \lambda = 60$ µm is the

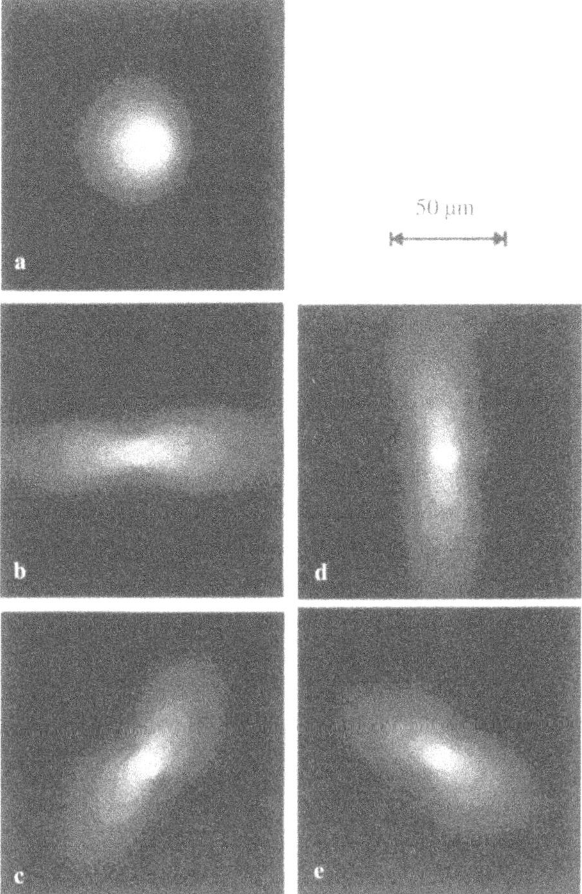

Fig. 1.19a-e. Photographs of the blue luminescence spots in the focus of the linearly polarized pump. (**a**) Pump is focused above the sample. (**b–e**) Pump with four different orientations of polarization is focused inside the sample. Notice that the blue luminescence spot is elongated in the direction of pump polarization. The pink spot is produced by the pump leaking through the dichroic mirror

waist length of a pump beam), the size of these inhomogeneities is estimated to be $d \leq \lambda_{\mathrm{UV}}/(2n \sin\varphi) = 90$ nm, where $\lambda_{\mathrm{UV}} = 267$ nm.

It should be pointed out that the scattering phenomenon described above must have strong wavelength dependence (λ^{-4}), which is similar to the wavelength dependence of Rayleigh scattering of light. Rayleigh scattering is normally caused by isotropic density fluctuations and the anisotropy in the scattering (the scattering is stronger in the direction perpendicular to the light polarization) is explained by the fact that a dipole does not radiate along its axis. In contrast to Rayleigh scattering the anisotropy in the observed scattering is caused by the anisotropy of the fluctuations themselves. The

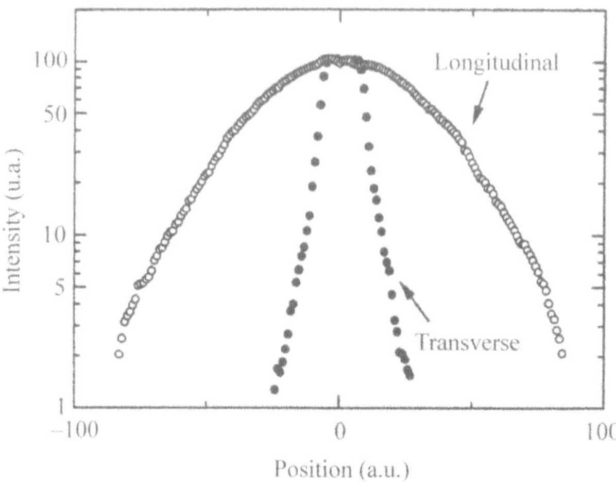

Fig. 1.20. Intensity distributions along the long axis of the "blue propeller" and in the perpendicular direction

strong dependence of the scattering on the wavelength explains the absence of noticeable changes in the shape of the infrared pump.

Alternatively, the photoelectrons involved in the movement in the direction of light polarization directly transfer their momentum to the UV photons, e.g., via Compton-like scattering. The electron momentum at a speed of 10^7 cm/s is about 50 times larger than the UV photon momentum. Even partial transfer of the electron momentum to the photons would create significant anisotropy in the light scattering. The photons, scattered indirectly (via the $\boldsymbol{k}$ vectors of the inhomogeneities) or directly by the photoelectrons, excite the anisotropic patterns of blue luminescence.

In other words, the pattern of the angular distribution of photoelectrons is imaged by the pattern of blue luminescence. In support of this explanation, it was found that there is a striking similarity between the observed patterns of the blue luminescence and the patterns of the angular distribution of photoelectrons in the experiments on the above-threshold ionization (ATI) of atoms [89]. Indeed, the angular distribution of photoelectrons elongated in the direction of light polarization has been observed in many experiments on atoms; the results reported here can be interpreted as the first evidence of such a distribution in glass.

2. Induction of Permanent Structures by Ultrashort Laser Pulses

2.1 Introduction

Glass was first found more than 5000 years ago. Now, it is widely used in daily life. We could even say that today's highly civilized society would not be what it is without glass. Why is glass so widely used? It is because glass is homogeneous, is transparent and can be easily fabricated to various forms such as bottles, large flat plates and fibers. Moreover, almost all of the elements in the periodic table, such as rare-earths, transition metals and noble metals, can be "stuffed" into glass. This results in splendidly colorful glass with various functions.

However, glass has its weak points due to its random network structure and defects introduced in fabrication processes. For example, glass is brittle and heavy, therefore the market of the glass bottle is now eaten away by metal, plastic, and paper containers. In addition, the intensity of luminescence of glass is weaker than that of a crystal with the similar composition due to the random structure of glass. In the coming information technology era, novel optical elements with the following functions are expected: ultrafast switching, optical memory with ultrahigh storage density, and optical amplification fabricated by glass. It is necessary to set up a new research concept for developing glass with novel optical functions.

As described in the Introduction, we proposed a basic research concept of "induced structure" in 1994 [3]. We especially paid attention to the fact that glass is metastable from the viewpoint of thermal dynamics. A metastable state of glass can be easily changed to other states after the injection of an external electromagnetic field. Novel optical functions can be achieved if the external structure induced by the electromagnetic field can be controlled in an active manner.

In Chap. 1, momentary electron states in Bi_2O_3-based, chalcogenide, and nanoparticle containing glasses, organic solution and Ge-doped silica glass induced by ultrashort laser pulses were discussed. When the irradiation conditions of the ultrashort laser pulses were controlled, the formation of various permanent induced structures in the glasses after the laser irradiation could be observed. In this chapter, the mechanism whereby an area with an altered refractive index is formed using a focused femtosecond laser is introduced [4]; in addition, a novel method of writing 3-dimensional optical waveguide in glasses by translating the focal point of the laser beam is described [5]. Three-dimensional control of the formation of microcrystals [7] and single crystals [13] is also demonstrated. Optical poling of Ge-doped silica glasses, Bi_2O_3-based glasses and dye-doped polymers for second harmonic generation is shown in the last section [11, 17, 91, 92]. All of the techniques open new possibilities in the field of integrated optics.

2.2 Induction of Permanent Structure with Femtosecond Laser Pulses and the Mechanism Utilized

Since the 1970s, many investigations on the effects of UV radiation damage in high-silica glasses (especially Ge-doped silica glass) have been performed with the objective of producing optical devices (e.g., Bragg gratings) in fibers and thin films [13]. In contrast, laser damage by visible and IR laser light has received little attention, owing to the low photon energy at these wavelengths. The development of high-energy-density femtosecond pulse lasers, however, has prompted us to investigate the unexplored potential for inducing multiphoton photochemical reactions and optical devices in glass by use of lasers of sub-UV photon energy. The results presented here show that stable, visible laser damage and photoinduced refractive-index alteration can be achieved with a visible-red-light femtosecond laser.

A regeneratively amplified 810-nm Ti:sapphire laser that emits 120-fs, 200-kHz, mode-locked pulses and delivers an average power of 975 mW was used in the present study. The 5-mm-diameter beam was focused through 5–20× microscope objectives and injected into polished plates of dry and wet silica, Ge-doped silica, borate, soda lime silicate, and fluorozirconate (ZBLAN) glasses (Fig. 2.1). The average power of the laser beam at the sample location was controlled to be between approximately 40 and 800 mW by neutral-density filters that were inserted between the laser and the microscope objective. With the help of an XYZ stage, the samples were translated at rates of 100–10 000 μm/s either parallel or perpendicular to the incident laser beam, thus creating visible damage lines inside the glasses.

For the silica and the Ge-doped silica glasses, cross sections of the damage lines were made by cutting the samples and polishing the exposed surfaces. Refractive-index profiles of the cross sections were measured with a microellipsometer. For UV and electron spin resonance (ESR) spectroscopic measurements, scans were taken before and after identical damage line patterns were written in glass plates using a 10× microscope objective and translating the samples perpendicular to the incident light at a rate of 100 μm/s. For these samples, the average laser power at the sample was ~470 mW. Assuming a square-wave pulse, a uniform beam intensity, and a diameter of the laser focal point that is equal to the thickness of the observed damage lines (~6 μm), the samples were found to experience 12 000 pulses/spot, and each spot was subjected to a dose of 100 MJ/cm^2 during a single pass of the laser.

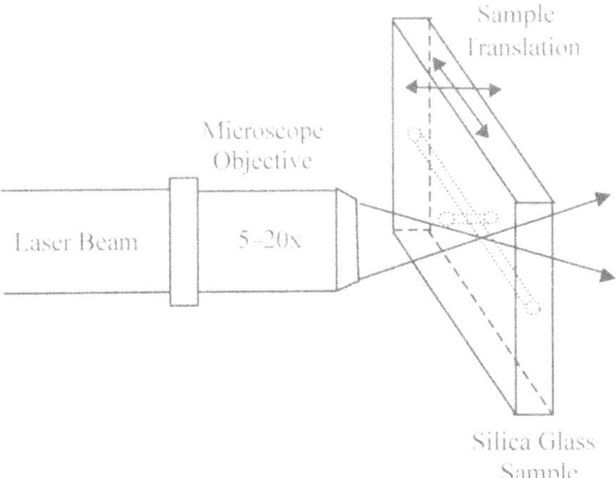

Fig. 2.1. Schematic of optical waveguide writing by femtosecond laser pulses

For all translation speeds and directions, structural changes were induced along the path traversed by the focal point of the laser, and colorless, transparent linear damage marks were produced inside every glass sample that was probed. These damage lines and their cross sections were visible when transmitted light optical microscopy was used and were stable at room temperature. When the laser beam was focused on the near surface of the samples, machining of the glass, most likely due to thermal shock, occurred at high laser powers; however, when the beam was focused on the interior of the samples, no cracking was detected in any of the glasses regardless of laser power. For the high-silica glasses, the damage lines produced when the samples were translated parallel to the axis of the laser beam were roughly cylindrical, with diameters of approximately 12 to 5 μm for the 5–20× microscope objectives. The cross sections of the lines created when the samples were translated perpendicular to the laser axis were elliptical because of the depths of focus of the lenses; the long dimension of the cross sections ranged from approximately 275 to 100 μm for the 5–20× lenses. For the high-silica glasses, the size of the damage area was fairly constant with changing translation speeds. For the soda lime silicate, ZBLAN, and borate glasses, however, the dimensions of the damage area changed significantly with translation speed, and when these glasses were held motionless in the laser beam, the damage spread radially from the focal point of the laser with time as if the glass were being slowly melted.

Because of the potential telecommunications applications for the pure and the Ge-doped silica glasses, the properties of the damage in these glasses were examined first. Using a microellipsometer, refractive-index profiles across the cross sections of damage lines formed perpendicular to the laser beam were measured. For the pure and the Ge-doped silica glasses, a single pass of the laser produced refractive-index increases of approximately 0.015 and 0.01,

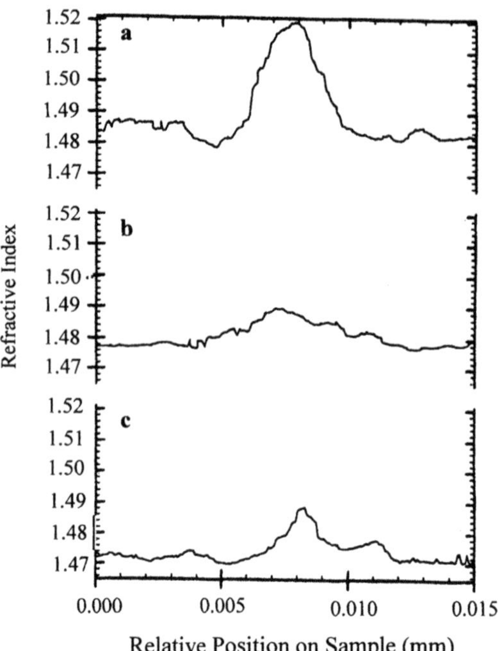

Fig. 2.2a–c. Refractive-index mappings across the cross sections of damage lines created by translation of the samples perpendicular to the laser beam with a 10× lens, an average laser power of 470 mW, and a sample translation rate of 100 μm/s for (**a**) $3GeO_2$–$97SiO_2$ after 10 passes of the laser along an identical route, (**b**) $3GeO_2$–$97SiO_2$ after a single pass of the laser, and (**c**) pure silica after a single pass of the laser. The visible dimensions of the damage cross sections are approximately 6 μm × 180 μm for all the damage marks, so the outer limits of the mappings represent the refractive index of the surrounding glass

respectively, at the center of the damage region (Fig. 2.2). After 10 passes of the laser, the refractive index at the center of the damage was ~0.035 higher than that of the surrounding glass in the Ge-doped silica. The refractive indices of the as-received glasses vary by less than ±0.0005 across the probed region according to the manufacturers' specifications, and the error in the ellipsometer measurements is less than ±0.01. Thus, the refractive-index increase shown in curve (a) of Fig. 2.2, at least, is unquestionably real.

According to ESR measurements [93] (Fig. 2.3), the pure and the Ge-doped silica glasses showed increases in the concentrations of Si E' and Ge E' centers, respectively, and the formation of peroxy radicals and nonbridging oxygen hole centers was observed in both glasses. The UV difference spectra (Fig. 2.4) are in agreement with these assignments [94–96]; they also show a possible decrease in the concentration of neutral-oxygen monovacancies (NOMVs) in the Ge-doped glass [97]. In addition, unidentified broad absorption bands running from 320 to 700 nm were formed in both glasses.

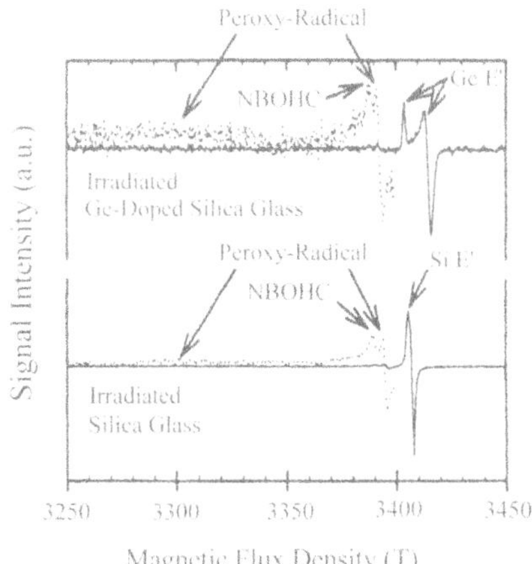

Fig. 2.3. Electron-spin-resonance (ESR) spectra of SiO_2 and $3GeO_2$ $97SiO_2$ glasses after laser irradiation. The *solid* and the *dotted curves* indicate ESR spectra collected with 1-mW and 50-mW microwave powers, respectively. The as-received pure-silica glass contained immeasurably small defect concentrations, and the as-received Ge-doped silica glass contained minute concentrations of ESR-detectable defects compared with the damaged glass. NBOHC: nonbridging oxygen hole centers

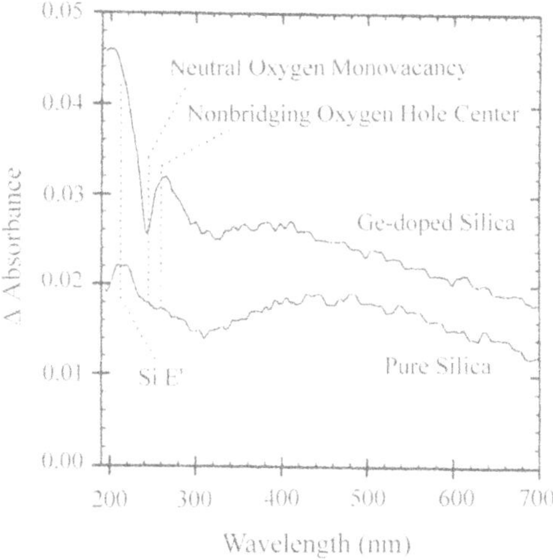

Fig. 2.4. UV difference spectra of the high-silica glasses before and after they were laser irradiated. The Ge-doped silica spectrum is vertically offset by +0.01 for clarity. The noise in these spectra is due to the damaged region, which comprises less than 5 vol. % of the glass probed by the spectrometer beam

The creation of defects in the high-silica glasses by 810-nm radiation suggests that the damage mechanism involves a multiphoton process. To our knowledge, such damage at this wavelength has not been reported, and it is suspected that the high pulse energy of the femtosecond laser is responsible for the effect. The photoinduced refractive-index increase in pure-silica glass also appears to be a new observation.

Traditionally, it has been suggested that the refractive-index increase resulting from UV irradiation of Ge-doped silica glasses arises from the bleaching of the NOMV band at 5.06 eV (245 nm), owing to the reaction of these sites to form Ge E' centers [75, 98]. More recently, however, it was shown that this bleaching mechanism can account for only a small portion of the refractive-index alteration [99], and a model based on densification and strain in the glass has been proposed [100]. The observed refractive-index increases in both Ge-doped and pure-silica glasses support the idea that the alteration is not caused primarily by the NOMV bleaching mechanism, as no NOMVs are found in the UV spectrum of the pure silica. From microscopic observation of the damage region during irradiation, the structural changes appear similar to what might be expected for localized melting, and it is suspected that the local structural rearrangement is significant. However, there is as yet no direct evidence of densification. It is also not known whether true melting and rapid quenching occur, whether the glass experiences a combination of defect formation and structural relaxation toward metastable equilibrium, or whether the structural changes are of a different nature. In addition, it is unclear what effect the unidentified absorption bands in Fig. 2.4 have on the refractive index.

The refractive-index increases observed here for the high-silica glasses are large enough for the creation of optical devices and waveguides in bulk glasses; the ability to restrict the refractive-index alteration to the region scanned by the focal point of the laser allows one to write complex, 3-dimensional patterns in the glass. Writing damage lines perpendicular to the incident light beam provides the most flexibility for writing planar patterns and allows multiple pattern layers to be created by simply changing the focus depth of the beam. Although the lines written perpendicular to the laser are elliptical, it should be possible to produce cylindrical damage lines that can serve as light conduits by varying parameters such as the aperture of the microscope lens, the laser wavelength, and the sample thermal history.

The possibility to create photoinduced refractive-index alteration in glass was demonstrated by focused, femtosecond laser irradiation at sub-UV wavelengths. This is important because it is easy to design optical systems that can manipulate this low-photon-energy light without causing laser damage except at the desired focal point of the beam. Moreover, it was possible to create visible but transparent laser damage without cracks in every type of glass examined. With improvements in the shape of the damage area, damage lines formed by this process may one day be used as waveguides in optical circuits. The formation of optical waveguide by femtosecond laser pulses will be discussed in the next section.

2.3 Photowritten Three-Dimensional Optical Waveguides

In the previous section, we reported the effect of femtosecond laser irradiation on various types of glasses [11]. Large increases ($>10^{-2}$) in the refractive index were observed in the damage area induced in bulk silica glass or germanosilicate glass samples by the femtosecond laser [11]. Moreover, round elliptical damage lines have been written inside various glasses with femtosecond laser pulses. The damage lines are expected to function as optical waveguides. Because of the similarities with optical fibers in terms of light guiding and confinement, the waveguide structures are very promising for realizing compact, all-solid-state lasers and amplifiers. However, most of the previous fabrication methods of optical glass waveguides have been confined to physical vapor deposition [101] or ionic exchange techniques [102]. There have been few attempts to produce an optical glass waveguide by photoinduced alteration of the refractive index with femtosecond laser pulses.

In this section, characteristics of permanent photowritten optical waveguides produced by scanning a focused ultrashort laser are introduced. The ultrashort pulses (120 fs) in Gaussian mode produced by a regeneratively amplified Ti:sapphire laser were utilized for the experiments.

Figure 2.5 shows an array of visible laser damage spots inside silica glass, each induced by a single pulse, where laser wavelength and peak power were 800 nm and 10^7 W, respectively. The visible laser damage is formed only in the focused region, only because there is the optical intensity of the nonlinear optical processes, such as multiphoton absorption, above the damage threshold. Using a femtosecond laser with a high repetition rate, it is possible to write waveguides by forming laser damage spots in a continuous trace. In

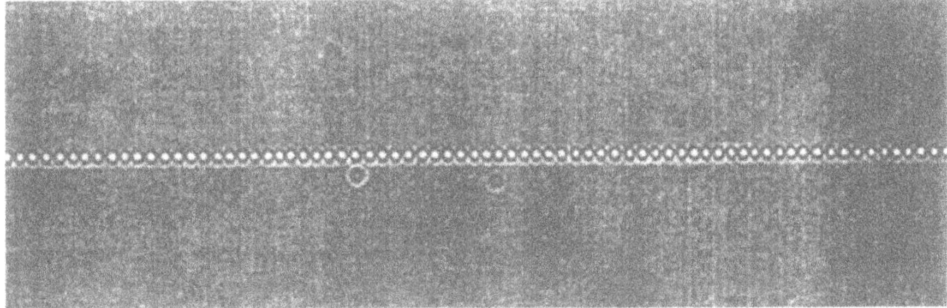

Fig. 2.5. Example of visible laser damage spots inside silica glass, each formed with a single pulse

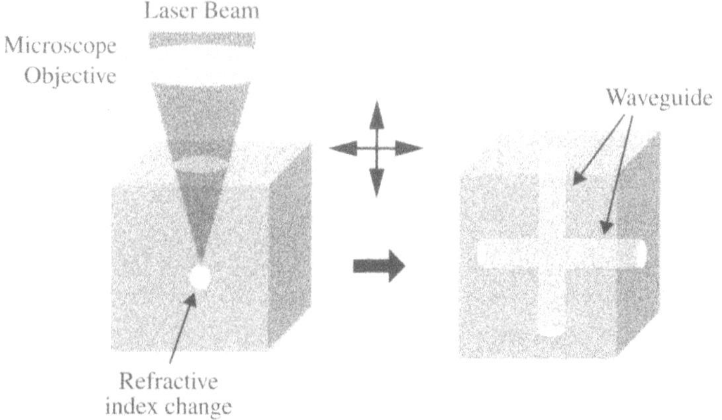

Fig. 2.6. Schematic of optical waveguide writing by high-repetition laser pulses

the present study, the waveguides were written by focusing the laser pulses through a microscope objective and translating the glass sample parallel to the axis of the laser beam (see Fig. 2.6). The refractive-index changes were induced along the path traversed by the focal point, and the waveguides were written inside various types of glasses such as fused and synthetic silica, Ge-doped silica, borosilicate, borate, phosphate, fluorophosphate, fluoride, and chalcogenide glasses. Figure 2.7 shows typical photowritten waveguides formed inside synthetic silica, borosilicate, fluoride, and chalcogenide glasses with 800-nm, 120-fs, 200-kHz, mode-locked pulses focused by a 10× microscope objective. The glass samples were translated at a rate of 20 μm/s in all cases. The waveguides were stable at room temperature. In the formation of waveguides, initial laser-induced damage thresholds differ for each type of glass. It is noted that the multiphoton absorption coefficient, the band-gap, the bond dissociation energy, and the thermal properties, such as the thermal conductivity, the thermal expansion coefficient, and the melting temperature, of each type of glass were essentially different. Therefore, the different damage thresholds can be explained by assuming that laser-induced damage results from multiphoton ionization, Joule heating, and/or conventional heating by multiphoton transition and/or plasma formation. Figure 2.8 shows an atomic-force microscope observation of the surface of the end of a silica glass core. This observation suggests that a densification of the glass is occurring in the laser-irradiated region. The increases in refractive index can be related to the local densifying which occurs at the end; however, the initial process of optical waveguide formation may be accompanied by various phenomena, such as the formation of color centers or lattice defects and melting of a very small area.

The effects of the pulse width, average power and radiation time of the laser on the refractive index variation and core size of optical waveguides were also examined. The results obtained indicated that control of the refractive-

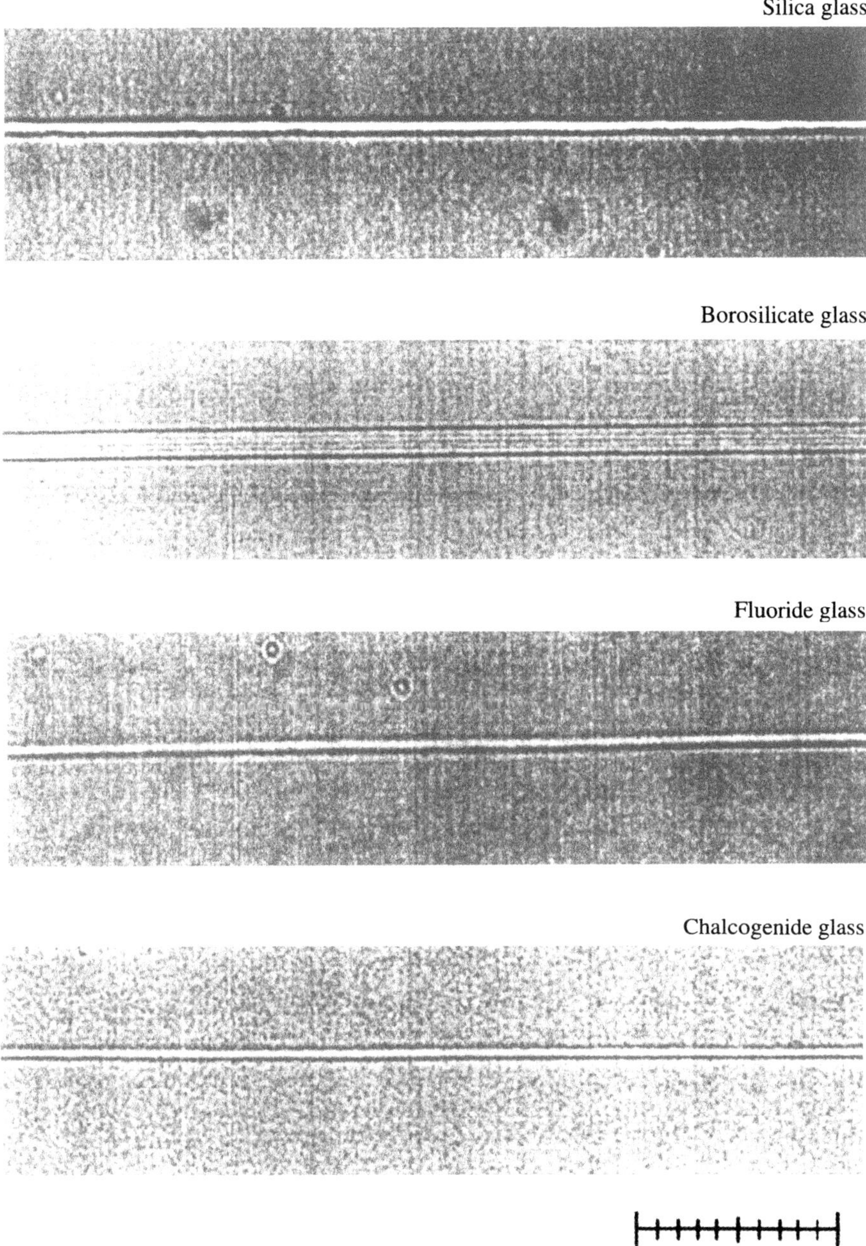

Fig. 2.7. Microscope photograph of photowritten optical waveguides in various glasses

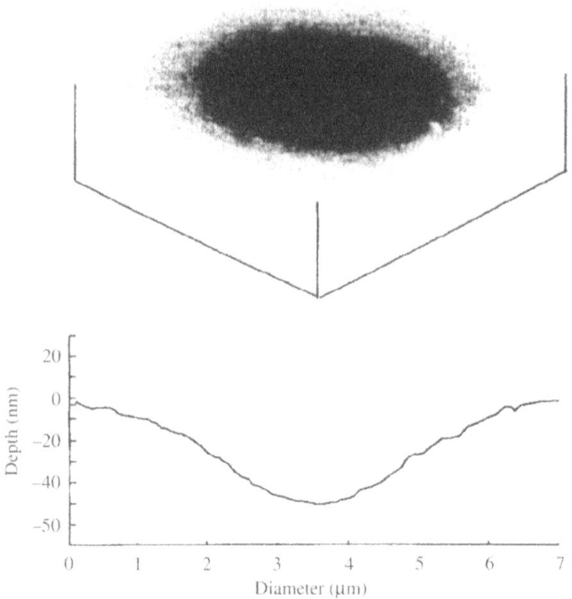

Fig. 2.8. Atomic-force microscope observation of the surface of the end of a silica glass core after laser irradiation

index difference and core diameter was possible by adjustment of the writing conditions. For the waveguides written in a fluoride glass, field-intensity distributions of a guided light were observed using a CCD camera. Near-field patterns at 800 nm for fluoride-glass waveguides of 15-mm length are shown in Fig. 2.9a–c, where the core diameters are 8, 17, and 25 μm, respectively. The core diameters of the waveguides shown in this figure were controlled by changing the average power of the writing laser. At a core diameter of 8 μm, it is only possible to propagate the LP_{01} fundamental mode, which is nearly Gaussian. In addition, it can be seen that the higher-order modes, such as LP_{11} and LP_{22}, were also propagated with an increase in the core diameter (see Fig. 2.9b and c). For the waveguide in Fig. 2.9a, the far-field patterns and intensity distributions of transmitted beams obtained at different wavelengths are shown in Fig. 2.10. For a wavelength of 633 nm, a complicated intensity distribution resulting from the overlap of several modes was observed, while the mode profile observed at 810 nm was nearly Gaussian. This fact reveals that the cutoff wavelength of the single mode exists between 633 and 810 nm. It was confirmed that the cutoff wavelength was around 800 nm by examining the wavelength dependence of the mode profiles at several wavelengths ranging from 633 nm to 1 μm. In addition, from the analysis of a near-field pattern by Hermite–Gaussian fitting, it was proven that this waveguide was

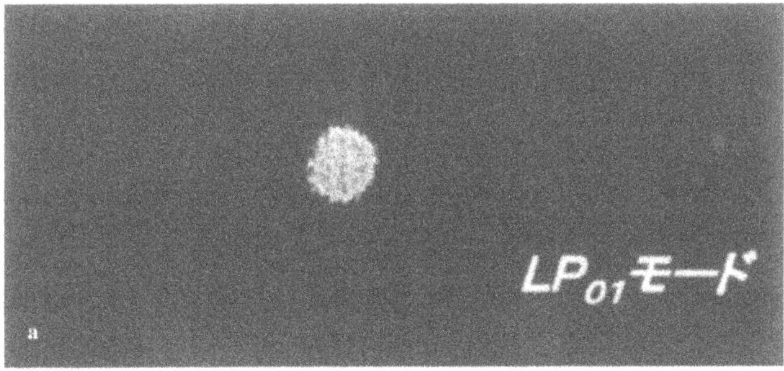

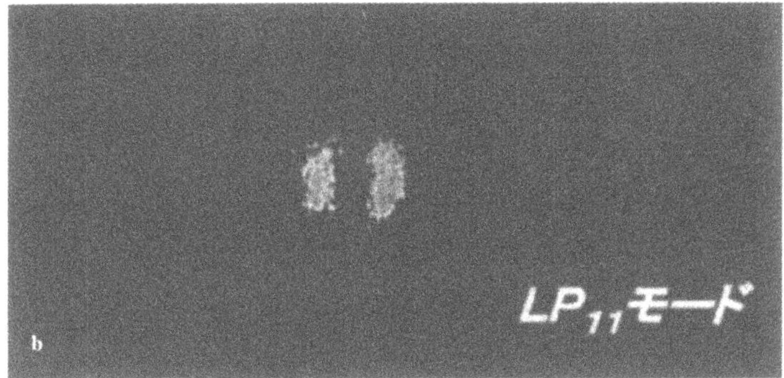

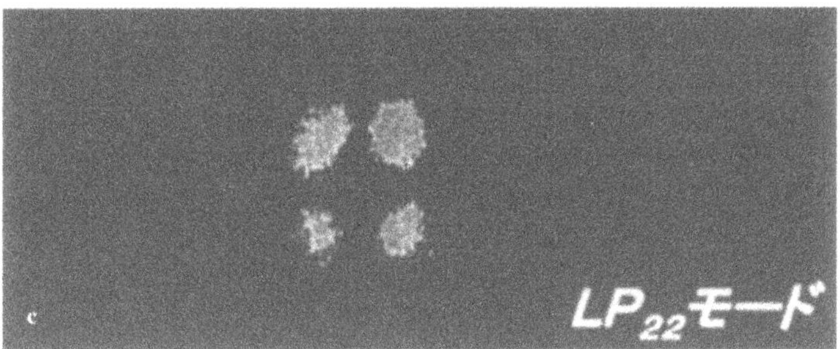

Fig. 2.9. Near-field patterns at 800 nm on fluoride-glass waveguides where the core diameters are (a) 8 μm, (b) 17 μm, and (c) 25 μm

a graded index type with a quadratic distribution in which the refractive indices of the core center and base glass were 1.502 and 1.499, respectively.

Because the reaction area can only be induced near the focal point of the laser beam, it is possible to write a 3-dimensional optical waveguide inside a glass using this technique. This technique will lead to new possibilities in the field of integrated optics and 3-dimensional optical circuits, especially for the development of compact, all-solid-state lasers, amplifiers, and optical switches.

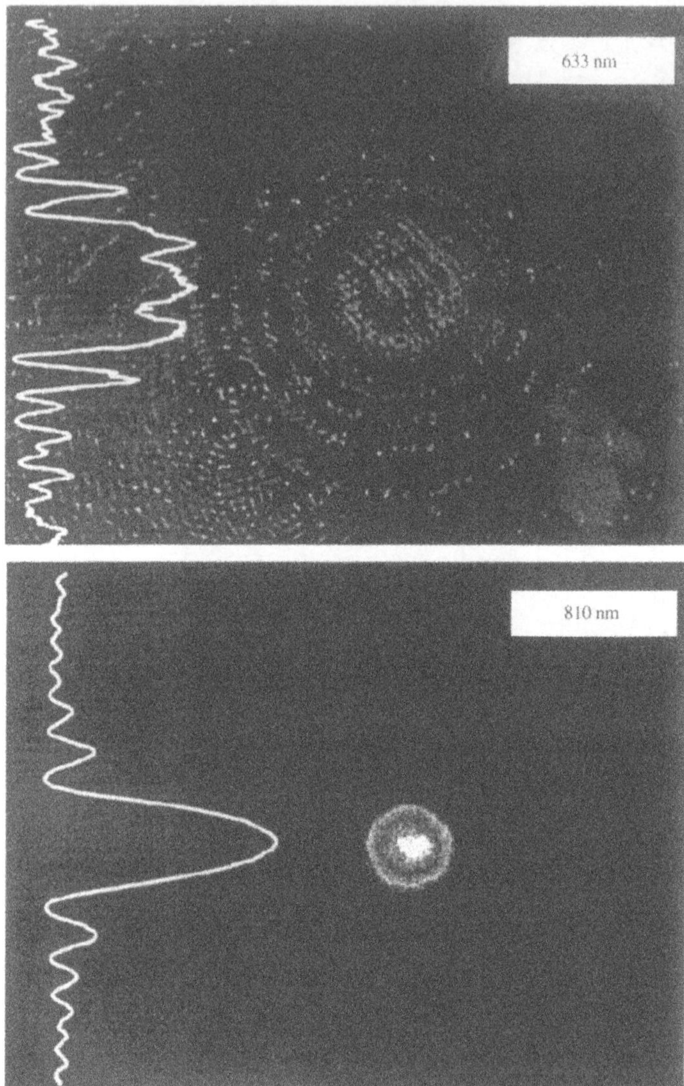

Fig. 2.10. Far-field patterns of a fluoride waveguide for different wavelengths. The sample was the same as that shown in Fig. 2.9a

2.4 Three-Dimensional Control of Microcrystal Precipitation in Glass

It is well known that glasses containing noble metallic photosensitive ions such as Ag^+ and Au^+ together with cerium ions as the sensitizer show precipitation of crystallites when irradiated by UV light and exposed to subsequent heat treatment above the glass transition temperature, T_g [103, 104]. According to the theory by Stookey [105] and Stookey and Schuler [106], the crystallization mechanism is explained as follows: Irradiation with UV light causes emission of photoelectrons from Ce^{3+}, whose absorption band is in the vicinity of 315 nm. These photoelectrons are trapped at Ce^{4+} and then captured by the noble metallic ions due to the subsequent heat treatment to form metallic atoms. When heated to higher temperatures, nonmetallic microcrystallites are precipitated using metallic colloids as nuclei. It should be noted that the use of UV light resonant with Ce^{3+} absorption results in the crystallization of the entire area exposed adjacent to the glass surface, and spot crystallization beneath the surface is impossible even when a mask is used. On the other hand, using a focused nonresonant short-pulse laser beam, crystallization seems to occur selectively because of a multiphoton reaction in the specific area where photon density is sufficiently high, similar to what has been described in the previous sections of this chapter. Such nonresonant photosensitive crystallization has not yet been investigated. In this section, the control of 3-dimensional microscopic crystallization within a photosensitive glass using femtosecond or nanosecond laser pulses is demonstrated.

The glass used in the experiments was an aluminosilicate glass containing Ag^+ ions and Ce^{3+} ions, in which NaF crystallites could be precipitated using the conventional process. The glass specimens were irradiated with a femtosecond laser, a nanosecond laser or a UV continuous-wave (cw) lamp. The irradiation sources employed were (a) an optical parametric amplifier (OPA) which emits 4-μJ, 150-fs, 1-kHz, mode-locked pulses by pumping with a regeneratively amplified 800-nm Ti-sapphire laser, (b) a YAG-laser-pumped dye laser which emits 1-mJ, 3-ns, 10-Hz pulses, or (c) a high-pressure Hg lamp whose power density is 13 mW/cm^2.

A laser beam of 630-nm wavelength, nonresonant with Ce^{3+} absorption, was focused through a 20× microscope objective or a focusing lens with 50-mm focal length. The diameters of the beam before focusing through the objective or the lens were 8-mm or 3-mm, respectively. The power of the laser beam was controlled by neutral-density filters so as not to damage the specimens. The irradiated specimens were heated at 540°C for 30 min and held at 100°C for 3 h; then they were heated again at 580°C for 30 min to precipitate NaF crystallites. Whether the crystallization occurred or not was primarily evaluated by using a 2000× microscope. The precipitated crystallites were analyzed by X-ray diffraction analysis using a Rigaku Rint 2000 diffractometer with CuKα radiation. Photoluminescence spectroscopic measurements were

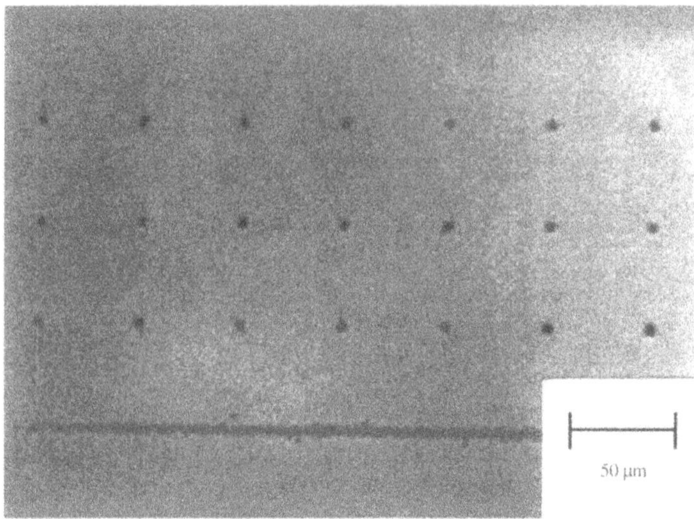

Fig. 2.11. Microscope photograph of the photosensitive glass containing Ag^+ and Ce^{3+} heat-treated after irradiation of femtosecond pulses focused by a 20× microscope objective at a wavelength of 630 nm with an average power of 80 μW at 1-kHz repetition for 5 s

performed using a monochromator (SPEX, 2704) with an ICCD (Princeton Instrument, ICCD-1024MG-1) to examine the photochemical process.

Figure 2.11 shows a microscope photograph exhibiting the features formed within the glass after spot irradiation of 5000 shots or scanning irradiation at the rate of 25 μm/s using the femtosecond pulses with a 80-nJ pulse energy though the objective, followed by heat treatment. It was determined that selective crystallization occurred at the focused irradiation area, and spot irradiation of femtosecond pulses caused precipitation of crystallites about 10 μm in diameter at the focal point beneath the surface. Since no damage or features were observed before the heat treatment, it was considered that the crystallites were precipitated from silver colloids caused by femtosecond laser irradiation or UV light irradiation. When using the nanosecond laser, on the other hand, no crystallization was observed even at a high energy density where plasma breakdown of the glass was likely to occur. Thus, a femtosecond nonresonant pulse is useful for 3-dimensional control of crystallite precipitation in photosensitive glasses. In order to investigate whether crystallization using a femtosecond laser has a threshold in pulse energy density, similar experiments were performed, varying the average power through the objective from 20 μW to 120 μW. Assuming a Gaussian beam profile, it was found that the threshold energy density existed at about 8 J/cm^2/pulse for spot irradiation at 1-kHz repetition for 5 s.

To confirm the precipitation of NaF microcrystallites, X-ray diffraction was measured for the samples which were heat-treated before and after ir-

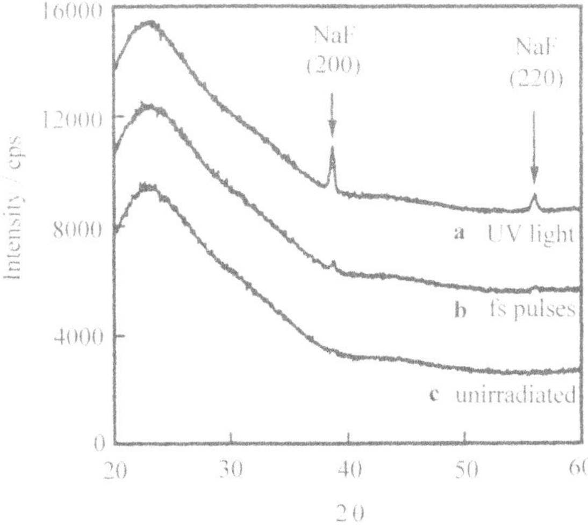

Fig. 2.12a–c. X-ray diffraction patterns of photosensitive glasses contaning Ag^+ and Ce^{3+}. Each sample was heat-treated after irradiation of (**a**) cw UV light from a high-pressure Hg lamp whose power density was 13 mW/cm^2 and (**b**) femtosecond pulses at a wavelength of 630 nm with an average power of 1.5 mW focused by a lens of 50-mm focal length. (**c**) Heat-treated without light irradiation. Miller indices of cubic NaF are indicated

radiation under various conditions. Figure 2.12 shows the X-ray diffraction patterns in a 2θ range of 20° to 60°. In this angular range, there are no peaks for the unirradiated sample. In contrast, two peaks were observed for the samples heat-treated after irradiation with (a) UV light and (b) femtosecond pulses. Since the crystallized region of the sample irradiated with femtosecond pulses is very small, the signal intensity is weak compared to that of UV light irradiation. The positions for the cubic structure of NaF are also shown in Fig. 2.12. The peak positions in the X-ray diffraction pattern of these two samples are in good agreement with those of cubic NaF. Thus, the precipitated crystallites in the femtosecond-pulse-irradiated glass are same as those in UV-light irradiated glass and have the cubic structure of NaF.

Figure 2.13 shows the photoluminescence spectra of the sample when excited by cw UV light from a xenon lamp monochromated at the wavelength of 315 nm and from a 630-nm femtosecond laser beam from the OPA. When the sample was excited using 315-nm UV light, emissions at about 380 nm were observed and are assignable to the 4f–5d transition of Ce^{3+} ions [107, 108]. This result indicates that the crystallization occurs using colloidal Ag as nuclei, which are created by the photochemical reaction $Ce^{3+} + Ag^+ \rightarrow Ce^{4+} + Ag^0$. When the sample was excited by a 630-nm femtosecond laser beam, the emissions were observed at about 450 nm. The peak at around 630 nm is due to the excitation light. Since the emission spectrum of the femtosecond-pulse-irradiated sample is different from that of the UV-light-

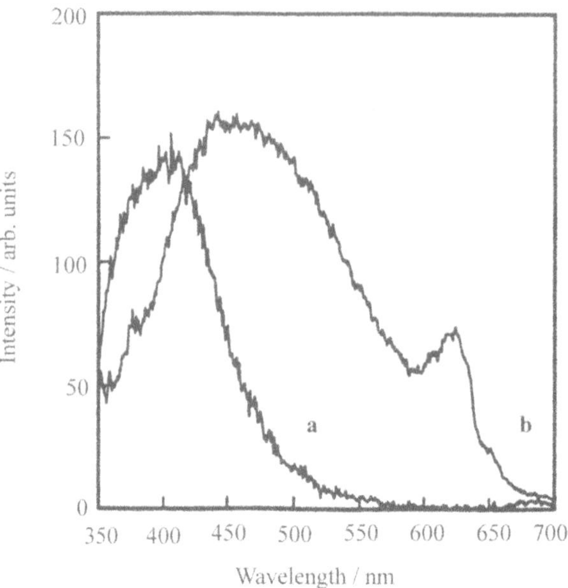

Fig. 2.13a,b. Photoluminescence spectra of photosensitive glass containing Ag^{+} and Ce^{3+} excited by (**a**) cw UV light from a Xe lamp monochromated at a wavelength of 315 nm and (**b**) femtosecond laser pulses at a wavelength of 630 nm with an average power of 700 μW focused by a lens of 50-mm focal length. The peak around 630 nm in (**b**) is due to the excitation light

irradiated sample, the photoreactions in these processes are considered to be different.

Generally, crystallization of glass occurs due to nucleation and crystal growth processes [109]. Impurities, structural imperfections and interfaces are well known to be nuclei. After femtosecond laser irradiation, no damage such as cracks, which can cause crystallization, exist. Therefore, even when using nonresonant femtosecond pulses, colloidal Ag may be formed by a photoreduction, $Ag^{+} + e^{-} \rightarrow Ag^{0}$, such as in the case of UV light irradiation. However, it is not yet known what emits an electron to Ag^{+}. The facts that crystallization occurs by irradiation of nonresonant femtosecond pulses, while no crystallization occurs by irradiation of nanosecond pulses, and a threshold in pulse energy exists for the crystallization by irradiation of femtosecond pulses are considered evidence for the nonlinear reaction in crystallization due to the focused irradiation of the femtosecond laser beam. Due to the use of transparent light and the presence of a threshold for crystallization, it is possible to precipitate microcrystallites 3-dimensionally within the photosensitive glass. Therefore, this technique can be applied to create 3-dimensionally structured materials such as photonic band-gap crystals, which offer unique ways to control the propagation of light [110,111]. However, the crystal shape, the crystal size and the pitch between crystals should be optimized for their use as photonic crystals.

2.5 Space-Selective Precipitation of Single Crystals with Nonlinear Optical Function Within Glass Using a Femtosecond Laser Irradiation

So far, ultrashort laser pulses have been useful for observing and evaluating at a very high time resolution the dynamics of phenomena that occur within materials at speeds ranging from picoseconds to femtoseconds [112–114]. Such phenomena include direct interaction between light and atoms or molecules, the saturation process associated with the coherent state of materials, and the elementary process of chemical reactions. A short pulse width gives an extremely high intensity power, up to 10^{14} W/cm^2 at the focal point of the laser. Nevertheless, in general, it is difficult to produce an interaction effect between glass and light by a one-photon process when the excitation wavelength does not match the wavelength of the absorption region of the glass. However, as has been shown in Sects. 2.2–4, using an ultrashort-pulse laser operating at a nonabsorption wavelength with femtosecond-order pulse widths can surprisingly produce various types of strong interactions with glass [4,115]. Therefore, the development of high-energy-density femtosecond-pulse lasers has prompted us to investigate the unexplored potential for inducing multiphoton photochemical reactions. There is considerable interest in using femtosecond lasers to generate various kinds of interactions with many types of materials, especially in metastable glass.

In Sects. 2.2–4, a variety of photoinduced structure changes that are permanent at room temperature were introduced that can only be produced near the area of beam focus inside bulk glasses with femtosecond laser pulses [5, 116, 117]. When we irradiate the interior of the material with an ultrashort (femtosecond) pulse, energy is accumulated at a minute area for a very short time. This might be caused by such effects as ionization and plasma vibration, which are presumed to produce a dramatic rise in the temperature and internal pressure in the region of focus [118]. In taking advantage of this phenomenon, spherical melting regions can be formed at arbitrary sites within a bulk glass, and for the first time single crystals with special components grown from the melt. This section describes how BBO (β-BaB_2O_4) was successfully grown with excellent characteristics inside a bulk glass using a novel method utilizing a nonresonant ultrashort-pulse laser. The BBO exhibited excellent performance when used as frequency conversion-devices, especially in the UV region.

The glass used in this study was prepared with components of BaO, TiO_2 and B_2O_3. Femtosecond laser pulses were tightly focussed inside bulk glass to create localized nonlinear optical crystals of BBO. The irradiation source employed was a regeneratively amplified 800-nm Ti:sapphire laser that emitted

4-μJ, 130-fs, 200-kHz, mode-locked pulses. A microscope system was used to tightly focus the laser pulses inside the glass sample to grow localized frequency-conversion crystals.

When the laser beam was focused in the interior of the samples, no cracking was detected, and the only atomic-scale damage observed was that resulting from various phenomena such as (a) the formation of color centers or lattice defects, (b) local densification or (c) melting of a very small area (see Fig. 2.14). (When a nanosecond laser instead of a femtosecond laser is used, cracking due to thermal shock occurs at the focal point of the laser pulse in the interior of the glass samples.) Frequency-conversion crystals are generated near the focal point after irradiation conditions such as those leading to the damage shown in Fig. 2.14c. By using the photosensitivity attributable to a nonlinear optical process, visible laser damage was formed only inside the focused region, because nonlinearity occurs only in regions with optical intensity above the damage threshold. Figure 2.15 shows microscope photographs taken near the focal point (a) directly after focused irradiation and (b) 20 min and (c) 30 min after irradiation of the laser (800-nm wavelength, 200-kHz repetition frequency, 600-mW average output) in $BaO–TiO_2–B_2O_3$ glass via a 50× objective lens. From the measurement of X-ray diffraction patterns, it was confirmed that only BBO crystals were grown in the laser focused area (see Fig. 2.16). In a similar way, it was possible to generate $LiNbO_3$ frequency-conversion crystals from $Li_2O–K_2O–Nb_2O_5–SiO_2$ glass using a femtosecond laser.

Figure 2.17 shows the variation of emission spectra obtained by moving the laser focal point that accompanies the growth of frequency-conversion crystals. Although only broadening of 800-nm femtosecond laser pulses due to self-phase modulation was observed immediately after laser irradiation, with the passage of time it was confirmed that the intensity of second harmonic generation increases with the growth of frequency-conversion crystals. In addition, after frequency conversion crystals are created by femtosecond laser irradiation, second harmonic generation of blue laser can also be observed by the incidence of an infrared nanosecond-order-pulse laser. A spectrum of second harmonic generation from frequency conversion crystals observed by the incidence of 800-nm nanosecond laser pulses is shown in Fig. 2.18.

Moving the focal point of a laser beam relative to the position of the glass sample enables the melting region to move freely. Continuous generation of frequency-conversion crystals inside the glass was attempted by moving the melting zone. Polarizing-microscope photographs of the side (a, b) and cross-sectional (c) views of the crystal are shown in Fig. 2.19. Figure 2.19a and b show polarizing-microscope photographs taken in extinction and diagonal positions, respectively. Region A in Fig. 2.19a shows a crystal grown while moving the melting zone at a speed of 100 μ/s, while region B shows a crystal grown when this speed is 10 μm/s. The melting zone was moved continuously from region A to region B. The glass layer situated at the periphery of the

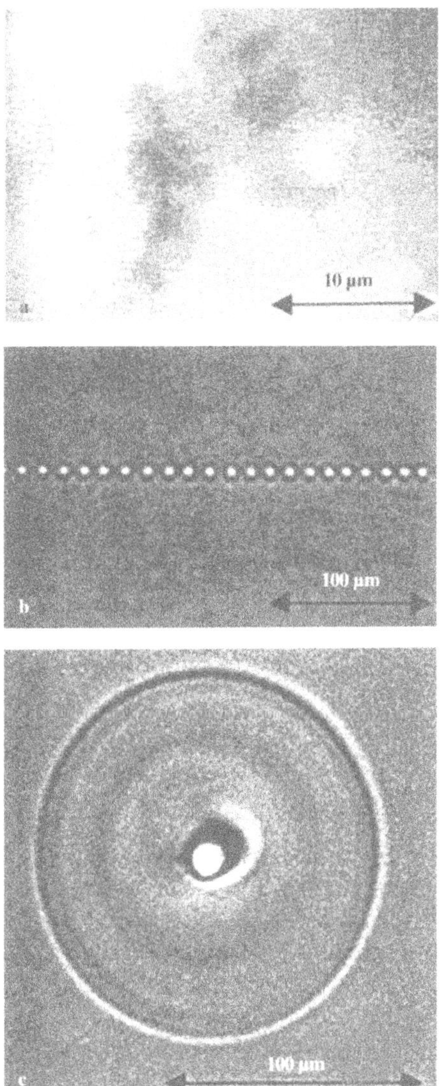

Fig. 2.14a–c. Damage caused by focusing a femtosecond laser in the interior of the glass. (**a**) Damage in the interior caused by 1-μJ pulses focused through a lens of 100-mm focal length. (**b**) Damage in the interior caused by 1-μJ pulses focused through a 10× objective lens. (**c**) Damage in the interior caused by 4-μJ pulses focused through a 50× objective lens. Each sample received 200 000 pulses/spot through a microscope objective

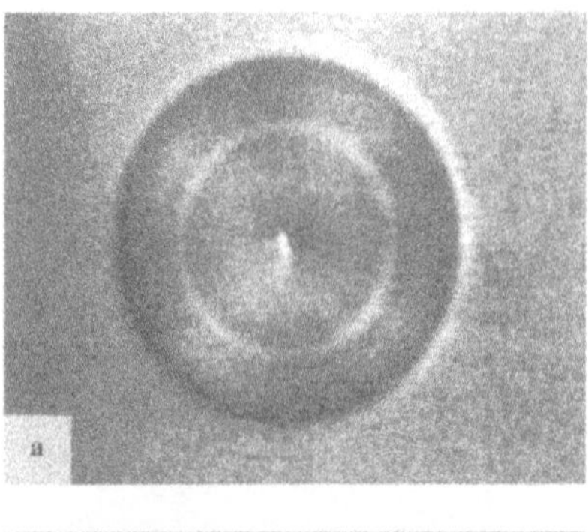

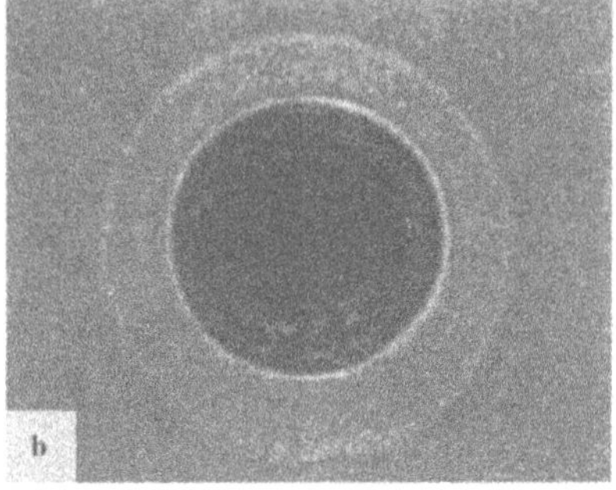

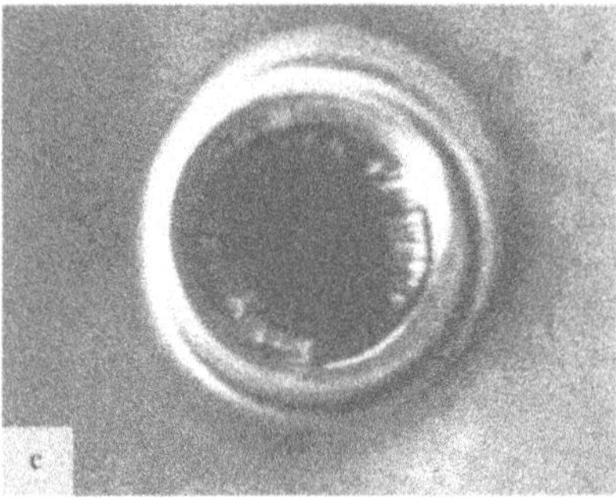

Fig. 2.15a–c. Microscope photographs taken near the focal point (**a**) directly after focused irradiation, (**b**) 20 min and (**c**) 30 min after irradiation. Wavelength, average power and pulse width of the laser were 800 nm, 600 mW and 130 fs at 200 kHz, respectively

crystals grown constitutes an area whose structure has changed due to the crystallization of specific components in the glass. The crystal of region A is clearly a polycrystal, due to the existence of grain boundaries revealed by a change in interference color. Surprisingly, on the other hand, the crystals of region B exhibit hardly any grain boundaries, indicating a fixed orientation. The phenomenon exhibited in region A indicates that by decreasing the movement speed of the fusion zone a stable structure with an accommodation layer is formed at the solid–liquid interface between a part of the polycrys-

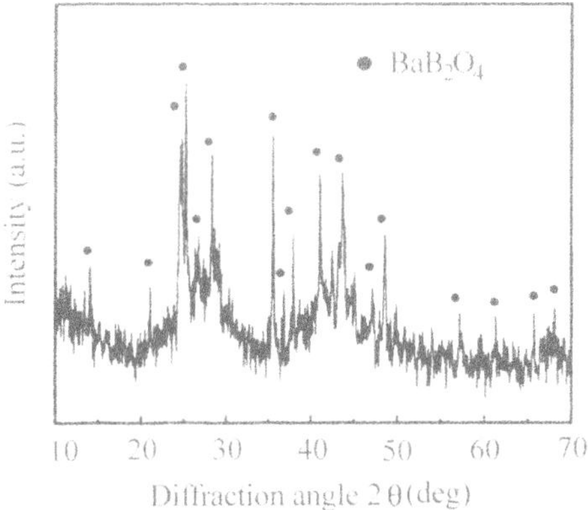

Fig. 2.16. X-ray diffraction pattern for crystals created by the irradiation of focused laser beam with a 50× microscope objective, an average power of 800 mW, and a irradiation time of 40 min

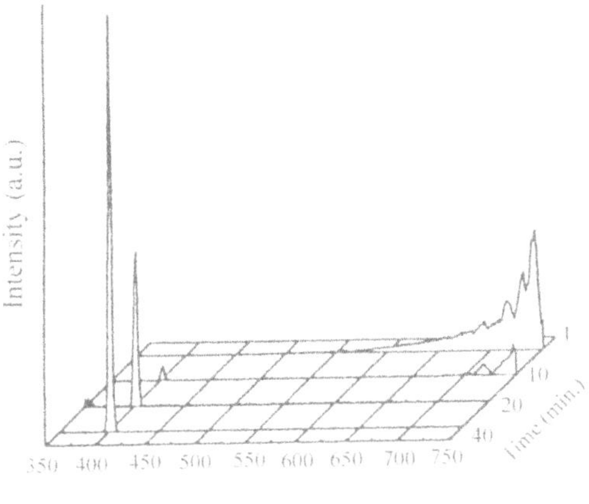

Fig. 2.17. Variation of emission spectra obtained from the laser focal point that accompanies growth of frequency-conversion crystals for various irradiation times. Wavelength, average power and pulse width of the irradiation laser were 800 nm, 450 mW and 130 fs at 20 kHz, respectively

tal and the fusion zone. It means that this technique leads to the growth of a single crystal or a crystal with a single-crystal-like structure. By using seed crystals in the phase-matching direction, it is possible to grow crystals adequate for use in frequency-conversion devices.

The possibility to form frequency-conversion crystals 3-dimensionally in glass by using a nonresonant femtosecond-order laser was demonstrated. This development will lead to new possibilities in the field of compact short-wavelength coherent light sources. Furthermore, forming frequency-conversion crystals continuously in glass enables an optical confinement effect

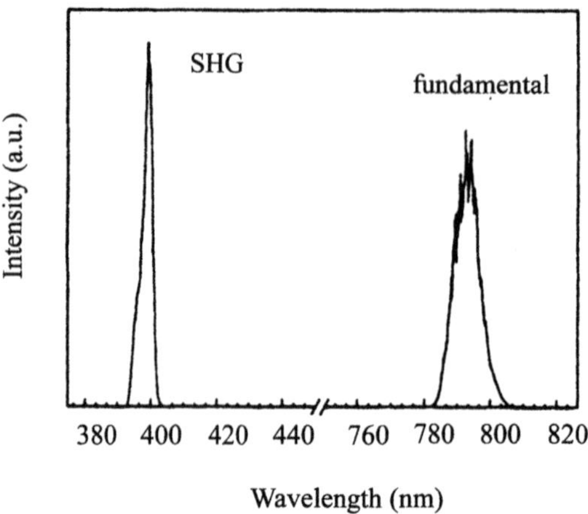

Fig. 2.18. (**a**) An emission pattern and (**b**) a spectrum of second harmonic generation (SHG) from frequency-conversion crystals observed by the incidence of 10 ns of 800-nm, 1-kHz laser light with a pulse energy of 1 mJ

to be achieved that makes use of the difference in the refractive indices of the glass and the crystals; such a formation may make it possible to develop new waveguide nonlinear optical frequency-conversion devices.

2.6 Optical Poling of Glasses

In the first part of this section, a brief review of the developments in studies on second-harmonic generation (SHG) in glasses is given; afterwards, the research results of the present study for photoinduced SHG in germanosilicate glasses and Bi_2O_3–B_2O_3–SiO_2 glasses are described.

2.6.1 Historical Background

SHG in glasses should not occur because glass has macroscopic inversion symmetry. However, in 1986 Österberg and Margulis observed SHG in a glass optical fiber after illuminating the fiber with intense infrared light for several hours [16]. A year later Stolen and Tom showed that when infrared fundamental light was introduced into a fiber along with its second-harmonic light the speed of the process increased from 10 h to 5 min [81]. To promote an understanding of this effect, many studies of its mechanism were carried out. Stolen and Tom presented a model in which they believed that the incident fundamental and its second-harmonic light beams caused a dc electric field to build up in the glass and that this semipermanent dc electric field not only broke the inversion symmetry of the glass but also permitted periodic phase matching of the SHG [81]. Explanations of the microscopic

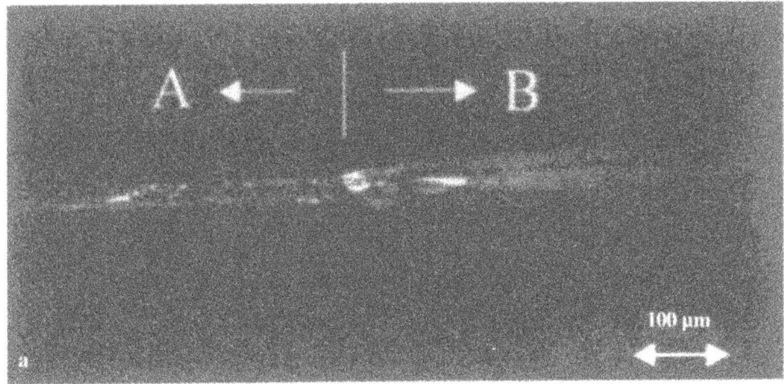

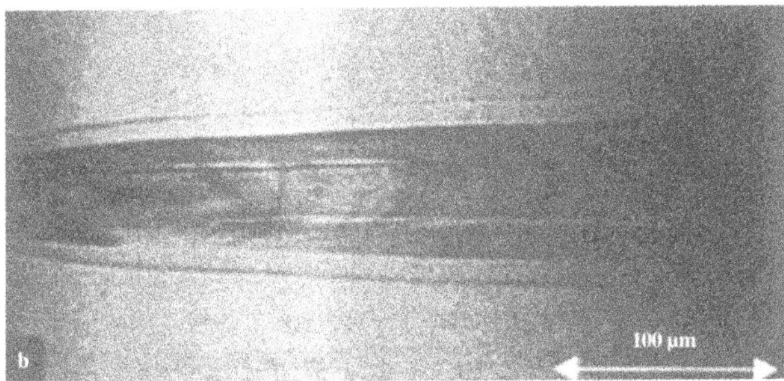

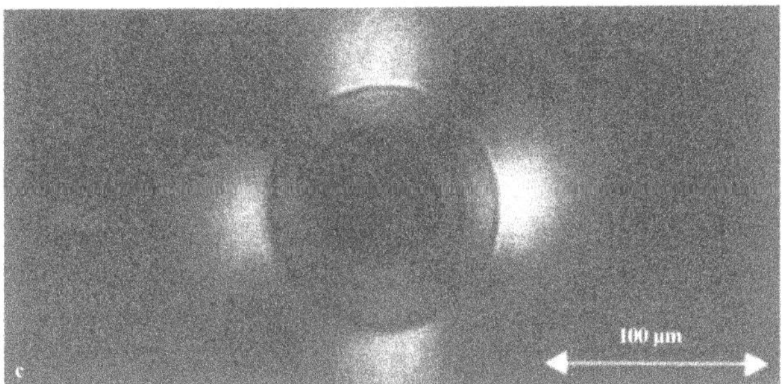

Fig. 2.19. Polarizing-microscope photographs of the (**a**,**b**) side and (**c**) cross-sectional views of the crystal. (**a**) and (**b**) show polarizing-microscope photographs taken in extinction and diagonal positions, respectively. Region A in (**a**) shows a crystal grown while moving the melting zone at a speed of 100 µm/s, and region B shows a crystal grown when this speed is 10 µm/s

mechanism of this photoinduced dc electric field cite either photoinduced currents [83,119] or structural orientation [81,120]. Dianov [83] and Dominic [121] ruled out structural reorientation models by comparing the measured spatial shapes of the dc electric field with the theoretical predictions of photocurrent models. Kyung and Lawandy spatially mapped the photoexcited electron distributions responsible for SHG with a charge-selective etching technique [122, 123]. Tsai demonstrated by electron-spin-resonance spectrometry that SHG in germanosilicate glass is related to the formation of the photoinduced Ge E' center [124]. The wavelength dependence and the compositional dependence of the photoinduced SHG in lead silicate glass were investigated by Krol [125, 126] and Nageno [127], respectively.

2.6.2 Photoinduced SHG in Germanosilicate Glasses Using a Femtosecond Laser

Most previous studies of photoinduced SHG in glasses were performed with a picosecond Nd:YAG laser, in which 1064-nm fundamental and 532-nm second-harmonic light were used as the preparation beams and the laser pulse intensities in glasses ranged from a few to several dozen gigawatts per square centimeter [127]. The SHG photoinduced in germanosilicate glasses by such a laser was believed to be related to the oxygen-deficient defect absorption band centered near 5.1 eV [128], which can be reached with an energy equivalent to four 1064-nm photons [119, 129]. Here, it is explained how SHG was encoded in germanosilicate bulk glass using femtosecond laser pulses at wavelengths of 810 and 405 nm, whose intensities in the glass ranged from 1 to 600 GW/cm^2. The SHG induced by these high-intensity laser pulses was expected to be different from that induced by Nd:YAG laser pulses. Measurements of the difference spectra between the absorption spectra of the glasses before and after preparation indicated that a band-to-band transition by multiphoton absorption is probably responsible for the photoinduced SHG.

A $10GeO_2$–$90SiO_2$ (mol. %) glass rod was prepared by Shin-Etsu Chemical Company as a fiber preform by a vapor axial deposition method. The rod was sliced and polished into 0.5-mm thick plates. A Ti:sapphire regenerative amplifier laser system was used for SHG preparation of the germanosilicate glass, which emitted 200-fs, 810-nm laser pulses at a repetition rate of 200 kHz. The average power of the laser was 960 mW. Seeding beam ω was split from the source beam and passed through a time-delay device and a $\lambda/2$ plate to control the path length and the polarization of the beam, respectively. Another beam separated from the source beam was frequency doubled using a KDP crystal and served as another seeding beam; it is denoted as seeding beam 2ω here. The two collinear seeding beams were introduced into the 0.5-mm-thick glass sample through a quartz lens with a focal length of 10 cm. Time superposition of pulses between the two seeding beams was achieved by adjusting the delay device and observing the optical Kerr effect of CS_2. During SHG preparation, the two seeding beams were introduced simultaneously into the glass sample; during the probe, beam 2ω was blocked by a shutter and only beam ω remained incident. The SHG signal of beam ω was detected by a photomultiplier and observed and averaged using an oscilloscope. A 405-nm bandpass filter was placed in front of the photomultiplier to allow only the second-harmonic (SH) signal to pass through it. The beam radius ($1/e^2$ of the intensity radius) at the sample and the pulse's maximum energy were approximately 12 μm and 0.75 μJ for beam ω and 10 μm and 0.02 μJ for

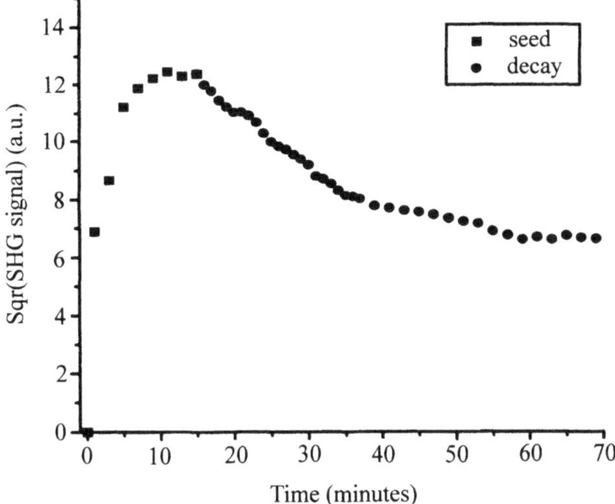

Fig. 2.20. Growth (*squares*) and decay (*circles*) of the SHG signal of the germanosilicate glass sample prepared by femtosecond laser pulses at wavelengths of 810 and 405 nm

beam 2ω, respectively. Absorption spectra were measured at 300 K with a Jasco V-570 spectrometer.

First, the growth and decay processes of the photoinduced SHG of the glass sample were measured, as shown in Fig. 2.20. For the preparation process the photoinduced SHG reached its saturation value after 10 min; laser intensities in the glass sample for light beams ω and 2ω were set at 81 and 1.2 GW/cm^2, respectively. When beam 2ω was switched off, nonexponential decay was observed. The induced second-order nonlinear susceptibility, $\chi^{(2)}$, was observed to remain constant for ~10 h if the irradiation of the intense beam ω was stopped, indicating that the decay results mainly from the erasure of $\chi^{(2)}$ by beam ω. Figure 2.21 shows the dependence of the induced $\chi^{(2)}$ on the preparation intensity in the glass sample. All the measurements were made after 2 min of preparation.

To understand what photochemical reaction is responsible for the induced SHG, the difference spectra between the absorption spectra of the glasses after and before preparation were measured for the various intensities shown in Fig. 2.21. The measurements of the absorption spectra for different preparation intensities were made on different spots of the sample, and the diameter of the spots was set at 2 mm for these measurements. The SHG preparation for each spot was scanned within the spot by translating the stage on which the sample was mounted in the transverse direction. Figure 2.22 shows two typical difference spectra; they correspond to preparation intensities of 36 and 322 GW/cm^2, respectively. As shown in Fig. 2.22, some new bands located near 4.7, 5.7, and 6.3 eV were induced after the SHG preparation;

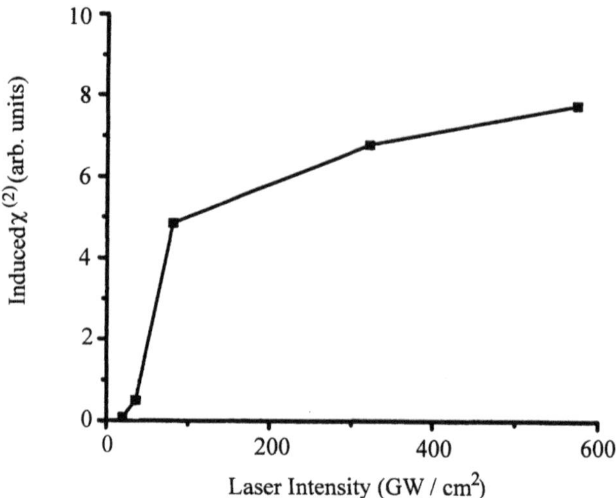

Fig. 2.21. Photoinduced second-order nonlinearity, $\chi^{(2)}$, versus laser intensity of preparation beam ω

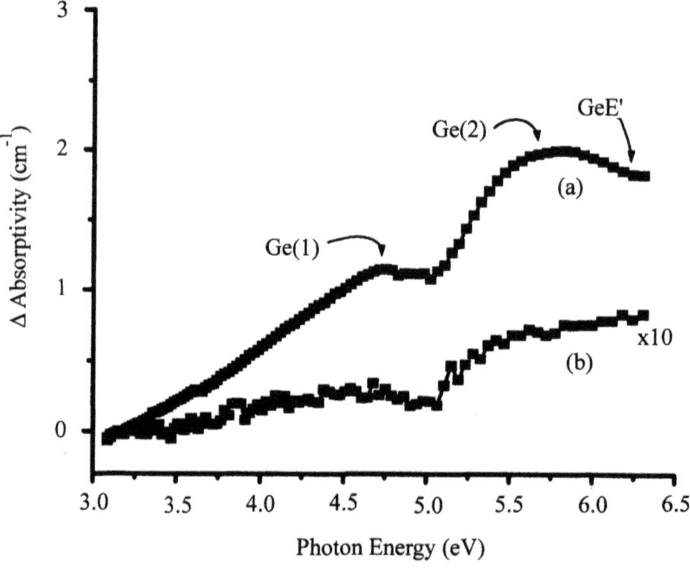

Fig. 2.22a,b. Difference spectra between the spectra after and before preparation. Difference spectra are shown for preparation intensities of (**a**) 322 and (**b**) 36 GW/cm^2

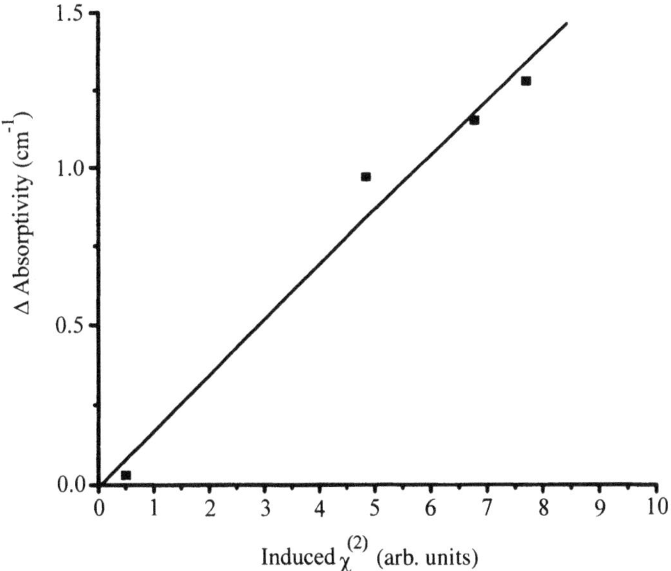

Fig. 2.23. Correlation between the induced $\chi^{(2)}$ and the absorption coefficient of the Ge(1) band

these are assigned, respectively, to the absorption of a Ge electron trapped center (GEC) [Ge(1) or Ge(2)] and a Ge E' center of $10GeO_2$–$90SiO_2$ glasses based on the earlier studies [130]. The GEC center is abbreviated as Ge(1) or Ge(2) depending on the number of nearest-neighbor Ge ions.The correlation between the induced $\chi^{(2)}$ and the absorption coefficient of the Ge(1) band is shown in Fig. 2.23. The results show clearly that with increasing laser intensity the absorption coefficients of the GEC bands increased along with the induced $\chi^{(2)}$.

These defect centers are produced by a band-to-band excitation as follows [130]: Under irradiation from a laser with high photon energy or high peak power, the lone pair electron on the bridging oxygen (BO), which occupies the uppermost level (2p orbit of O) of the valence band, is excited to the conduction band by band-to-band excitation and then trapped on the fourfold-coordinated Ge ions (GeO_4), yielding a GEC^- center. Furthermore, the GEC center can be converted into a Ge E' center and an NBO^- center, where NBO^- is the nonbridging oxygen trapping an electron. In contrast, the BO is converted into a self-trapped hole center, termed STH^+, after releasing the electron. The photochemical reaction can be given by

$$\mathrm{GeO_4} + \mathrm{BO} \xrightarrow{\mathrm{h}\nu} \mathrm{GEC}\left(\mathrm{GeO_4} + \mathrm{e^-}\right) + \mathrm{STH}\,, \tag{2.1}$$

$$\mathrm{GEC} \rightarrow \mathrm{Ge}\ E' + \mathrm{NBO}\,. \tag{2.2}$$

As described above, the experimental data suggest that SHG of germanosilicate glass induced by a femtosecond laser with high power is related to the band-to-band transition by means of multiphoton absorption. Therefore, the following mechanism is proposed for formation of the photoinduced dc field in germanosilicate glass: Under the combined action of the fields at ω and 2ω, the lone pair electrons on BO are excited to the conduction band through a multiphoton absorption process, transferred in the conduction band, and then trapped on the fourfold-coordinated Ge ions (GeO_4). This directional electron transfer associated with the creation of the an STH^+ with a positive charge and a GEC^- with a negative charge results in a periodic frozen-in dc field that is satisfied for SHG phase matching. In this model, the Ge E' center, which has no nominal charge, is produced only as an incidental defect, as described in (2.2). In addition, the concentration of the intrinsic structure unit GeO_4 is much higher than that of the intrinsic oxygen-deficient defect [130,131], because these are, respectively, the intrinsic structure unit and the intrinsic defect of germanosilicate glass. Therefore, it is expected that the dc field in germanosilicate glass induced through band-to-band excitation will be stronger.

2.6.3 Band-Gap Dependence of Photoinduced SHG in Bi_2O_3–B_2O_3–SiO_2 Glasses

As shown above, there is a correlation between photoinduced SHG and the creation of a Ge electron center in germanosilicate glass, suggesting that a band-to-band transition by multiphoton absorption is responsible for SHG. Therefore, it can be expected that the band gap of glass may have a large influence on photoinduced SHG in glass. Here, the dependence of photoinduced SHG on the band gap of Bi_2O_3–B_2O_3–SiO_2 glasses is shown. The large third-order nonlinear optical susceptibility of these glasses [132], which originates from pure electronic polarization, will benefit the photoinduced SHG. The experiments showed that both the saturation intensity of the IR preparation beam for photoinduced SHG and the relaxation time of SHG increase with an increase in the band gap of the glasses. In addition, these glasses were found to have lower saturation intensities for the 1064-nm preparation beam for photoinduced SHG, due to their small band gaps, compared to that for germanosilicate glass.

Four Bi_2O_3–B_2O_3–SiO_2 glasses with different Bi_2O_3 concentrations, ranging from 84.2 to 92.0 wt %, were used in the experiments, and are denoted, respectively, BI-3, BI-5, BI-6, and BI-7 here. The composition and the preparation of these glasses has been described in [132]. The band gap E_g of the glasses decreases with an increase in the Bi_2O_3 concentration, which ranges from 2.65 to 3.00 eV [132]. All of the glasses were polished into 1.95-mm-thick plates.

A Q-switched Nd:YAG laser was used for the SHG preparation of the glasses; it emitted 3.5-ns, 1064-nm and 3-ns, 532-nm laser pulses at a repeti-

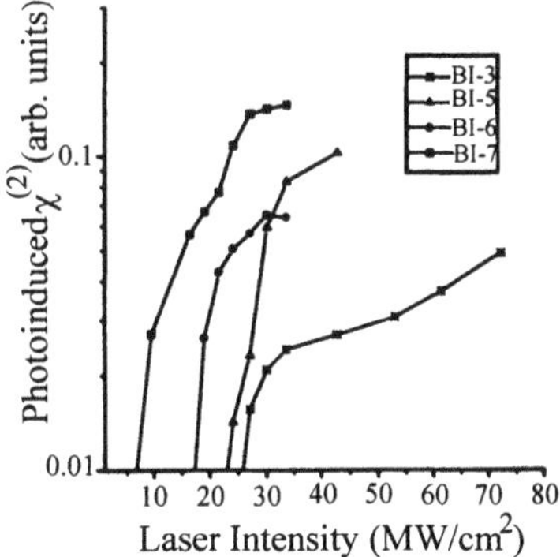

Fig. 2.24. Plot of the photoinduced $\chi^{(2)}$ for the BI glasses at different ω preparation intensities while the intensity of the 2ω preparation light was kept at 0.61 MW/cm^2

tion rate of 50 Hz. The 1064-nm and 532-nm pulses were used as SHG preparation beams, and are denoted, respectively, beam ω and beam 2ω here. The two beams were coaxially introduced into the glass sample through a quartz lens with a focal length of 25 cm. Two HA30 filters (heat-absorbing filter) and a 532-nm bandpass filter were placed behind the sample to allow only the SHG signal to pass through it. During SHG preparation, the two beams were simultaneously introduced into the glass sample, and during the probe beam 2ω was blocked and only beam ω remained incident. The SHG signal was detected by a photomultiplier and observed and averaged using an oscilloscope. Absorption spectra were measured at 300 K with a Jasco V-570 spectrometer.

First, we measured the preparation intensity dependence of photoinduced $\chi^{(2)}$ for the glasses. The intensity of beam ω was varied while the intensity of beam 2ω was kept at a constant value of 0.61 MW/cm^2 during SHG preparation. The measured results are shown in Fig. 2.24; all of the measurements were made after the SHG was encoded to the saturation value for each preparation intensity. From Fig. 2.24, one can see that the smaller the band gap E_g of the glass, the lower the preparation intensity needed for the photoinduced SHG. The saturation preparation intensity I_s as a function of the optical band gap for these glasses is shown in Fig. 2.25. I_s is defined here as the preparation intensity corresponding to half of the saturated $\chi^{(2)}$. The BI-7 glass exhibited the lowest saturation preparation intensity of approximately 18 MW/cm^2.

The decay of the photoinduced $\chi^{(2)}$ of these glasses was also measured during the readout process. The decay rate was observed to increase with an increase in the power and repetition rate of the readout laser. The measured decay for a readout peak intensity of 27 MW/cm^2 is shown in Fig. 2.26. The photoinduced $\chi^{(2)}$ of all these glasses showed a nonexponetial decay. A stretched exponential fit ($\chi^{(2)}(t) = \chi^{(2)}(0)\exp[-(t/\tau)^{\beta}]$) for the decay of

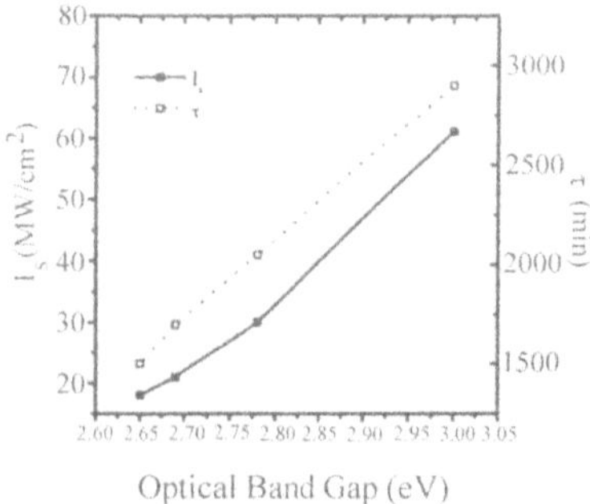

Fig. 2.25. Band-gap dependence of the saturation intensity of the ω preparation beam (*solid squares*) and the relaxation time (*open squares*)

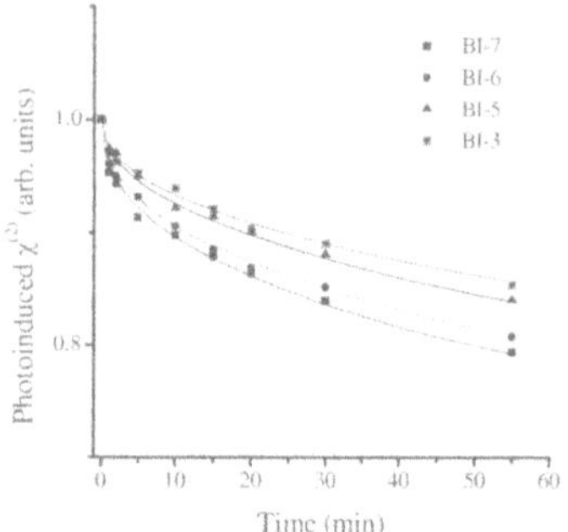

Fig. 2.26. Decay of the photoinduced $\chi^{(2)}$ for the BI glasses under ω beam irradiation. The intensity and repetition rate of the ω beam were kept at 27 MW/cm^2 and 50 Hz, respectively

these glasses was made to compare the relaxation rates of the photoinduced $\chi^{(2)}$ in these glasses. From the fit, it was found that the smaller the band gap of the glass, the faster the relaxation rate. The parameter β for all these glasses remained constant at approximately 0.46, suggesting that the effect responsible for photoinduced SHG is essentially of the same origin in all these glasses. The band-gap dependence of the relaxation time τ is also shown in Fig. 2.25.

Absorption spectra of the glasses are shown in Fig. 2.27. The wavelength of 532 nm is located at the band-edge absorption regions of these glasses; it corresponds to the two-photon energy of the ω beam. In the wavelength region of band-edge absorption, the absorption coefficients for both one-photon and two-photon absorption usually decrease when the wavelength of the laser is longer than the optical band gap. However, it is well known that the saturation intensity I_s is inversely proportional to the absorption cross-section σ_0 ($I_s = \hbar\omega/2\sigma_0\tau_s$, where τ_s is the excited-state lifetime) in a saturable absorber system [133]. Obviously, the saturation intensity in a saturable absorber system increases with an increase in the band gap. Moreover, the photoinduced

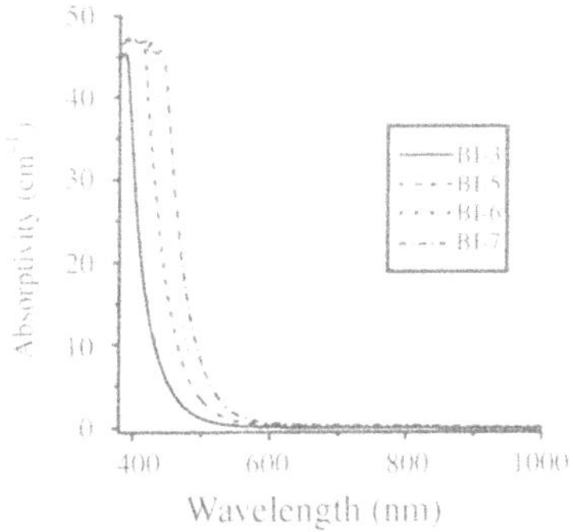

Fig. 2.27. Absorption spectra of the BI glasses

$\chi^{(2)}$ in these glasses results from the band-to-band transition by the quantum interference excitation between the one-photon absorption (2ω) and the two-photon absorption ($\omega+\omega$) [126]. Therefore, the photoinduced $\chi^{(2)}$ should show saturation properties similar to the saturation absorption. The band-gap dependence of the relaxation time can also be explained in terms of the band-gap dependence of the two-photon absorption coefficient at the wavelength of ω. As described above, the decay of photoinduced $\chi^{(2)}$ was caused mainly by erasure by the readout beam ω. The erasure was due to the recombination between the electron centers and the hole centers that are related to the photoinduced $\chi^{(2)}$. This recombination can be achieved through two-photon excitation of beam ω or through thermal excitation due to beam ω irradiation. Hence, the relaxation rate for the same readout intensity will depend on the two-photon absorption coefficient of the glasses.

Photoinduced $\chi^{(2)}$ in glass can usually be induced through either band-to-band excitation or excitation for intrinsic defects [134]. However, the dc field in glass induced through band-to-band excitation may provide a stronger dc field, because the concentration of the intrinsic structure unit that is related to band-to-band transition is much higher than that of the intrinsic defects. Further studies are needed to know what defects produced through band-to-band transition in these glasses are responsible for photoinduced $\chi^{(2)}$.

2.7 Optical Poling of Dye-Doped Inorganic Glass for Second-Harmonic Generation

The optical poling in glasses was described in Sect. 2.6. In this section, optical poling of dye-doped inorganic glass using a nanosecond laser and a femtosecond laser will be discussed. There were two problems to overcome in the application of this optical poling technique in photonic devices: the relaxation of the induced polar orientation of the azodye molecules, and the low SHG conversion efficiency. In order to solve the first of these, thermally assisted optical poling (see Sects. 2.7.2 and 6.5) and the successfully achieved thermosetting enhancement of the induced polar orientation stability in polymers and glasses are utilized. In a resonant optical excitation process, it appears difficult for the SHG conversion efficiency to benefit from phase matching achieved automatically in large propagation distances owing to the material absorption. Therefore, all-optical poling under a nonresonant excitation using a femtosecond laser was utilized (see Sect. 2.7.3). Nonresonant excitation should permit the use of a larger film thickness, which should in turn result in a significant increase in the conversion efficiency.

2.7.1 Historical Background

A second-order nonlinear optical effect is used for photonic devices, and many kinds of effects have been reported in the application of these devices, for instance, SHG [135] and electro-optic light modulation [136]. Some organic dyes show high nonlinearity, and the azo-dye chromophore is one of the most probable candidates because of its high second-order nonlinear optical susceptibility. Some polymers grafted with azo-dye have been intensively studied [137]. The second-order process is normally dipole forbidden in centrosymmetric materials. A noncentrosymmetric order for the polymer film has to be achieved in order to obtain second-order nonlinearity, and many studies have been carried out using electric poling [138, 139]. Poled polymers have serious problems associated with them, for example, the nonlinearity decreases with time because of orientation relaxation. With a sol-gel method, the organic dye can be doped in a higher concentration into a strong inorganic matrix in which the dye can be fixed and stabilized for a long time. Sugihara et al. reported that an azo-dye-doped silica film made using a sol-gel method with an electric poling technique had high second-order nonlinear optical and long-term stability [140, 141]. However, the electric poling technique has difficulty controlling the poling state of devices, for example, SHG in optical waveguides requires strong phase control. Meanwhile, optical poling techniques can develop noncentrosymmetric structures and automatically achieve SHG phase matching [81, 142]. In the electric poling technique, an azo-dye with a dipole in a sample is rotated and oriented by the dc electric field applied between electrodes. In contrast, the physical mechanism of optical poling techniques consists of two processes: orientational hole burning and the reorientation of azo-dye molecules [143, 144]. Under the excitation of a fundamental beam together with its SH beam, orientational hole burning of azo-dye molecules occurs through the interference of two-photon absorption at the fundamental frequency and one-photon absorption at the doubling frequency. Orientational hole burning is followed by a momentary trans–cis–trans photoisomerization (Fig. 2.28), which leads finally to a net permanent poled orientation of molecules. The orientation with the largest excitation probability is depopulated in favor of the opposite orientation. Fiorini et al. prepared phase-matched azo-dye grafted polymer films using

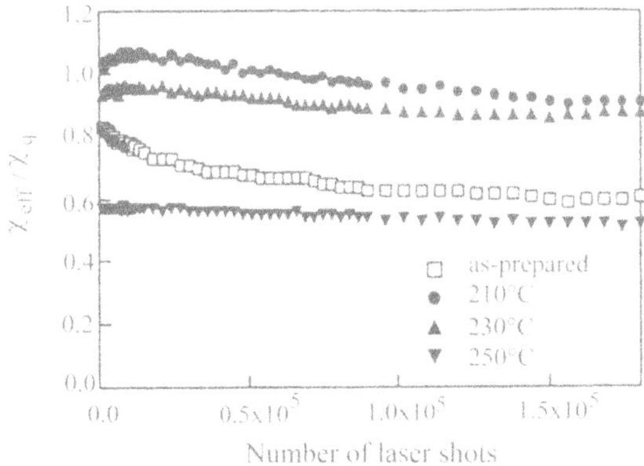

Fig. 2.28. Photoisomerization of Disperse Red 1 (DR1)

this technique [143, 145]. Si et al. investigated the light-induced SHG of azo-dye grafted polyimide films, and they showed the ascendancy of optical poling over electric poling with an optical storage demonstration [146, 147].

2.7.2 Thermosetting Enhancement of Photoinduced SHG Stability in Dye-Doped Glasses

Here, how the preparation of optical-poled DR1 doped silica films made using a sol-gel method was optimized is explained. The thermal evolution of the gel and the term stability of the photoinduced SHG of the films were investigated, and it was found that the rigid silica matrix prevented relaxation of polarized structure.

Tetraethyl orthosilicate ($(C_2H_5O)_4Si$; Nacalai Tesque, Kyoto, Japan) and 4-[N-ethyl-N-(2-hydroxyethyl)] amino-4'-nitro-azobenzene (Disperse Red 1, DR1; Aldrich, Milwaukee, USA) were used as starting materials. The sol procedure is illustrated in Fig. 2.29 and is based on an approach reported by Izawa et al. [148]. First, 1.432 g of tetraethyl orthosilicate and 1.005 g of N,N-dimethylformamide ($HCON(CH_3)_2$; Nacalai Tesque) were put into 0.633 g of ethanol (Nacalai Tesque). Then, 0.108 g of DR1 was dissolved in the solution at 25°C. Finally, a mixed solution consisting of 0.633 g of ethanol, 0.072 g of 35% hydrochloric acid (Nacalai Tesque), and 0.696 g of deionized water was added to the dye mixed solution. After stirring for 30 min at 25°C, sols were obtained. Gel films were spin coated onto alkali-free glass substrates (AF-45; Schott Japan, Japan). Immediately after spin coating, the gel films were put into an oven and dried at 150°C for 20 min to remove solvents for one film coating. For two film coatings, the first and second dry times were 5 and 20 min, respectively.

Differential thermal analysis/thermogravimetry (DTA/TG) measurements were performed on a gel film dried in an oven at 150°C for 20 min. Measurements were made for both the films scratched off the glass substrates and

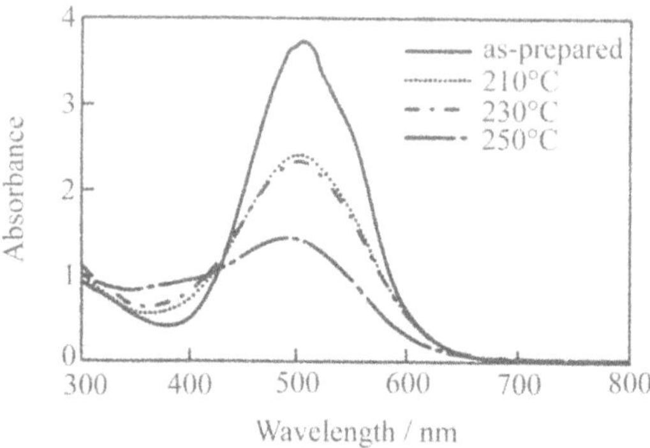

Fig. 2.29. Flowchart showing the procedure for preparing the optically poled films

DR1. The measurement of each powder was conducted in air while heated at 5°C/min with a differential thermal analyzer (Model Thermo Plus TG8110; Rigaku Co.). The thickness of the films was measured using a surface roughness measure (Model Surfcorder SE-2300; Kosaka Laboratory), for which parts of the films were scratched away from the glass substrates and measured. Refractive indices of heated films were measured using an ellipsometer (Model DVA–36VW; Mizojiri); gel films were coated on alkali-free glass substrates, dried in an oven at 150°C for 20 min, and heat-treated at 210–250°C for 10 min. The measurement was carried out at 1064 nm.

The experimental setup shown in Fig. 2.30 was used in the preparation and measurements on SHG relaxation of the optically poled films. First, the dried films were treated by optical poling without or with heat treatment at 210–250°C for 10 min to build the polarized structure. Two seed beams for the optical poling of 1064 nm (3.5-ns pulse width, 1.09 J/cm^2) and 532 nm (3.0 ns, 5.48×10^{-3} J/cm^2 from a Q-switched Nd:YAG laser (50 Hz) were coaxially applied to the films with heat treatment at 210–250°C for 10 min; then the polarized light of the two seed beams was aligned. Next, the seed beams were eliminated from the samples, and the temperature of the oven was reduced to 25°C. The SHG intensity was consecutively measured by applying the 1064 nm beam. The SHG intensity was compared with the SH generated by a Y-cut quartz crystal. Ultraviolet and visible absorption spectra of optically poled films were measured using an ultraviolet and visible light spectrophotometer (Jasco Model V-570).

Figure 2.31a and b show the DTA/TG curves of DR1 and the gel film with DR1 dried at 150°C for 20 min, respectively. Two endothermic peaks attributed to the melting point were observed at 141 and 164°C without weight loss in the DTA curve for DR1. Gradual weight loss from approximately 200°C and sharp weight loss from approximately 250°C were observed in the TG curve for DR1, accompanied by exothermic behavior at higher than approximately 240°C. In contrast, a slight exothermic peak at approximately

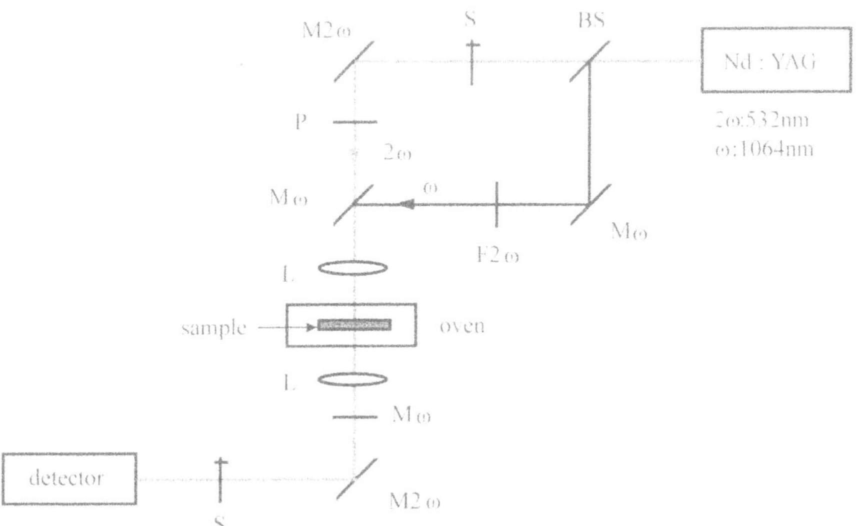

Fig. 2.30. Experimental setup for optical poling. BS: beam splitter for 1064 nm; S: shutter; M2ω: mirrors for 532 nm; P: polarizer; Mω: mirrors for 1064 nm; F2ω: filter for 532 nm; L: lenses

210°C was observed in the DTA curve for the gel film with DR1, followed by monotonous endothermic behavior. Figure 2.31c shows the DTA/TG curves for a silica gel film without DR1. Measurements were performed from room temperature to 500°C. A monotonous decrease in weight shown by the TG curve, and a slight exothermic peak position in the DTA curve were similar to those of the gel film containing DR1. A constant decrease in weight was observed from 300 to 500°C in the TG curve in Fig. 2.31c.

Thicknesses and refractive indices of the gel-derived films are shown in Table 2.1. The thicknesses and refractive indices decreased as the heat-treatment temperatures increased. The thickness of the two film coatings was more than twice as large as that of the one film coating.

Figure 2.32 shows the laser shot dependence of SH $\chi_{\mathrm{eff}}/\chi_{\mathrm{q}}$ of the optically poled films heat-treated at various temperatures, where χ_{eff} is the effective second-order susceptibility and χ_{q} is the second-order susceptibility of quartz. The values of $\chi_{\mathrm{eff}}/\chi_{\mathrm{q}}$ [137] are shown as

$$\frac{\chi_{\mathrm{eff}}}{\chi_{\mathrm{q}}} = \frac{2 l_{\mathrm{qc}} T_{\mathrm{q}}^{1/2} n_{\mathrm{s}}^{3/2} \cos\theta_{\mathrm{s}} \sqrt{I_{\mathrm{s}}^{2\omega}/I_{\mathrm{q}}^{2\omega}}}{\pi L_{\mathrm{s}} \mathrm{sinhc}[\alpha_{\mathrm{s}}^{2\omega} L_{\mathrm{s}}/2] \exp\left(-\alpha_{\mathrm{s}}^{2\omega} L_{\mathrm{s}}/2\right) n_q^{3/2} T_s^{1/2}} , \tag{2.3}$$

where l_{qc} is the coherence length of quartz ($l_{\mathrm{qc}} = 20\ \mu\mathrm{m}$ at 1.063 μm [149]), T is the transmittance of fundamental and SH waves, n is the refractive index at 1.064 μm ($n_{\mathrm{q}} \approx 1.55$ [150]), θ_{s} is the angle between the boundary normal and the direction of phase propagation inside the film ($\theta_{\mathrm{s}} = 0$), L_{s} is the

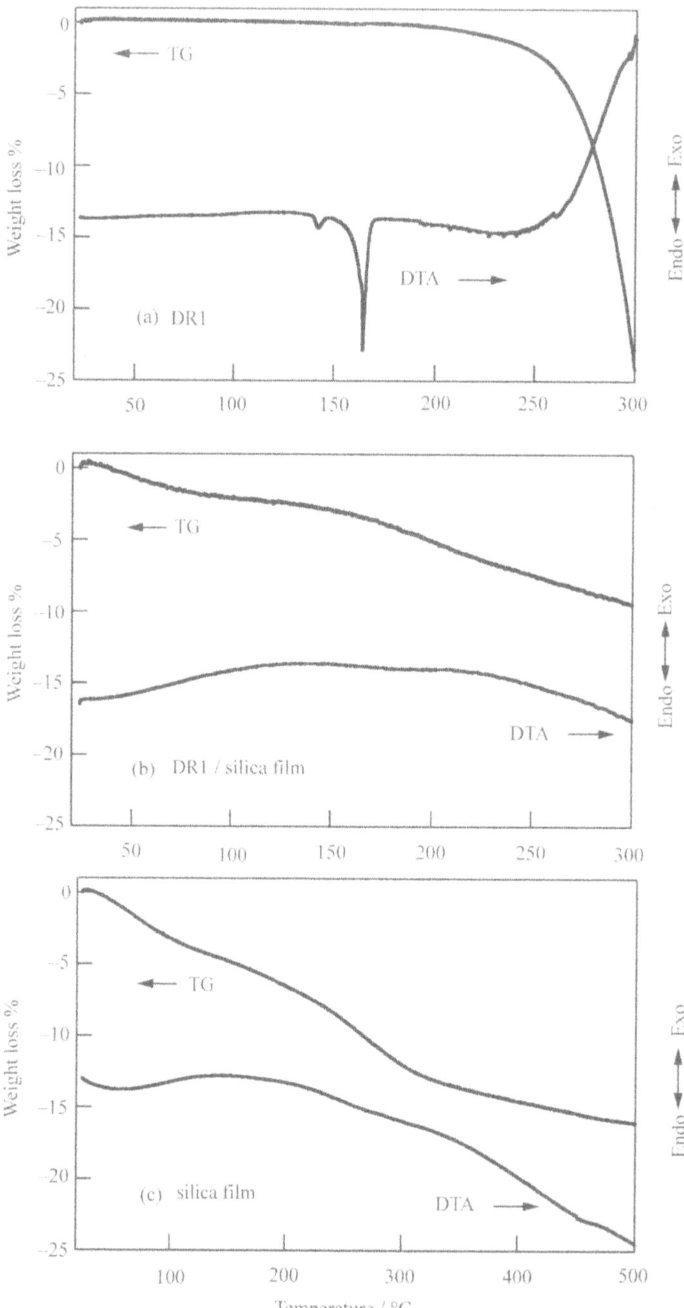

Fig. 2.31. DTA/TG curves of (**a**) DR1, (**b**) gel film with DR1 and (**c**) gel film without DR1; the gel films were dried at 150°C for 20 min, and the measurements were conducted in air at a heating rate of 5°C/min

Table 2.1. Variation in absorption peaks, thickness and refractive indices of heat-treated and optically poled films

		Preparation conditions			Absorption peak			
Sample number	No. of film coatings	Heat treatment Temp (°C)	Heat treatment Time (min)	Optical poling time (min)	Wavelength (nm)	Absorbande	Thickness (μm)	Refractive index at 1064 nm
1	2	-	-	-	506	3.73	1.15	–
2	2	210	10	10	502	2.41	1.08	–
3	2	230	10	10	502	2.34	1.08	–
4	2	250	10	10	492	1.45	1.03	–
5	1	–	–	–	–	–	0.40	1.58
6	1	210	10	–	–	–	0.35	1.56
7	1	230	10	–	–	–	0.32	1.54

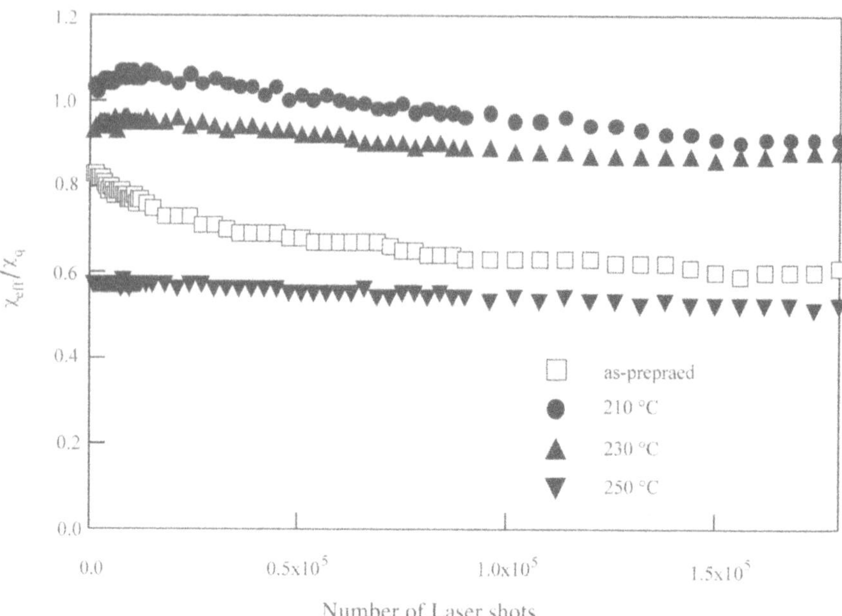

Fig. 2.32. Laser shot dependence of second-harmonic $\chi_{\text{eff}}/\chi_{\text{q}}$ of the optical-poled films heat-treated at 210, 230 and 250°C for 10 min

sample thickness, $\text{sinhc}(x) = \sinh(x)/x$ and α is the attenuation constant. The subscripts s and q refer to the sample and quartz, respectively. The SH intensity $I_{\text{s}}^{2\omega}/I_{\text{q}}^{2\omega}$ of the optically poled films was measured, where $I_{\text{s}}^{2\omega}$ and $I_{\text{q}}^{2\omega}$ are the sample and quartz intensities, respectively. As shown in Fig. 2.32, the SH $\chi_{\text{eff}}/\chi_{\text{q}}$ of the optically poled films heat-treated at 210 and 230°C were higher than that of the optically poled film heat-treated at 250°C. Moreover, the SHG relaxation rate of the poled films decreased with increasing the heat-treatment temperature.

In the plots of $\chi_{\text{eff}}/\chi_{\text{q}}$ heat-treated at 210 and 230°C slightly increasing behavior of $\chi_{\text{eff}}/\chi_{\text{q}}$ was observed at the beginning, and then the signals decreased. While applying the two seed beams with heat treatment, the optically poled films were observed to shift from red to orange. A similar color shift was observed when a gel film was heat-treated in the oven without applying the seed beams.

To investigate the differences between optical poling and electric poling, corona poling was performed, applying a high voltage of 8 kV/cm with the same heat-treatment condition as the sample optically poled at 250°C. The value of $\chi_{\text{eff}}/\chi_{\text{q}}$ and the relaxation of SHG were measured with the same experimental set up as shown in Fig. 2.32 by rotating the sample stage (the oven) against the 1064-nm beam. The $\chi_{\text{eff}}/\chi_{\text{q}}$ value was measured to be 0.20,

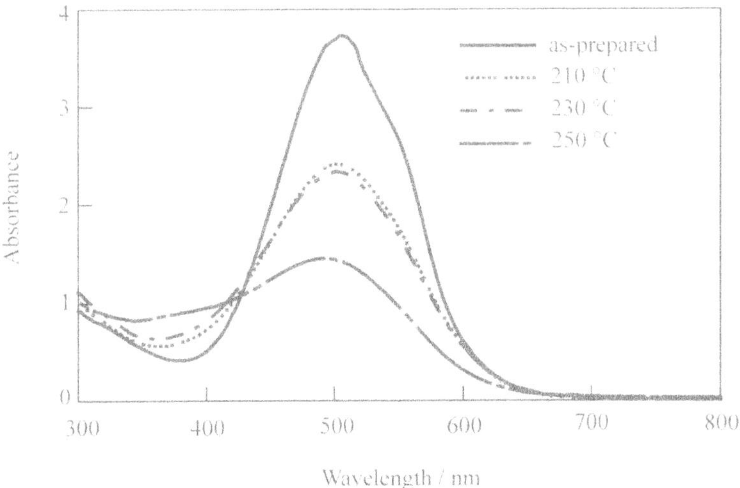

Fig. 2.33. Absorption spectra of optically poled films heat-treated at different temperatures for 10 min

and no measurable difference between the relaxation plots for optical poling and electric poling was observed.

Figure 2.33 shows the absorption spectra of gel-derived films optically poled at different heat-treatment temperatures. As shown in Fig. 2.33 and Table 2.1, reduction of peak heights and blue shifts of the absorption spectra were observed when the heat-treatment temperature was increased. Moreover, a new peak at approximately 350–400 nm was observed.

The gradual weight loss above approximately 200°C accompanied by exothermic behavior starting at approximately 240°C as shown in the DR1 system in Fig. 2.31a is considered to be due to the evaporation and/or oxidation of DR1. In the DR1/silica system in Fig. 2.31b, a small endothermic peak at approximately 210°C was observed, followed by monotonous endothermic behavior; sharp weight loss was not observed. The difference in weight loss between the two systems may result from the difference between the two exothermic peak temperatures and the difference between the two curves. The decrease in weight observed in the DR1/silica system was similar to that in the silica system. The slight exothermic peak and monotonous weight decrease in the DR1/silica system could be due to the decomposition and oxidation of the organic materials in the matrix. The silica matrix alone may prevent the evaporation and/or oxidation. In the silica system as shown in Fig. 2.31c, a constant weight decrease was observed from 300 to 500°C. This could be due to the elimination of OH and the condensation of the silica matrix. From the TG curves in Fig. 231b and c, there should be residual organic materials in the matrix even if the film was heat-treated at 250°C. The fact that the thickness of two film coatings was more than twice as large as that of one film coating must be due to the heat-treatment temperatures and times. Thus, the silica matrix made in this study was not a completely inorganic material.

Orientation-selective excitation of DR1, orientational hole burning [143, 144] occurs because of the interference of two seed beams. One-photon absorption at the SH beam and two-photon absorption at the fundamental beam cause momentary photoisomerization, which leads to a net orientation of DR1. The orientation with the largest excitation probability is depopulated in favor of the opposite orientation. It can be said that the polarized structure is induced by this mechanism.

The $\chi_{\mathrm{eff}}/\chi_{\mathrm{q}}$ value (0.20) of electrically poled film was considerably lower than those reported by Sugihara et al. [140], who electrically poled gel films with a heat treatment at 150°C. The low $\chi_{\mathrm{eff}}/\chi_{\mathrm{q}}$ value is probably due to the relatively rigid matrix. In addition, the fact that the $\chi_{\mathrm{eff}}/\chi_{\mathrm{q}}$ values of optically poled films were higher than that of the electrically poled film is believed to be related to the effect of the photoisomerization.

As shown in Fig. 2.31b, solvent and organic compounds in the silica matrix were removed by heat treatment. Measurement of film thickness showed that shrinkage occurred with higher heat-treatment temperature (Table 2.1). In addition, as the heat-treatment temperature was increased, the SHG relaxation rate of the poled films decreased (Fig. 2.32). It is possible that the polarized DR1 was fixed in the silica matrix and the matrix was made tougher through polycondensation as a result of heat treatment. In the rigid matrix, the polarized structure might be stabilized.

The SHG intensity reduced as the heat-treatment temperature increased, as shown in Fig. 2.32. As mentioned above, absorption of the 532-nm beam is needed for the photoisomerization between *trans* and *cis* in this azo-dye doped system. The degree of photoisomerization depends on the resonance absorption of the azo-dye, so the more the absorbance at 532 nm, the easier the dipole rotation and the DR1 orientation. As shown in Fig. 2.33, the absorbance at 532 nm was reduced as the heat-treatment temperatures increased. Therefore, it is suggested that the difference in SHG intensity was caused by the amount of absorption by the film.

Slight increases in $\chi_{\mathrm{eff}}/\chi_{\mathrm{q}}$ were observed at the beginning in the plots for the films heat-treated at 210 and 230°C, and a color shift from red to orange was observed when a gel film was heat-treated in the oven without applying the seed beams. Temperature increase in the films could be caused by a thermal effect from the 1064-nm beam pulses. The color shift could lead to a decreased absorption of green. The absorption for SHG might be reduced because of the thermal effect of the 1064-nm beam. Therefore, the appearance of an increase in $\chi_{\mathrm{eff}}/\chi_{\mathrm{q}}$ could be observed.

It is difficult to specifically understand the nanoscopic structure of this DR1/silica system. However, there are some keys in the absorption spectra and the results of other studies. A reduction of peak heights, blue shifts, and a new peak at about 350–400 nm can be observed in Fig. 2.33. Films made by the sol-gel method have many pores when the films are heat-treated at a low temperature. DR1 could have evaporated through the pores. Nakanishi et al. [141] reported results on the UV exposure of DR1/silica films made with a sol-gel method. They studied the absorption spectra of the exposed films. From thin-layer ^{1}H-NMR studies, they determined that DR1 changed into two materials, one having a *p*-nitroaniline-like structure with an absorption peak near 370 nm. A similar decomposition occurred with heat treatment. In addition, another structure change might have occurred; it is described in the following: DR1 has a hydroxy group. Si–O–C chemical bonds can be produced during the hydrolysis of TEOS and polycondensation between the hydroxy group of DR1 and hydrolyzed TEOS. The Si–O–C bonds can be hydrolyzed again, but some parts of the bonds that are held in the dense silica matrix remain after the heat treatment. A reverse reaction cannot be made because of the lack of water. DR1 has a donor group [$-N(CH_2CH_3)(CH_2CH_2OH)$] and an acceptor group ($-NO_2$) at separated positions. Charge transfer is caused by an absorption band between approximately 400 and 600 nm in a DR1 molecule. If the new chemical bond is produced between DR1 and the silica matrix, the structure change of the donor can cause decreased electron-release behavior and change the resonance absorption. As a result, a reduction of peak heights and blue shifts could possibly occur.

2.7.3 Optical Poling of Azo-Dye-Doped Thin Films Using an Ultrashort Pulse Laser

Here, optical poling of DR1-doped PMMA films and DR1-doped silica gel films achieved by the coherent superposition of the 1500-nm fundamental and the 750-nm SH light from a 130-fs Ti:sapphire laser is described. In the optical poling process, the multiphoton absorption and the photoisomerization of DR1 can produce the polarized structure of the molecules. DR1 does not have one-photon absorption at the wavelength of SHG; hence, this method provides the possibility for practical waveguides in optical communications.

DR1-doped PMMA (DR1/PMMA) films and DR1-doped silica gel (DR1/silica gel) films were used in this work. For the DR1/PMMA films, PMMA was dissolved into telrahydrofuran (THF). DR1 was mixed into the solution, and the starting solution was obtained. The reagent's weight ratio of the starting solution was PMMA:DR1:THF = 5:1:45. Polymer films were spin coated onto alkali-free glass substrates. Immediately after spin coating, the polymer films were put into an oven and dried at 80°C for 20 min to remove solvents. The thickness and transmission at 750 nm of the DR1/PMMA films were measured to be 2.1 μm and 99.9%, respectively.

Tetraethyl orthosilicate (TEOS) and DR1 were used as starting materials for the DR1/silica gel films. *N,N*-dimethylformamide (DMF) and ethanol were used as solvents. 35% hydrochloric acid (HCl) and deionized water were used for the hydrolysis of TEOS. The procedure for preparing the starting solutions is described in detail above. The reagent's mole ratio of the starting solution was TEOS:DR1:DMF:ethanol:HCl:H_2O = 1:0.05:2:4:0.1:10. Gel films were spin coated on alkali-free glass substrates. Immediately after spin coating, the gel films were put into an oven and dried at 150°C for 5 min, to remove solvents. After the films were cooled to 25°C, the sol was spun again and dried at 150°C for 20 min. The thickness and transmission at 750 nm of the DR1/silica gel films were measured to be 1.4 μm and 99.6%, respectively.

A Ti:sapphire regenerative amplifier laser system and an optical parametric amplifier were used for the optical poling of the thin films, which emitted 130-fs, 1500-nm laser pulses at a repetition rate of 1 kHz. The laser's average power was 3.0 mW. The 1500-nm beam was divided with a beam splitter, and a SH of 750 nm was generated from the beam by a KTP crystal. The other 1500-nm beam and the 750-nm beam were mixed using a dichroic mirror and coaxially applied to the thin film samples through a silica glass lens (100-mm focal length) at the same time by an optical delay line. The polarization of the two seed beams was adjusted in the same direction by a $\lambda/2$ plate in the 1500-nm beam line. Two seed beams were applied to the samples during the optical poling. After the seeding process, the 750-nm beam was discontinued and the SHG from the samples was measured by applying the 1500-nm beam using a photomultiplier tube. The SHG intensity was consecutively measured by applying the 1500-nm beam. The fluences of 1500-nm and 750-nm beams were 6.7–203 GWcm^{-2} and 17.6–19.7 MWcm^{-2}, respectively. The SHG intensity was compared with the SH generated by a 1-mm-thick Y-cut quartz crystal.

Figure 2.34 shows the dependence of the induced SHG intensities from DR1/PMMA thin films on the two seed beams' temporal correlation. The correlation time was adjusted with the optical delay line. The full width at half maximum measured from a Gaussian fitting curve was 117 fs, which was almost equivalent to the pulse width of the two seed beams. Therefore, the SHG resulted from the coherent superposition of the fundamental and SH laser pulses.

To investigate the induction of SHG, the evolution of the induced SHG signals from a DR1/PMMA film and a DR1/silica gel film was measured. As shown in Fig. 2.35, the signals from the DR1/PMMA film and the DR1/silica gel film became saturated in as short as 30 and 120 s, respectively. These phenomena can be said to be remarkable results compared with the result of a PMMA copolymer grafted with pNA [145]; in that case, the optical poling used to induce a saturated SHG signal took as long as approximately 20 h. The fast growth of the SHG signal probably results from the photoisomerization of the dye molecules. This phenomenon will be discussed later. The photoinduced SH intensity ratios $I_s I_q$ (I_s: the SH intensity from samples; I_q, the SH intensity from a Y-cut quartz) of a DR1/PMMA film and a DR1/silica gel film were 1.38×10^{-2} and 0.44×10^{-2}, respectively. This difference of the induced SHG intensity between the DR1/PMMA film and the DR1/silica gel

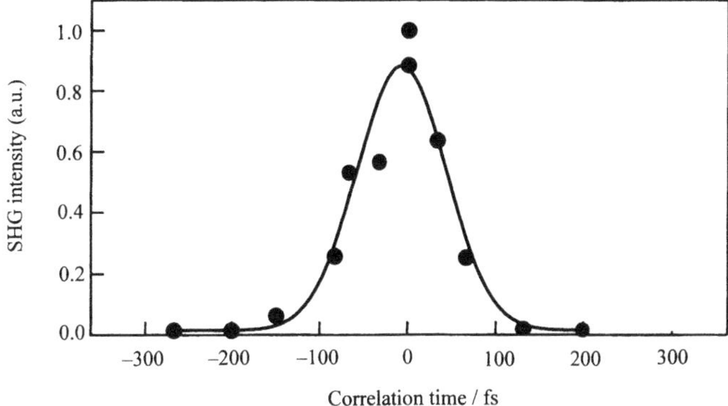

Fig. 2.34. Dependence of the induced SHG intensities from DR1/PMMA thin films on the two seed beams' temporal correlation; the fluences of the 1500-nm and 750-nm beams were 12.7 GW/cm^2 and 18.3 kW/cm^2, respectively

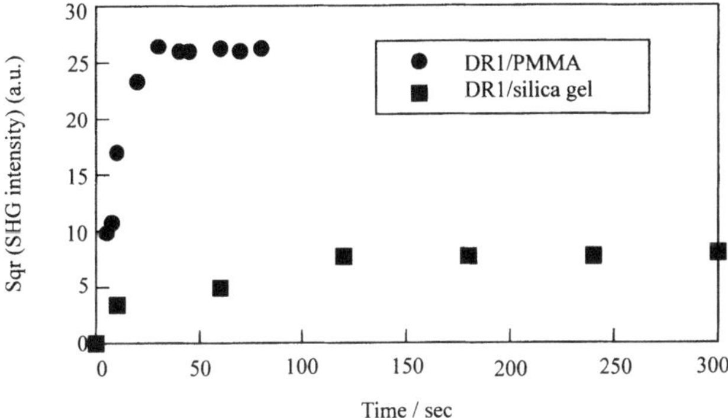

Fig. 2.35. Evolution of the induced SHG signals from a DR1/PMMA film and a DR1/silica gel film; the fluences of the 1500-nm and 750-nm beams were 203 GW/cm^2 and 19.7 MW/cm^2, respectively

film could be due to differences in the thickness and hardness of the matrix between them.

Figure 2.36 shows the relaxation of the SHG signal from DR1/PMMA and DR1/silica gel films. There are two decay processes in optical poling; an initial fast decay that occurs after the interruption of the seeding process, and a slower multiexponential decay. The first component is attributed to a reverse isomerization based on the decay time. The second component can be attributed to the orientational diffusion of the molecules inside the matrix [152]. The relaxation rate of the DR1/silica gel film was lower than that of the DR1/PMMA film. As described earlier, the relaxation rate depends on the hardness of the matrix. For DR1/silica gel films, heat treatment can be applied to fix the polarized structure of the dye molecules, and long-term stabilized SHG can be attained [18].

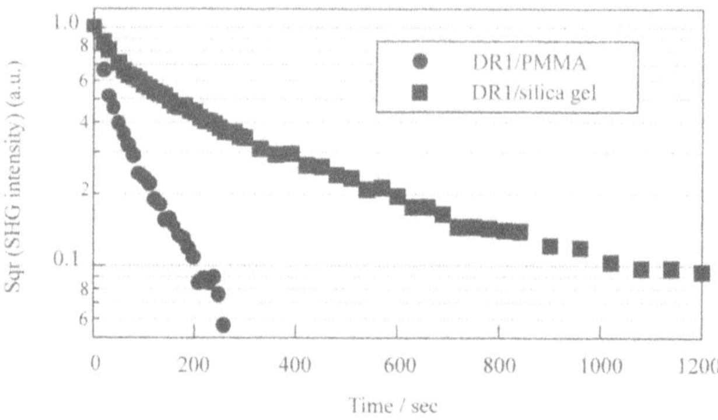

Fig. 2.36. Relaxation of the SHG signal from DR1/PMMA and DR1/silica gel films; the fluence of the 1500-nm beam was 203 GW/cm^2

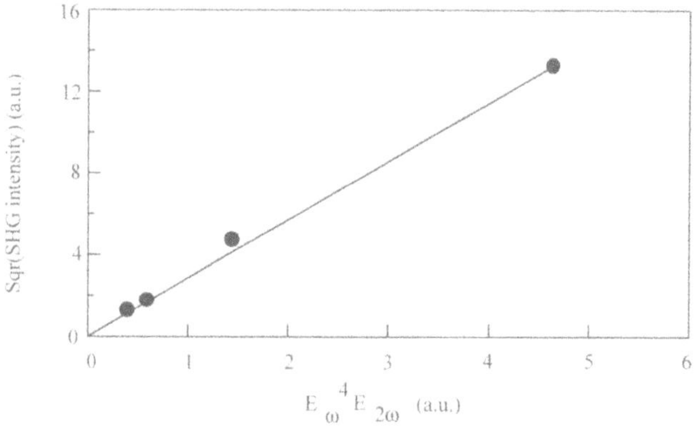

Fig. 2.37. Dependence of saturated SHG on the seed beams' electric fields $E_\omega{}^4E_{2\omega}$

The physical mechanism for the ordinary optical poling of azo-dye consists of two processes: orientational hole burning and reorientation of azo-dye molecules [143, 144]. A resonance absorption of the seed beam promotes the orientation of the dye molecules through a momentary *trans–cis–trans* photoisomerization. We studied the dependence of the saturated SHG from DR1/PMMA films on the seed beams' energy. The seed beams' power was changed by shifting the distance between the focus lens and the samples. Figure 2.37 shows the $E_\omega{}^4E_{2\omega}$ dependence [145] of the saturated SHG. In this study, the high peak power fundamental beams, which are higher than those used in a previous study [145], were used. Despite the low fluences of the seed beams, we could observe the fast growth of the SHG. The coherent superposition of the subpicosecond two-seed pulses could induce simultaneous two-photon ($\omega + 2\omega$) and three-photon ($\omega + \omega + \omega$) absorption on the same electric level. Multiphoton ($\omega+2\omega$ or $\omega+\omega+\omega$) absorption corresponds to the resonance absorption band of DR1. Even if multiphoton absorption takes place, a change in the molecular structure, such as photoisomerization, cannot occur in the case of *p*NA. However, in the case of DR1, the momentary *trans–cis–trans* photoisomerization can be induced by multiphoton absorption. Therefore, the fast SHG growth in this DR1-doped system is probably due to the orientation caused by momentary *trans–cis–trans* photoisomerization.

3. Generation of Induced Structures in Rare-Earth-Ions-Doped Glasses

3.1 Introduction

Rare earths have been used widely in various fields, such as phosphor, magnetic material and superconductor. The effect of rare-earth ions can be divided into two parts: one due to the electron configuration of their 4f orbit, and the other due to their chemical bonding state, e.g. ion radius and chemical bond length. The most important properties of rare-earth-containing materials come from the special 4f electronic structure of the rare earth. As was pointed out in the Introduction, a large amount of rare-earth ions can be stuffed into glass. Glass is an excellent matrix for rare-earth ions to realize various optical functions. The optical properties of glasses doped with rare-earth ions have been investigated intensively, and these glasses have been used as materials for lasers, optical amplifiers and so on. However, only a few studies have been made of the induced structure in rare-earth-ion-doped glasses.

We expect that if we can control the external-electromagnetic-field-induced structure and concentration, species and valence states of rare-earth ions in glass, especially if we can space-selectively control the induced structure or induce 3-dimensional periodically distributed electronic structure, novel optical functions of rare-earth-ion-doped glass can be obtained. From the viewpoint of practical application, it is expected that we can obtain a glass with properties excellent in comparison with those of single crystals.

In this chapter, room-temperature spectral hole burning in an Sm-doped glass fiber is introduced [153]. The observation may have practical application in optical communication. Novel phenomena and promising applications such as photostimulated luminescence induced by X-rays [21, 108, 154, 155], long-lasting phosphorescence induced by ultraviolet light and infrared femtosecond lasers [6, 156, 157], space-selective manipulation of the valence state of rare-earth ions [9, 10, 158] by using a focused femtosecond laser are reviewed.

3.2 Room-Temperature Spectral Hole Burning of Sm-Doped Glass Fibers

Recently, persistent spectral hole burning (PSHB) of rare-earth-doped inorganic materials has attracted much attention in view of its application to high-density optical memories. In particular, it seems that glass materials are advantageous for application in wavelength-selective optical devices, as well as memory devices, because of their large inhomogeneous linewidth. Wavelength-selective devices are key components in wavelength-division multiplexing systems, which are important for the next-generation optical communication technology. The problem for practical application lies in the fact that PSHB of rare-earth ions in glasses is usually observed only at temperatures below 20 K. However, room-temperature PSHB has been observed recently for Sm^{2+}-doped crystals [159, 160] and glasses [20, 161–163].

Optical fibers are the most important medium for telecommunication at present. An optical device in a fiber form is easy to connect with optical communication fiber with a small splice loss. We consider that room-temperature PSHB in optical fibers can be applied for demultiplexers in wavelength-multiplexing optical communication systems.

The optical fiber grating usually used as the wavelength-selective device is a refracting device. Thus, the optical fiber grating requires another optical fiber to guide the refracting light. In contrast, the wavelength-selective optical device using PSHB is a transmission device, and thus an optical fiber to guide the refracting light is not necessary.

As a first step in the development of the optical demultiplexers, room-temperature PSHB in Sm^{2+}-doped glass fibers was attempted. Sm-containing silica-based fibers were prepared and room-temperature PSHB for Sm^{2+} was successfully observed in the fiber. The ratio of inhomogeneous linewidth (Γ_{ih}) to homogeneous linewidth (Γ_{h}) in this system is $\sim$15.

As a source material for the fiber, core rods doped with Sm and Al were fabricated by the VAD method in a reducing atmosphere (H_2/He $= 1/10$). The concentration of Sm was 1000–10000 ppm and that of Al was 2–3 wt. %. The core rods obtained were orange in color. The preform was fabricated by jacketing the core rod with a pure SiO_2 tube. The preform was drawn into 10/125-μm fiber in the inert gas, and the core-cladding index difference Δn was 0.3–0.5%.

The absorption spectrum of the core rod is shown in Fig. 3.1, which indicates that both Sm^{3+} and Sm^{2+} are present. The broad band at 300–600 nm corresponds to the $4f^{6}{}^{7}F_0$–$4f^{5}5d$ transition that gives the spectrum its orange color. In this study, the absorption of Sm^{2+} near 600 nm was small. Therefore, room-temperature PSHB of Sm^{2+} to the fluorescence in optical fibers was tried as a first step. Fig. 3.2 shows the fluorescence spectrum of the Sm^{2+}-doped fiber and the core rod excited by 514-nm emission from an Ar^{+} laser. The peaks around 680 nm and 725 nm correspond to ${}^{5}D_0$–${}^{7}F_0$ and ${}^{5}D_0$–${}^{7}F_2$ transitions of Sm^{2+}, respectively. It was found that the Sm^{2+} ions

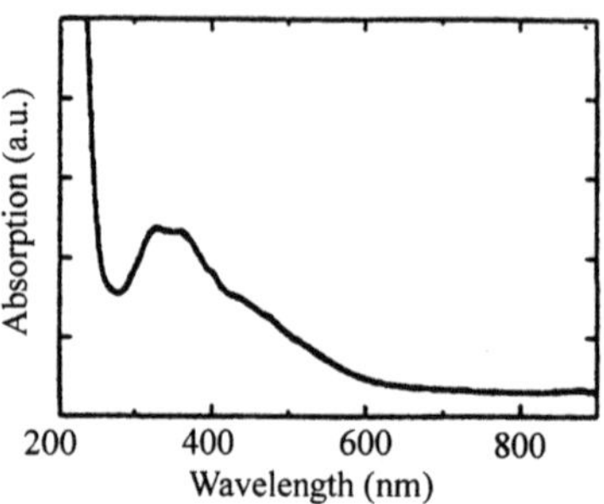

Fig. 3.1. Absorption spectrum of Sm^{2+}-doped glass (core rod) measured at room temperature

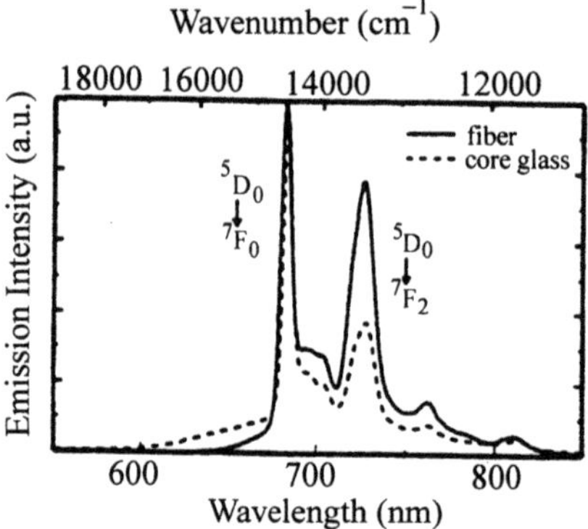

Fig. 3.2. Fluorescence spectrum measured at room temperature of Sm^{2+}-doped glass (core rod) and fiber excited by an Ar^+ laser (514 nm)

exist in both the fiber and the core rod, indicating that the process of fiber formation does not affect the valence state of Sm.

Hole-burning experiments were performed at room temperature for the $^5D_0$–$^7F_0$ transition of Sm^{2+} by using a DCM-special dye laser with a linewidth of about 1.3 cm^{-1} pumped by an Ar^+ laser. The dye laser beam was coupled into the fiber through a microscope objective lens. The laser power density in the fiber core during the burning was estimated to be 1×10^4 W/cm^2 from the fiber output power and core area. A typical burning time was 30 min. After the burning process, the hole-burning spectrum was measured by fluorescence excitation spectroscopy with a beam whose intensity was attenuated by a factor of 100. For the excitation spectroscopy, the fluorescence of the $^5D_0$–$^7F_2$ transition of Sm^{2+} near 725 nm was collected from the end of the fiber and detected by a photomultiplier through a 25-cm monochrometer.

Figure 3.3 shows the excitation spectrum of Sm^{2+}-doped fiber obtained after 30-min irradiation with the dye laser tuned to 683 nm at room tem-

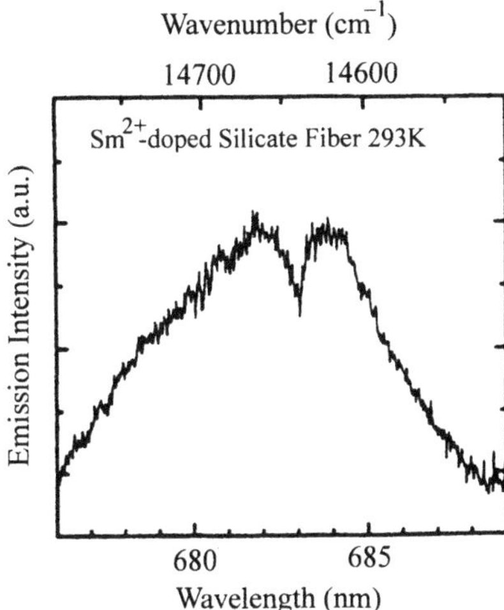

Fig. 3.3. Room temperature excitation spectrum of Sm^{2+}-doped fiber obtained by monitoring the $^5D_0$–$^7F_2$ emission after irradiation with a DCM dye laser at 683 nm. Persistent spectral hole burning (PSHB) is clearly observable at 683 nm

perature. It was found that the hole width is about 6/cm, and the inhomogeneous linewidth for the $^5D_0$–$^7F_0$ transition is about 93/cm. The ratio of homogeneous to inhomogeneous linewidths was calculated to be about 15. The dye laser used in this study shows its largest power near 640 nm; at longer wavelengths, the power gently diminished. At 675–690 nm, the wavelength range for the present measurement, the excitation spectrum seemed to become asymmetric, since the laser power at 675 nm is higher than at 690 nm. A symmetrical excitation spectrum was obtained by correcting the original spectrum using the power spectrum of the dye laser.

In this study, Sm and Al were co-doped in the core glass. Al is important for the presence of Sm^{2+} ions in the SiO_2-based glass matrix, as suggested by Arai et al. [164]. To obtain pure SiO_2, it is difficult to disperse the Sm ions because there is little nonbridging oxide. The doping of Al produces Sm^{3+}–O–Al bonds, leading to the dispersion of Sm^{3+} ions in the glass. Since the Al–O bond acts as a covalent bond, electron emission from the Sm^{3+}-O bond is easy. Thus, it becomes possible to introduce the stable Sm^{2+} ions in the SiO_2-based glass and to realize room temperature PSHB.

In addition, the PSHB performance of the fiber was compared to that of the bulk core rod. The core rod was cut into a $10 \times 10 \times 30$-mm^3 block, and similar hole-burning experiments were performed. In this case, the laser power density was limited to 3×10^3 W/cm^2, which was considerably smaller compared to the fiber experiment because of the different focusing lens used. The excitation spectrum was measured after the Sm^{2+}-doped core rod was irradiated for 60 min at room temperature with the dye laser beam tuned

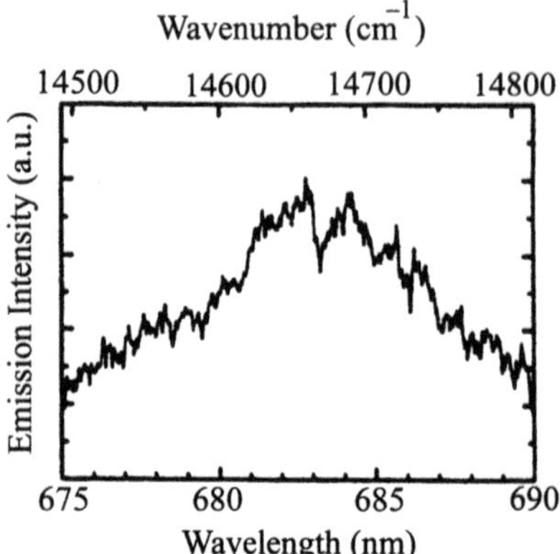

Fig. 3.4. Room temperature excitation spectrum of Sm^{2+}-doped fiber obtained by monitoring the $^5D_0$–$^7F_2$ emission after irradiation with a DCM dye laser at 683 nm. The power density used was similar to that used in the core rod experiment. PSHB is observable at 683 nm

at 683 nm. It was found that the PSHB of the core rod was very much smaller than that of the fiber. Since this result seems to be attributed to the difference in power level, the PSHB performance of the fiber was checked at a reduced power density, similar to that used in the core rod experiment. The resultant excitation spectrum is shown in Fig. 3.4, where the hole is still clearly observable at about 683 nm. The reason for this discrepancy is not understood at present. It is thought that the nature of the core material does not change through the fiber-drawing process, because the fluorescence spectra of the core rod and the fiber are similar, as shown in Fig. 3.2. A possible explanation is that there is a local concentration of laser power in the fiber core which results in the enhancement of the PSHB. The observation suggests the possibility of applying the PSHB to wavelength-selective devices suitable for optical communication systems.

3.3 X-ray-Induced Structure and Photostimulated Luminescence in Reduced Rare-Earth-Ion-Doped Glasses

Photostimulated luminescence, a phenomenon caused by the photostimulated recombination of holes and electrons at traps, which leaves electrons in a long-lived excited state, has attracted considerable attention in recent years [165, 166]. In photostimulated luminescence, a material excited by light 1 after X-ray irradiation, for example, emits light 2, the wavelength of which is usually shorter than that of excitation light 1, and the intensity of light 2 is proportional to the X-ray irradiation quantity in a certain dynamic range [165].

Photostimulable phosphor, $BaFX{:}Eu^{2+}$ (X = Br, I), is now widely used as a detector in X-ray radiography [165, 166]. An imaging plate made of $BaFX{:}Eu^{2+}$ (X = Br, I) has excellent characteristics, such as a wide dynamic range, extending over more than five orders of magnitude, and high sensitivity, which is one hundred or one thousand times higher than that for silver chloride films, which are still used as X-ray image receptors [165, 166].

It is well known that glasses have important advantages over crystals because of the potentially higher doping levels with rare-earth ions and their flexible geometry (glasses can be easily drawn into fibers and fabricated into large flat plates). If photostimulable luminescence phosphor could be made of glass, it would be an important breakthrough from the viewpoint of practical application. In this section, the observation of a photostimulated luminescence phenomenon in reduced rare-earth-ion-doped glasses is described. The mechanism for the photostimulated luminescence in the glass is assumed to be similar to that of the well-studied $BaFBr{:}Eu^{2+}$ photostimulable phosphor [165].

3.3.1 Photostimulated Luminescence in Eu^{2+}-Doped Fluoroaluminate Glasses

The glass sample used in the study was $0.1EuF_2 \cdot 14.9YF_3 \cdot 10MgF_2 \cdot 20CaF_2 \cdot 10SrF_2 \cdot 10BaF_2 \cdot 35AlF_3$ (mol. %). High-purity EuF_3, YF_3, MgF_2, CaF_2, SrF_2, BaF_2, and AlF_3 were used as raw materials. A batch of 10 g was mixed in a glovebox filled with Ar gas. In order to convert residual oxides into fluorides, 10 wt. % ammonium bifluoride NH_4HF_2 was mixed into the batch. The batch was first melted in a covered platinum crucible at 1000°C for 1 h under an Ar atmosphere. The liquid was cooled by pouring it onto the surface of a stainless steel plate, then pressing another plate down on top of it. The glass obtained was then put into a glassy carbon crucible and treated in an Ar + H_2 (5 vol. %) atmosphere at 1000°C for 1 h in a horizontal carbon furnace, while reducing gas flowed from the top to the bottom of the furnace at a flow rate of 5 L/min. The specimen was obtained by cooling the melt at room temperature. The transparent sample was cut and polished for the measurement of optical properties. The absorption spectrum of the sample was measured with a spectrophotometer (Jasco V-570). The photoluminescence spectrum of the sample was measured using an Hitachi 850 fluorescence spectrophotometer. When the sample was excited by an He–Ne laser (633 nm) after X-ray irradiation, photostimulated luminescence at ~400 nm was observed; the luminescence decayed with further He–Ne laser irradiation of the glass. The photostimulated luminescence decay curve was measured. For the photostimulated luminescence decay spectrum measurement, the glass specimen was first irradiated with 40-kV/30-mA X-rays from a W target for 600 s, and an He–Ne laser (633 nm) with a power of 170 $\mu W/cm^2$ was used as an excitation source. To eliminate the influence of background light, a stack of four B-410 filters (Hoya Company, Ltd., Japan) was set in front of the

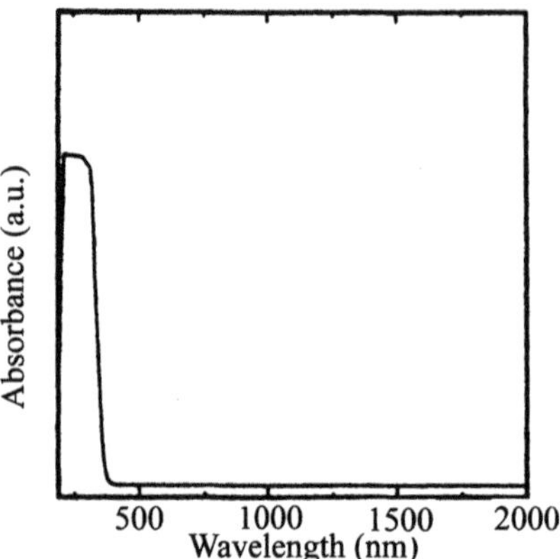

Fig. 3.5. Absorption spectrum of Eu^{2+}-doped fluoroaluminate glass

photomultiplier detector. For the measurement of the photostimulated excitation spectrum, the sample was first X-ray irradiated for 1200 s, then it was excited by 450–700 nm monochromatic light from a xenon lamp with a monochrometer; the photostimulated luminescence at 400 nm was monitored.

X-ray absorption spectra were measured for glass specimens unirradiated and X-ray irradiated by 6.94-keV X-rays for various durations. The measurements were carried out in the BL-7C beam line in the photon factory of the National Laboratory for High Energy Physics, with an electron beam energy of 2.5 GeV and a maximum stored current of 350 mA. Absorption data were collected at 301 energy points, ranging from 6.94 to 7.04 keV, utilizing an Si(111) double-crystal monochromator. A transmission mode was employed, and intensities were measured with an ionization chamber. Harmonies were rejected by detuning of the monochromator. The I_o ionization chamber was filled with nitrogen gas, and the I ionization chamber was filled with a mixture of nitrogen (85 vol. %) and argon (15 vol. %). The absorption spectra of Eu_2O_3 and EuF_2 crystals were also measured, as references. All measurements were carried out at room temperature.

Figure 3.5 shows the absorption spectrum of the sample. The sample is transparent in the wavelength region from 380 nm to 2 μm. A broad band was observed at ~300 nm, ranging from 200 to 380 nm. Since undoped fluoroaluminate glass is transparent in the wavelength regions from 200 nm to 6 μm, the band can be assigned to the absorption of Eu^{2+} ions [167].

Figure 3.6 shows the photoluminescence spectrum of the sample excited by 250 nm UV light. There is a sharp peak at 360 nm and a broad band at ~400 nm; these are attributable to the $^6P_{7/2}$–$^8S_{7/2}$ and 5d–4f transitions of Eu^{2+}, respectively [167]. Eu^{3+} shows strong absorption at 250 nm; glass containing Eu^{3+} would show strong emission at 500–600 nm due to the $^5D_j(j = 0, 1, 2)$–$^7F_j(j' = 0, 1, 2, 3)$ transitions of Eu^{3+} when excited by

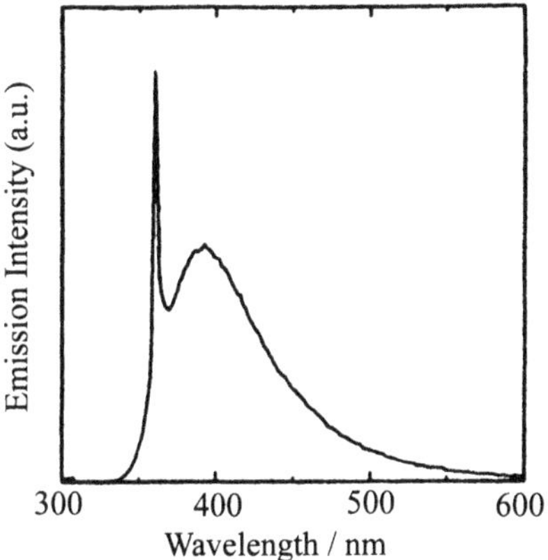

Fig. 3.6. Photoluminescence spectrum of the glass. The wavelength of the excitation light was 250 nm

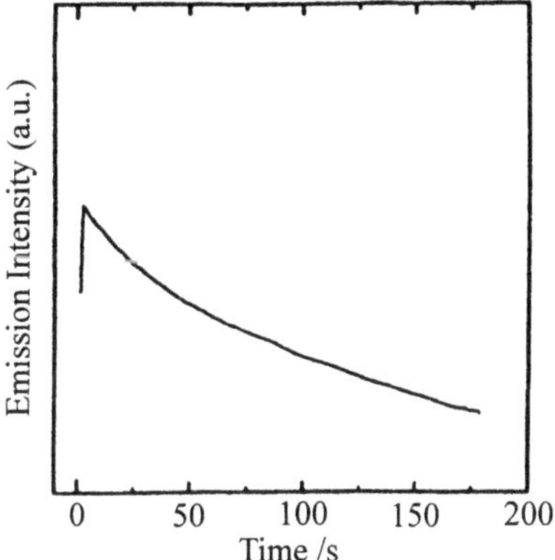

Fig. 3.7. Decay curve of photostimulated luminescence at ~400 nm for the X-ray-irradiated glass when excited continuously by an He–Ne laser (633 nm) with a power of 170 $\mu W/cm^2$

250 nm light [167]. Because no emission due to Eu^{3+} transition was observed, it is Eu^{2+} ions that are present in the glass.

Figure 3.7 shows the photostimulated luminescence decay curve at ~400 nm of the X-ray-irradiated sample when excited continuously by the He–Ne laser. The emission at 400 nm can be assigned to the 5d–4f transition of Eu^{2+} ions. The emission decayed when the sample was continuously irradiated by the He–Ne laser. No emission at 400 nm was observed in the unirradiated sample. Therefore, the emission at 400 nm is not due to upconversion or to a multiphoton absorption process. It is a phenomenon typical of photostimulated luminescence, as observed in $BaFBr:Eu^{2+}$ phosphor [168, 169].

The mechanisms of photostimulated luminescence have been investigated intensively [168–174]. Even for BaFBr:Eu^{2+}, however, the exact mechanism is still not clear enough. There are at least three models which describe the photostimulated luminescence process in BaFBr:Eu^{2+}. Takahashi et al. performed experiments to study the mechanism of photostimulated luminescence in BaFBr:Eu^{2+} [170]. The proposed mechanism is that Eu^{2+} ions are ionized by X-ray irradiation and converted to Eu^{3+} ions either directly or by trapping holes, and electrons excited to the conduction band are caught by F^+ centers (halogen ion vacancies) to form F centers. Then the irradiation of light in green to red stimulates luminescence, trapped electrons are liberated to the conduction band and return to Eu^{3+} ions, converting them to excited Eu^{2+} ions, and thus Eu^{2+} luminescence is produced. However, a study by Hangleiter et al. has shown that no Eu^{3+} is formed as a result of X-ray irradiation [171]. Moreover, the model proposed by Takahashi et al. does not specify how charge compensation is achieved when the negative ion vacancies (F^+ center) are present during crystal growth. Seggern et al. attributed the photostimulated luminescence to a recombination of an F center and a hole center in close proximity [172], where charge transfer after photostimulation occurs through tunneling and not through the conduction band. More recently, a new model of photostimulated luminescence was proposed by Harrison et al., in which photostimulated luminescence occurs when trapped electrons and holes migrate together to form loose clusters around Eu^{2+} and recombine after photostimulation [173].

All of the models propose that electrons and holes are formed in BaFBr: Eu^{2+} after the X-ray irradiation. Some of the electrons are caught by F^+ centers to form F centers, while some of the holes are caught by the hole-trapping center. Then, by the excitation of the He–Ne laser, trapped electrons are liberated and recombined with the trapped holes, resulting in the characteristic luminescence of Eu^{2+} ions.

Figure 3.8 shows the X-ray absorption spectra of Eu^{2+}-doped fluoroaluminate glasses, upon X-ray irradiation. Compared with crystals containing Eu^{2+} and Eu^{3+}, it is clear that a part of Eu^{2+} converted to Eu^{3+} upon X-ray irradiation; the concentration of Eu^{3+} increases with increasing the duration of X-ray irradiation. Eu^{2+} ions are ionized by X-ray irradiation and converted to Eu^{3+} either directly or by trapping holes.

A broad absorption band peaking at 500 nm and ranging from 400 to 700 nm was observed in the photostimulated excitation spectrum of X-ray-irradiated BaFBr:Eu^{2+}; this was considered due to the absorption of an F (F^-) center [174]. Electron and hole traps have also been observed in γ-ray irradiated fluoride glasses containing RF_2 (R = alkaline earth ion)–AlF_3 [175, 176]. Figure 3.9 shows the photostimulated excitation spectrum of the X-ray-irradiated sample when the emission at 400 nm was monitored. The spectrum has three broad bands – 540, 630, and 680 nm. These bands were assigned to the absorption due to electron traps, i.e., quasi-F-centers,

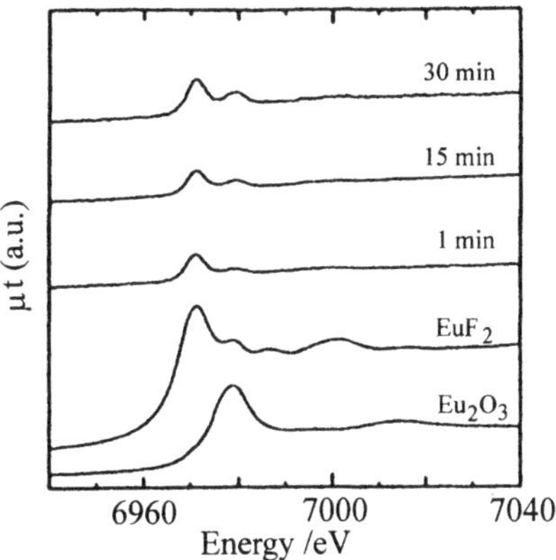

Fig. 3.8. X-ray absorption spectra of the glass irradiated by 6.94 keV X-rays for various duration

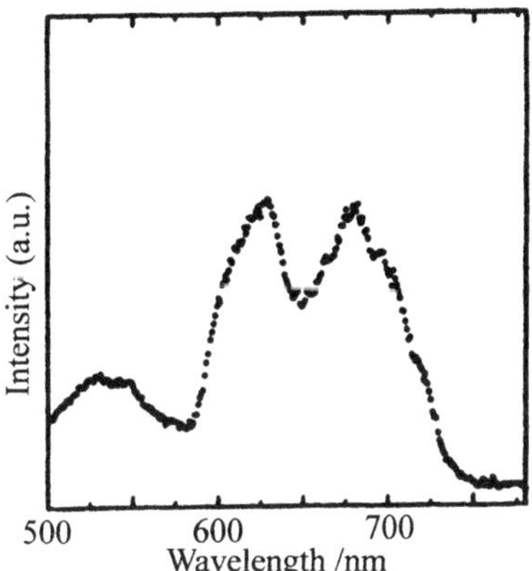

Fig. 3.9. Photostimulated excitation spectrum of the X-ray-irradiated glass where the photostimulated luminescence at 400 nm was monitored

which may have a deformed structure compared with F centers in crystals. It is assumed that quasi-F^+-centers and Eu^{2+} ions or other defects act as electron and hole traps in the photostimulated luminescence of the glass studied, respectively.

3.3.2 Photostimulated Luminescence in Ce^{3+}-Doped Alkali Borate Glasses

Photostimulated luminescence was also observed in other rare-earth-ion-doped glasses. There, the photostimulated luminescence characteristics of Ce^{3+}-doped alkali borate glasses are discussed. Composition of the samples used in this study was $25R_2O \cdot 75B_2O_3 \cdot 0.5CeO_2$ (R = Li, Na, K) (mol. %). Reagent-grade B_2O_3, Li_2CO_3, Na_2CO_3, K_2CO_3, and CeO_2 were used as starting materials. Mixed 10-g batches were melted in a covered Pt crucible at 1000°C for 30 min under an ambient atmosphere. The melts were then poured onto a stainless steel plate. Samples were reduced by melting them in glassy carbon crucibles in an $Ar_2 + H_2$ (5 vol. %) atmosphere at 1250°C for 60 min in a horizontal carbon furnace and quenching the melts to room temperature. Transparent samples were obtained. Samples were cut and polished to have a size of 7 ($\pm$0.1) $\times$ 7 ($\pm$0.1) $\times$ 3 ($\pm$0.1) mm.

X-ray absorption spectra were measured for samples unirradiated and X-ray irradiated by 5.22 keV X-rays for various durations. The absorption spectra of CeO_2 and CeF_3 crystals were also measured as references.

Photoluminescence spectra of the samples were measured using a Hitachi 850 fluorescence spectrophotometer. When the samples were excited by an He–Ne laser (633 nm) X-ray irradiation, photostimulated luminescence at about 360 nm was observed. Photostimulated luminescence decay spectra and photostimulated excitation spectra were measured. For the measurement of the photostimulated luminescence decay spectra, samples were first irradiated with a 40-kV/30-mA X-ray from a W target for 600 s; an He–Ne laser (633 nm) was used as the excitation source. To eliminate the influence of the background light, a U360 filter (Hoya Company, Ltd.) was set in front of the photomultiplier. The integrated intensity of the X-ray-induced photoluminescence of the samples during X-ray irradiation was also measured. For the measurement of the photostimulated excitation spectrum, samples were first X-ray irradiated for 1200 s, then they were excited by 450–700-nm monochromatic light from a xenon lamp (100 W) with a monochrometer; the photostimulated luminescence at 360 nm was monitored. All measurements were carried out at room temperature.

Figure 3.10 shows the X-ray absorption spectra of the cerium-ion-doped sodium borate glass samples fabricated in ambient and reducing atmospheres. Only an absorption band at 5.725 keV, which is assignable to the absorption of Ce^{3+}, was observed in the spectrum of the sample fabricated in the reducing atmosphere. An absorption band at 5.737 keV, attributable to the absorption of Ce^{4+}, and the 5.725 keV band were observed in the sample fabricated in the ambient atmosphere. Therefore, Ce ions exist in a trivalent state in the glass fabricated in the reducing atmosphere, while a part of the Ce ions remains in a Ce^{4+} state in the sample fabricated in the ambient atmosphere.

Figure 3.11 shows the photoluminescence spectra of the Ce^{3+}-doped alkali borate glass samples under excitation with 300 nm UV light. A broad emission band at about 360 nm was observed, which can be assigned to the 5d–4f transition of Ce^{3+} ions. The wavelength of the emission shifts slightly to a longer wavelength for the different samples in the following order: lithium borate $<$ sodium borate $<$ potassium borate. This can be regarded as the effect of the basicity of the glass matrix on the splitting of the 5d levels of Ce^{3+}. The 5d levels of Ce^{3+} ions are highly affected by the ligand field of

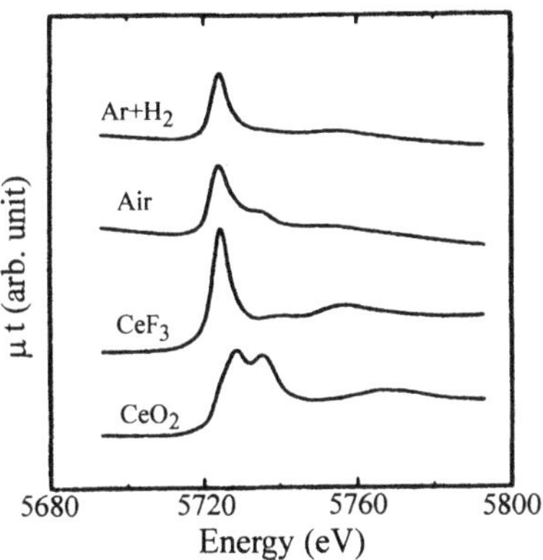

Fig. 3.10. X-ray absorption spectra of Ce^{3+}-doped sodium borate glass fabricated in the ambient and reducing atmospheres

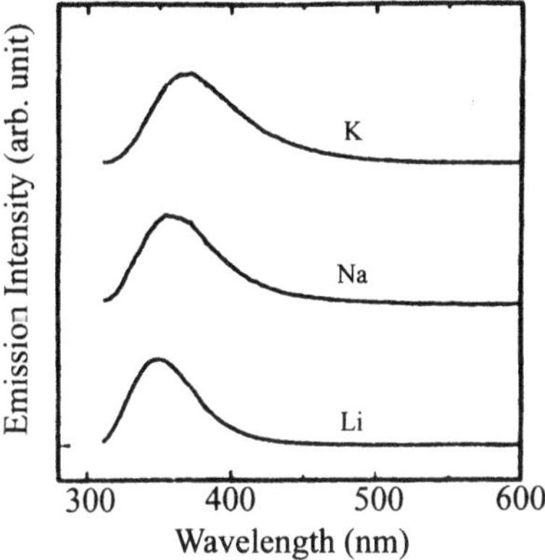

Fig. 3.11. Photoluminescence spectra of the Ce^{3+}-doped alkali borate glasses. The wavelength of excitation light was 300 nm

the first coordinating sphere. The higher electron density in oxygen ions of the potassium borate glass, due to it's larger basicity, results in the larger splitting of the 5d levels of Ce^{3+} ions, leading to the longer wavelength of the emission associated with the 5d–4f transition of Ce^{3+} ions.

When the Ce^{3+}-doped samples were excited by the He–Ne laser (633 nm) after the X-ray irradiation, emission at about 360 nm was observed, and it decayed with further excitation by the He–Ne laser. Figure 3.12 shows the decay curves of the emission. It is clear that the emissions at about 360 nm observed in the X-ray-irradiated samples is not due to upconversion or to a two-photon absorption process, since no emission at 360 nm was observed in the unirradiated samples under excitation with the He–Ne laser. It is a phenomenon typical of photostimulated luminescence, as observed in $BaFBr{:}Eu^{2+}$ phosphor [168, 169].

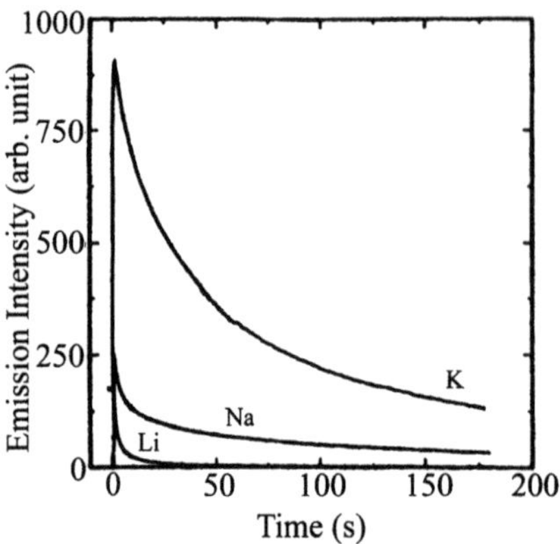

Fig. 3.12. Photostimulated luminescence decay curves of the Ce^{3+}-doped alkali borate glasses. The excitation source was an He–Ne laser (633 nm) with a power of 170 μW/cm^2

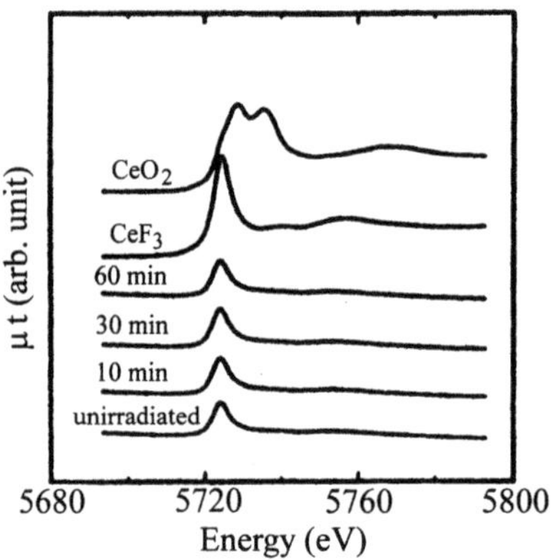

Fig. 3.13. X-ray absorption spectra of the Ce^{3+}-doped sodium borate glass after X-ray irradiation for various durations. The X-ray energy was 5.22 keV

It is usually considered that Ce^{3+} ions act as strong hole traps in the glasses [177]. Figure 3.13 shows the X-ray absorption spectra of Ce^{3+}-doped sodium borate glass after X-ray irradiation for various durations. No apparent variation of the valence state of Ce ions is observed for Ce^{3+}-doped sodium borate glass upon X-ray irradiation. This result is different from that in Eu^{2+}-doped sodium borate glasses, in which some Eu^{2+} converted to Eu^{3+} upon X-ray irradiation [178]. Therefore, Ce^{3+} ions do not seem to directly act as hole traps, which is different from the role of Eu^{2+} in BaFBr:Eu^{2+} proposed by Takahashi et al. Other defects may act as hole traps in our samples.

The absorption spectra of alkali borate glasses irradiated by various radiation sources have been investigated extensively [177]. After γ-ray irradiation, an absorption band peaking at about 600 nm, ranging from 400 to

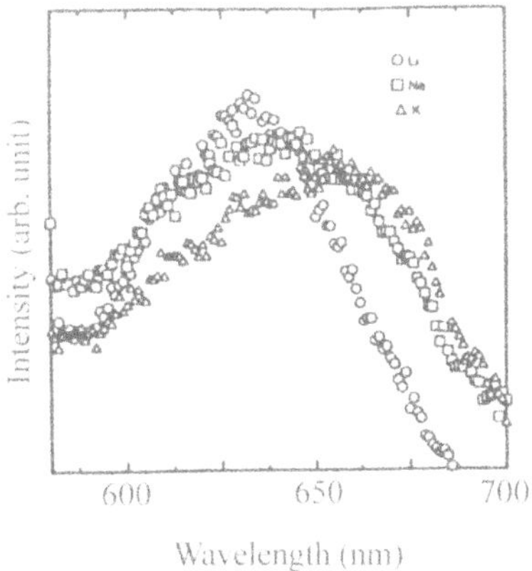

Fig. 3.14. Photostimulated excitation spectra of the X-ray-irradiated glasses when the photostimulated luminescence at 360 nm was monitored

800 nm, was observed in alkali borate glasses. This band was assigned to the absorption due to the electron traps, i.e., quasi-F-centers, in the borate glasses [177]. Figure 3.14 shows the photostimulated excitation spectra of the samples when the emission at 360 nm was monitored. The spectra have a broad band with the maximum at about 650 nm. This band has been attributed to electron traps (the quasi-F-centers) in the alkali borate glasses after γ-ray irradiation [177].

Based on the proposed mechanism of photostimulated luminescence in BaFBr:Eu^{2+}, the following model of photostimulated luminescence in our samples is suggested: After X-ray irradiation, electrons and holes are formed in the samples. Some of the electrons are caught by the quasi-F^+-center to form a quasi-F-center, and some of the holes are caught by other defects (hole centers). When excited by the He–Ne laser, the trapped electrons are liberated and combined with the trapped holes, and thus they release an energy which excites the electrons at the ground state of the Ce^{3+} ions to the excited state, finally leading to the characteristic Ce^{3+} emission.

Figure 3.15 shows the dependence of the photostimulated luminescence intensity I_p and I_{int}) and X-ray-induced photoluminescence intensity (I_x) on the alkali ion species. I_p is the peak value at the beginning of the excitation by the He–Ne laser, and I_{int} is the time-integrated intensity. The intensity of photostimulated luminescence increases exponentially with increasing the molecular weight of glasses.

The photostimulated luminescence intensity is determined by several factors including the X-ray absorption efficiency of the glass matrix, the recombination probability of the hole and electron traps, the energy-transfer efficiency from recombination centers to Ce^{3+} ions and the emission efficiency of Ce^{3+} ions. The larger the alkali element, the larger the X-ray absorption efficiency of the glass matrix. Therefore, it seems that the order of the photostimulated

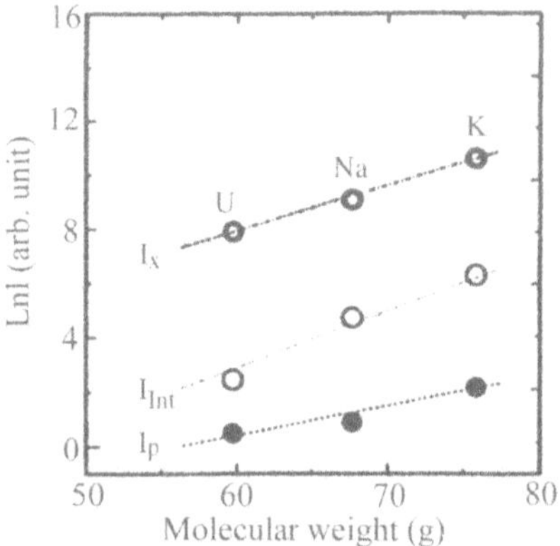

Fig. 3.15. Dependence of the peak value of photostimulated luminescence at the beginning of the excitation by the He–Ne laser (I_p), the integrated intensities of photostimulated luminescence (I_{int}), and X-ray-induced photoluminescence (I_x) on the Ce^{3+}-doped borate glasses and alkali ion species

luminescence intensity is determined by the X-ray absorption efficiency of the glass matrix. However, the question of why the photostimulated luminescence intensity exponentially increased with increasing molecular weight of the glass matrix still remains unanswered.

The photostimulated luminescence intensity of the glass samples used here is relatively weak compared to commercially available $BaFBr:Eu^{2+}$ phosphor. The main reason is assumed to be the low concentration of electron traps, as well as an unsuitable ratio of electron and hole traps in the glass. However, by selecting appropriate glass compositions and controlling the precipitation of photostimulable luminescence microcrystal in glass, it should be possible to fabricate a rare-earth-ion-doped glass with desirable photostimulable luminescence characteristics.

3.4 Creation of Long-Lasting Phosphorescence in Rare-Earth-Ion-Doped Glasses

As has been discussed in the previous section, glass is an excellent matrix for rare-earth ions to perform various optical functions. So far, the optical properties of glasses doped with trivalent rare-earth ions have been investigated intensively, and these glasses have been used as materials for lasers, optical amplifiers, etc. [2, 179, 180]. Only a few studies have been performed on reduced rare-earth-ion-doped glasses, although glasses containing reduced rare-earth ions exhibit various useful optical properties, such as a large Faraday effect, photostimulated luminescence, spectral hole burning memory, etc [20, 154, 181–183]. The main reason may be that reduced rare-earth-ion-doped glass must be fabricated in a strong reducing atmosphere. Compared to glasses doped with other reduced rare-earth ions, Eu^{2+}-doped glasses are easier to fabricate. Some interesting phenomena in Eu^{2+}-doped glasses have been observed during the past few decades [154, 167, 182, 183].

Cohen and Smith reported a photochromic phenomenon in Eu^{2+}-doped sodium silicate glasses early in 1962 [183]. Absorbed energy, for example, sunlight, quickly creates visible color centers in the glasses, so that the number of centers reaches an equilibrium state, and the visible color spontaneously decays and disappears almost completely in a few seconds upon removal of the activating light. They proposed that these glasses are promising materials as glass window curtains and visible-intensity windshields as well as ophthalmic and space devices. In Sect. 3.2, the photostimulated luminescence phenomenon in Eu^{2+}-doped glasses was introduced [154]. In photostimulated luminescence, a material excited by light 1 (visible or infrared light) after X-ray irradiation, emits a light (light 2) whose wavelength is usually shorter than that of excitation light 1, such that the intensity of light 2 is dependent on the excitation intensity of the X-rays. These glasses are expected to become a new family of materials for two-dimensional X-ray sensors and optical memory. It seems that Eu^{2+}-doped glasses with various optical functions may be obtained by selecting the appropriate glass matrix. If the activating energy of the trapped electron or hole released from the trapping center is far lower than that in the case of photostimulated luminescence, then the temporarily trapped electron or hole can be released by the thermal energy and the energy due to electron and hole recombination may be released as long-lasting phosphorescence at room temperature. In Sect. 3.4.1 an interesting phenomenon in Eu^{2+}-doped transparent aluminosilicate glasses is introduced. The glasses show bright and very long-lasting phosphorescence. The mechanism of long-lasting phosphorescence is also discussed. In Sect. 3.4.2 a three-dimensional long-lasting phosphorescence phenomenon in calcium aluminosilicate glasses doped with Ce^{3+}, Tb^{3+}, and Pr^{3+} induced by an 800-nm femtosecond pulsed laser is introduced. The focused part of the laser in the glasses emits bright and long-lasting phosphorescence able to be clearly seen with the naked eye in the dark even 1 h after the removal of the activating laser. By selecting appropriate glass compositions and species of rare-earth ions, optional three-dimensional image patterns emitting long-lasting phosphorescence in various colors, including blue, green, and red, can be formed within glass samples by moving the focal point of the laser. The mechanism of long-lasting phosphorescence is discussed based on the absorption spectra of the glasses before and after femtosecond laser irradiation.

3.4.1 Long-Lasting Phosphorescence in Eu^{2+}-Doped Glasses Induced by UV Light

The compositions of the glass samples prepared were $40SrO \cdot 30Al_2O_3 \cdot 30SiO_2 \cdot 0.05Eu_2O_3 \cdot 0.05Dy_2O_3$ (EDSAS) and $40SrO \cdot 30Al_2O_3 \cdot 30SiO_2 \cdot 0.05Eu_2O_3$ (ESAS) (mol. %). Dy^{3+} ions were introduced into one of our samples; we expected them to act as electron traps, as they act in $SrAl_2O_4$ doped with Eu^{2+} and Dy^{3+} [184]. Reagent-grade $SrCO_3$, Al_2O_3, SiO_2, Eu_2O_3 and Dy_2O_3 were used as starting materials. Approximately 10-g batches were mixed and then melted in Pt crucibles at 1550°C for 60 min in an ambient atmosphere. The crucibles containing the melts were then taken out of the furnace and cooled to room temperature. The glasses obtained were then pulverized, put into glassy carbon crucibles and remelted in an Ar + H_2 (5 vol. %) atmosphere at 1550°C for 60 min. The melts were then quenched to room temperature. The glass samples thus obtained were cut, polished and subjected to optical measurement. $SrAl_2O_4$ doped with Eu^{2+} and Dy^{3+} was prepared under the Ar + H_2 (5 vol. %) atmosphere at 1450°C for 60 min. The crystal phase was confirmed with X-ray diffraction analysis.

The absorption spectra of the samples were measured using a spectrophotometer (Jasco V-570). The normal fluorescence spectra of the samples were measured by a fluorescence spectrophotometer (Hitachi 850) using 394-nm UV light from a xenon lamp as the excitation source. For the phosphorescence spectrum and the decay curve of the phosphorescence measurements, glass samples were first irradiated by a white-color fluorescent lamp with a power density of 2×10^4 lux for 30 min. The thermal luminescence curves of the irradiated glass samples were measured with a thermal luminescence detector reader (Kasei Optonics Co. Ltd., Japan) at a heating rate of 2°C/s.

X-ray absorption spectra of the Eu^{2+}–Dy^{3+} co-doped $SrAl_2O_4$ and EDSAS sample irradiated with 6.981-keV X-rays for Eu ions and with 7.790-keV X-rays for Dy ions for various durations were measured. The measurements were carried out in the BL-7C beam line in the photon factory of the National Laboratory for High Energy Physics, with an electron beam energy of 2.5 GeV and a maximum stored current of about 400 mA. Absorption data were collected at 301 energy points in the measured range, utilizing an Si(111) double-crystal monochromator. A transmission mode was employed, and intensities were measured with an ionization chamber. Harmonies were rejected by detuning of the monochromator. The I_0 ionization chamber, which was used for intensity reference, was filled with nitrogen gas, and the I ionization chamber was filled with a mixture of nitrogen (85 vol. %) and argon (15 vol. %) for Eu-ion measurement and a mixture of nitrogen (50 vol. %) and argon (50 vol. %) for Dy ions measurements. The absorption spectra of Eu_2O_3, EuF_2, EuF_3, EuS, Dy_2O_3, DyF_3 and Dy_2S_3 crystals were also measured, as references. All measurements were carried out at room temperature, except for the measurement of the thermal luminescence curve.

Figure 3.16 shows the optical absorption spectra of EDSAS samples fabricated in ambient and reducing atmospheres. The sample fabricated in the ambient atmosphere is transparent in the wavelength region from 300 nm to 1 μm, while a strong absorption band is observed at about 380 nm, ranging from 350 to 500 nm, in the spectrum of the sample fabricated in the reducing atmosphere. This band can be assigned to the absorption of Eu^{2+} ions.

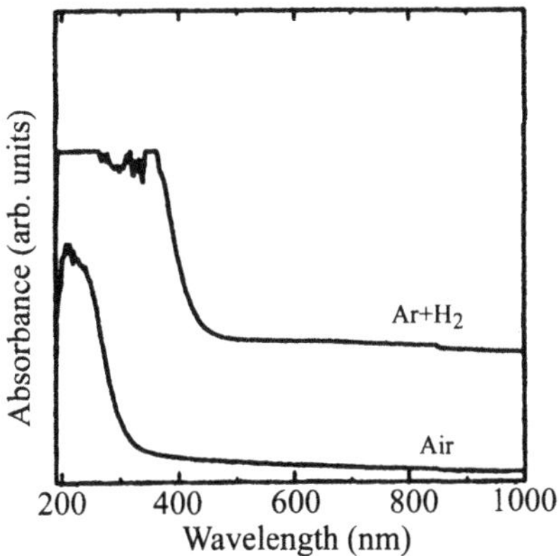

Fig. 3.16. Optical absorption spectra of EDSAS samples fabricated in various atmospheres. Flat top in the absorption spectrum of glass fabricated in the Ar + H_2 atmosphere is due to absorbance over the permissible measurement level

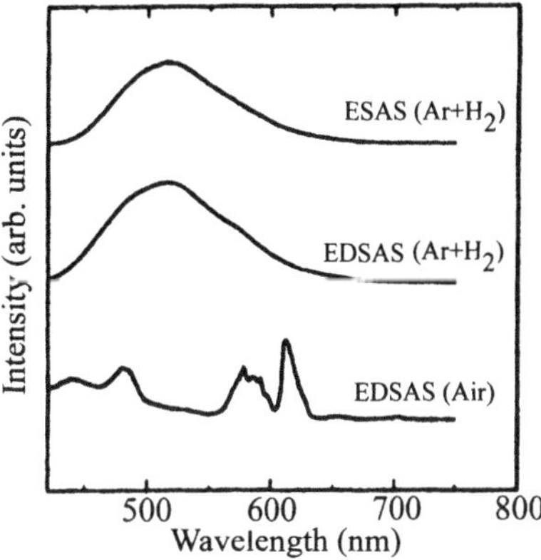

Fig. 3.17. Photoluminescence spectra of EDSAS and ESAS samples fabricated in the reducing atmosphere and EDSAS sample fabricated in the ambient atmosphere. The excitation wavelength was 394 nm

Figure 3.17 shows the photoluminescence spectra of the ESAS and EDSAS samples fabricated in the reducing atmosphere together with the photoluminescence spectrum of EDSAS sample prepared in the ambient atmosphere. The excitation wavelength was 394 nm. There are several peaks ranging from 400 to 700 nm in the spectrum of the EDSAS sample fabricated in the ambient atmosphere. The peaks can be attributed to the $^5D_i(i = 0, 1)$–$^7F_j(j = 0$–$4)$ Eu^{3+} transitions [167]. In contrast, EDSAS and ESAS samples fabricated in the reducing atmosphere showed an emission band at 510 nm due to the 5d–4f Eu^{2+} transition [167]. No emission peaks due to the $^5D_i(i = 0, 1)$–$^7F_j(j = 0$–$4)$ Eu^{3+} transitions were observed. Therefore, most of the Eu ions are present

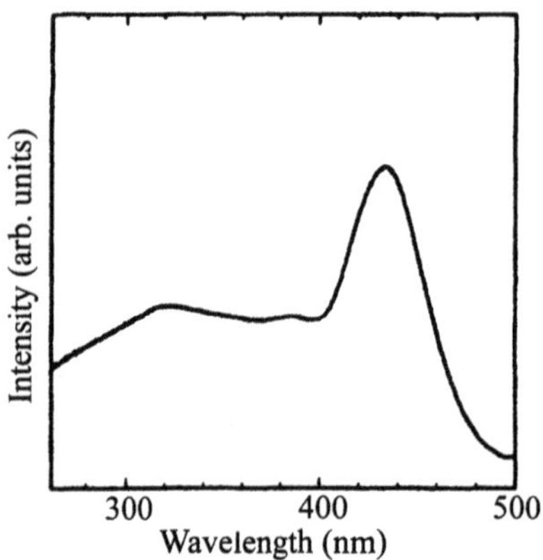

Fig. 3.18. Excitation spectrum of EDSAS sample fabricated in the reducing atmosphere. The emission at 510 nm was monitored

in the divalent state in the reduced samples. The spectrum of ESAS has an appearance similar to that of EDSAS.

Figure 3.18 shows the excitation spectrum of the EDSAS sample fabricated in the reducing atmosphere when the emission at 510 nm was monitored. A strong band peaking at 440 nm, with a shoulder at about 325 nm, was observed in the spectrum. It can be ascribed to the Eu^{2+} transitions. We also observed that there was no apparent difference between the excitation spectra of EDSAS and ESAS.

After irradiation by a white-color fluorescent lamp with a power density of 2×10^4 lux for 30 min, no phosphorescence was observed in the samples fabricated in the ambient atmosphere, while glass samples fabricated in the reducing atmosphere showed a bright and long-lasting phosphorescence. Figure 3.19 shows a photograph of the phosphorescence in the reduced EDSAS sample 8 h after removal of the activating lamp. An ISO 100 film made by Fuji Photo Film Co. Ltd. was used to take the photograph. The exposure time was 40 min. The phosphorescence can still be clearly seen with the naked eye in the dark even 24 h after the removal of the exciting lamp. The emission spectra of the phosphorescence have similar appearances to the photoluminescence spectra excited by 394-nm light. Figure 3.20 shows the decay curve of the phosphorescence at 510 nm in the EDSAS sample fabricated in the reducing atmosphere. The emission decays quickly at first and then the intensity slowly decreases. The decay curves of EDSAS and ESAS samples were found to overlap with each other. Figure 3.21 shows the thermal luminescence curves of the EDSAS and ESAS samples irradiated by the light from a fluorescent lamp for 5 min. There is a broad band with a maximum at about 50°C, ranging from room temperature to 230°C.

Figures 3.22 and 3.23 show the X-ray absorption spectra due to the absorption of Eu and Dy ions of $SrAl_2O_4$ doped with Eu^{2+} and Dy^{3+} and X-

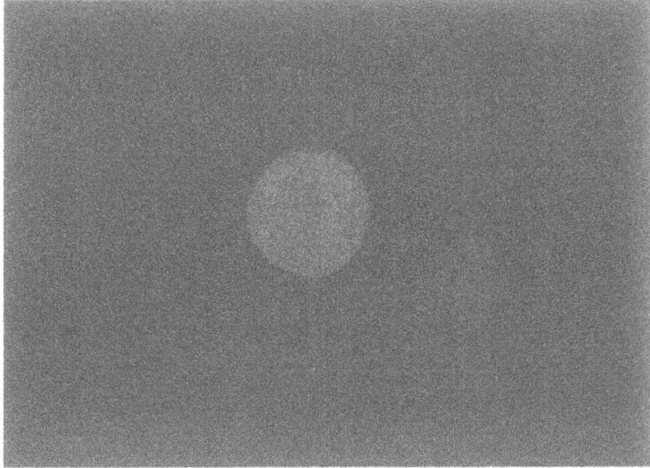

Fig. 3.19. Photograph of the phosphorescence in the reduced EDSAS sample 8 h after removal of the activating lamp

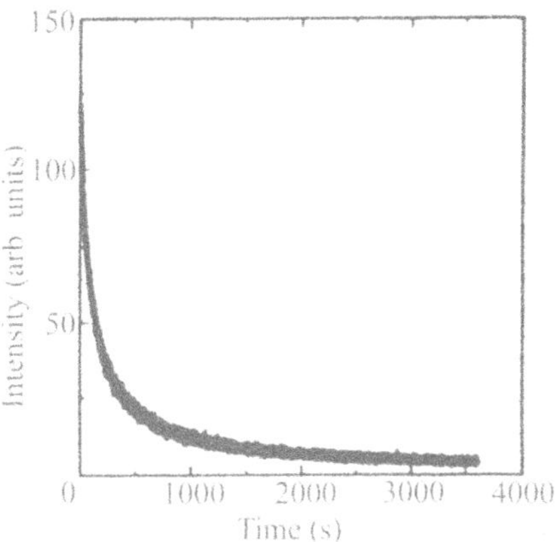

Fig. 3.20. Decay curve of the long-lasting phosphorescence at 510 nm in EDSAS sample fabricated in the reducing atmosphere

ray irradiated for various durations. The X-ray absorption spectra of Eu^{2+}-, Eu^{3+}- and Dy^{3+}-doped crystals are also shown in Figs. 3.22 and 3.23 for comparison. The bands at 6.973 keV and 6.981 keV are assigned to the absorption due to $Eu^{2+}$and Eu^{3+}, respectively. A new band should appear in the wavelength regions shorter than 6.973 keV if Eu^{+} is formed (Eu^{2+} + electron) after X-ray irradiation. However, little difference can be found between the absorption spectra before and after X-ray irradiation. The same results were obtained for the X-ray absorption spectra of the EDSAS sample.

Long-lasting phosphorescence is suggested to be due to the thermostimulated recombination of holes and electrons at traps that leave electrons or

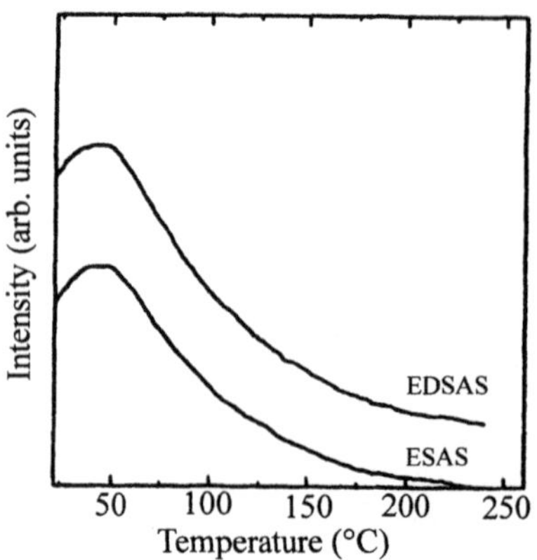

Fig. 3.21. Thermal luminescence curves of EDSAS and ESAS samples fabricated in the reducing atmosphere

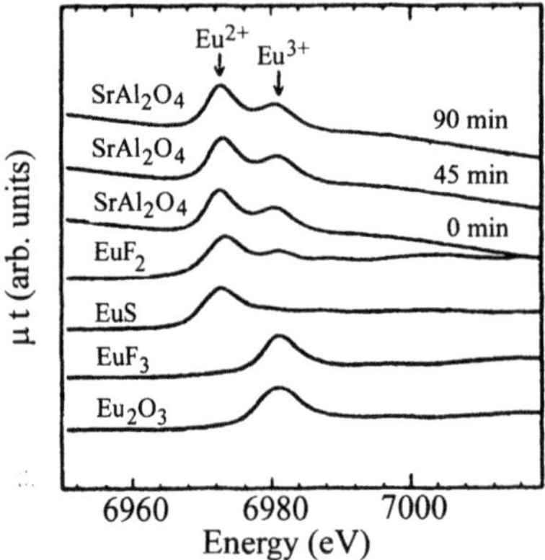

Fig. 3.22. X-ray absorption spectra of Eu ions in an Eu^{2+}–Dy^{3+}-doped $SrAl_2O_4$ crystal X-ray irradiated for various durations. The energy of the X-ray irradiation was 6.981 keV

holes in a metastable state at room temperature [185]. Usually, incorporation of rare-earth ions such as Eu^{2+}, Sm^{3+}, Dy^{3+} into phosphors can dramatically change the phosphorescence properties of the phosphors; therefore, such rare-earth ions are proposed to act as electron or hole trapping centers [186]. The mechanism of long-lasting phosphorescence in Eu^{2+}–Dy^{3+}-doped strontium aluminate phosphor has been investigated by Matsuzawa et al [184]. Based on photoconductivity measurements, they proposed that the Dy^{3+} ion acts as a hole trap (Dy^{3+} + hole $\rightarrow$ Dy^{4+}) and Eu^{2+} acts as an electron trap (Eu^{2+} + hole $\rightarrow$ Eu^{+}). Introduction of Dy^{3+} into the Eu^{2+}-doped strontium aluminate results in the creation of a highly dense trapping level which is located at a suitable depth so that the trapped hole is thermally released at

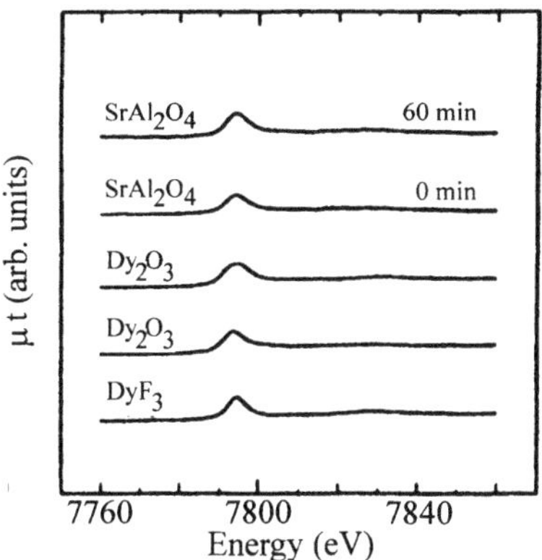

Fig. 3.23. X-ray absorption spectra of Dy ions in an Eu^{2+}–Dy^{3+}-doped $SrAl_2O_4$ crystal X-ray irradiated for various durations. The energy of the X-ray irradiation was 7.790 keV

a steady rate at room temperature. Thus, bright and long-lasting phosphorescence takes place.

However, no evidence was observed for the conversion of Eu^{2+} to Eu^{+} after the X-ray irradiation from X-ray absorption spectra of Eu ions in $SrAl_2O_4$ doped with Eu^{2+} and Dy^{3+} shown in Fig. 3.22. Moreover, little difference can be found between the absorption spectra of Dy ions in $SrAl_2O_4$ doped with Eu^{2+} and Dy^{3+} before and after X-ray irradiation (Fig. 3.23), although bright and long-lasting phosphorescence was observed after the X-ray irradiation. In addition, it was observed that the valence state of Eu and Dy ions in the EDSAS sample remain unchanged after X-ray irradiation. Moreover, the photoluminescence spectrum, excitation spectrum, decay curve of phosphorescence and thermal luminescence curve in the ESAS sample were observed to be nearly the same as those in the EDSAS sample. Therefore, it is suggested that Dy^{3+} and Eu^{2+} ions do not directly act as hole and electron traps.

Recent results giving electron spin resonance (ESR) spectra showed that the valence state of Eu^{2+}remains unchanged after the UV light irradiation. ESR signals due to the defects in glass matrix were observed after UV light irradiation and decayed with time. The results agree with the decay in phosphorescence.

Calcium aluminate glasses, without containing any rare-earth ions, melted in a reducing atmosphere have been found to show photochromism [187]. Upon exposure to ultraviolet radiation, a broad absorption band with an apparent peak at around 2 eV and a shoulder at around 3.5 eV was induced; after interruption of the light illumination, both bands faded at room temperature. The photochromism is suggested to originate from an electron trapped at a site of oxygen vacancy surrounded by Ca^{2+} ions. The oxygen vacancy in the glasses was formed due to the strong reduction in the reducing atmosphere. It is suggested that such oxygen vacancies surrounded by Sr^{2+} ions also exist in the glass samples fabricated in a reducing atmosphere and may act as electron-trapping centers, since the physicochemical behaviors of Ca^{2+} and Sr^{2+} are very similar. After irradiation by a white-color fluorescent lamp, electrons and holes are formed in the samples. Some of the electrons are trapped by oxygen defects and some of the holes are captured by other defects in the glass matrix. Since the electron-trap depth is broadly distributed and shallow, the electrons can be thermally released at room temperature and long-lasting phosphorescence is brought about. The detailed mechanism of long-lasting phosphorescence in Eu^{2+}-doped strontium aluminosilicate glasses should be investigated further.

Eu^{2+}-doped glass samples are transparent in the region with wavelengths longer than 400 nm and can absorb UV and visible light with a shorter wavelength to emit light at 510 nm, which fits well with the wavelength region corresponding to a larger conversion efficiency of conventional Si solar cells [188]. Moreover, glasses in the $SrO–Al_2O_3–SiO_2$ system are thermally and chemically stable. Therefore, the glasses developed may be used not only as material for energy-saving display but also as material for the enhancement of the conversion efficiency of solar cells.

3.5 Femtosecond-Laser-Induced, Three-Dimensional, Bright and Long-Lasting Phosphorescence Inside Calcium Aluminosilicate Glasses Doped with Rare-Earth Ions

Since long-lasting phosphorescence was observed in rare-earth-ion-doped glass samples after UV light irradiation, we suspected that it should be possible to induce 3-dimensional long-lasting phosphorescence by irradiation of a focused ultrashort infrared pulsed laser via a multiphoton process.

The composition of the glass samples prepared was $40CaO \cdot 30Al_2O_3 \cdot 30SiO_2 \cdot 0.05Ln_2O_3$ (Ln = Ce, Tb, Pr, Nd, Sm, Eu, Dy, Ho, Er, Tm, and Yb) (mol. %). Reagent-grade $CaCO_3$, Al_2O_3, SiO_2, and rare-earth oxides were used as the starting materials. Approximately 30-g batches were mixed and then melted in Pt crucibles at 1550°C for 60 min in an ambient atmosphere. The crucibles containing the melts were then taken out of the furnace and cooled to room temperature. For the Tb^{3+}-doped glass sample, a part of the obtained glass was pulverized, put into a glassy carbon crucible, and remelted in an Ar + H_2 (5 vol. %) atmosphere at 1550°C for 60 min. The melt was then quenched to room temperature. All of the glasses obtained were transparent. The glass samples were cut, polished, and subjected to optical measurement. The absorption spectra of the samples were measured by a spectrophotometer (Jasco V-570). The normal fluorescence spectra of

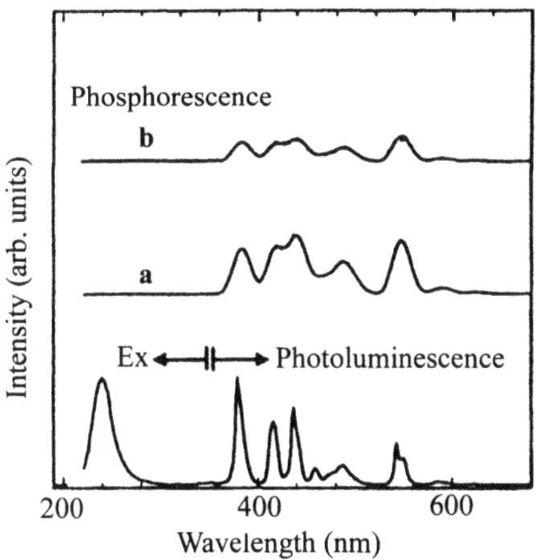

Fig. 3.24. Photoluminescence, phosphorescence, and excitation spectra of a Tb^{3+}-doped calcium aluminosilicate glass. For the measurement of the excitation spectrum, the luminescence at 437 nm was monitored. Phosphorescence spectra of the glass 350 (*curve a*) and 1000 s (*curve b*) after laser irradiation are shown

the samples were measured by a fluorescence spectrophotometer (Hitachi 850) using 250 nm UV light from a xenon lamp as the excitation source.

A regeneratively amplified 800-nm Ti:sapphire laser was used for our study to emit 120-fs, 200-kHz, mode-locked pulses. The laser beam, with an average power of 400 mW, was focused by a lens with a 100-mm focal length in the interior of the glass samples with the help of an XYZ stage. For the phosphorescence spectra and decay curves, the glass samples were first irradiated with the focused laser. All of the measurements were carried out at room temperature.

After irradiation with the focused laser, no apparent phosphorescence was observed for the Nd^{3+}-, Sm^{3+}-, Eu^{3+}-, Dy^{3+}-, Ho^{3+}-, Er^{3+}-, Tm^{3+}-, and Yb^{3+}-doped glass samples, while visible, bright, and long-lasting phosphorescence from the focused area was observed for the Ce^{3+}-, Tb^{3+}-, and Pr^{3+}-doped glass samples in the dark after removal of the femtosecond laser. As shown in Fig. 3.24, the emission spectrum of the phosphorescence in the Tb^{3+}-doped glass sample has the same appearance as the photoluminescence spectrum excited by 250-nm UV light. The emission peaks in the wavelength region from 350 to 600 nm can be ascribed to the ${}^5D_i(i = 3, 4)$–${}^7F_j(j = 1$–$6)$ Tb^{3+} transitions [189]. From Fig. 3.24, it is clear that the phosphorescence intensity decreases with time, while the appearance of the phosphorescence spectrum remains unchanged.

Figure 3.25 shows the decay curve of the phosphorescence at 437 nm in the glass sample doped with Tb^{3+} ions. The time dependence of the inverse of the phosphorescence intensity is also shown in Fig. 3.25. The intensity of

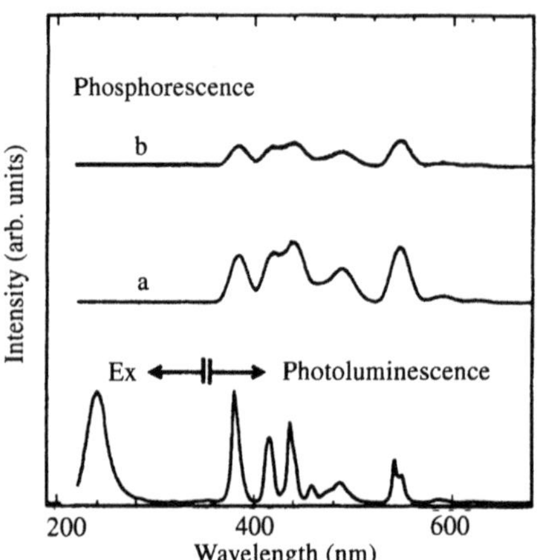

Fig. 3.25. Decay curve of the phosphorescence at 437 nm in a Tb^{3+}-doped calcium aluminosilicate glass

the phosphorescence decreases in inverse proportion to time, indicating the phosphorescence may be a decay process due to heat-assisted tunneling effect.

Figure 3.26 shows a photograph of the emission states of phosphorescence in Ce^{3+} (blue)-, Tb^{3+} (green)-, and Pr^{3+}(red)-doped glasses. The insides of the glass samples were scanned randomly by a focused laser beam moving at a rate of 1000 μm/s. It is surprising that the phosphorescence can still be clearly seen in the dark even 1 h after the removal of the activating laser.

The absorption spectra of the Tb^{3+}-doped glass sample before and after laser irradiation were measured and are shown in Fig. 3.27. A broad absorption band can be observed peaking at 400 nm in the wavelength region from 280 to 750 nm after laser irradiation. The band can be ascribed to, for instance, the absorption of aluminum–oxygen hole centers, which has been observed for a UV-irradiated CaO–Al_2O_3-based glass sample [187]. The band fading at room temperature shown in Fig. 3.27 agrees with the decay in phosphorescence. Moreover, the phosphorescence can only be observed in the laser-focus area, where color centers were observed under a microscope to form after laser irradiation. Therefore, the disappearance of defects at room temperature is considered to be related to the decay of the phosphorescence. The time constant of the phosphorescence was estimated to differ from that of the decay of the absorbance due to laser-induced defect centers. Consequently, phosphorescence and absorption may not be simply related; other factors should be considered.

Long-lasting phosphorescence phenomenon in the Ce^{3+}-, Tb^{3+}-, and Pr^{3+}-doped glass samples was observed. However, the same phenomenon was not observed in the other rare-earth-ion-doped glass samples. It is therefore suggested that the mechanism of long-lasting phosphorescence in the glass

Fig. 3.26. Photograph of the emission states of phosphorescence in glass samples 5 min after the removal of the exciting laser. The Ce^{3+}-doped calcium aluminosilicate glass sample shows blue-light emission. The Tb^{3+}-doped calcium aluminosilicate glass sample shows green-light emission. The Pr^{3+}-doped calcium aluminosilicate glass sample shows red-light emission

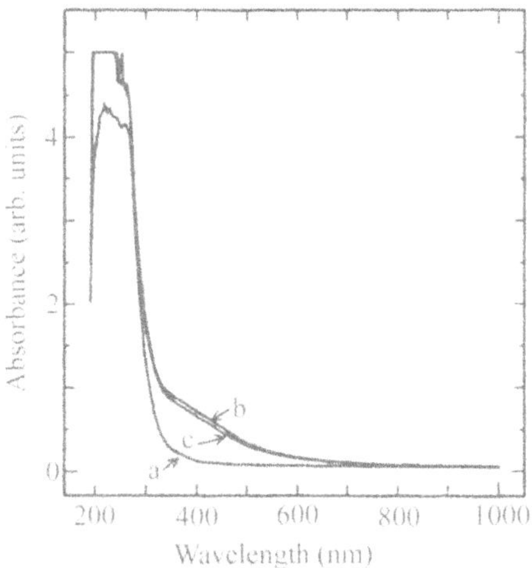

Fig. 3.27. Absorption spectra of a Tb^{3+}-doped calcium aluminosilicate glass before and after irradiation with a femtosecond laser. *Curve a:* Before the laser irradiation. *Curve b:* Upon the removal of the femtosecond laser. *Curve c:* 30 min after the removal of the femtosecond laser

samples is as follows: Ce, Tb, and Pr are elements that lead to the easy formation of Ln^{4+} (Ln = rare earth) [189]. Since all of the glasses were fabricated in an ambient atmosphere, Ce, Tb, and Pr may have already existed as mixed states of Ln^{3+} and Ln^{4+}. Ln^{3+} can possibly act as a hole-trapping center, while Ln^{4+} is known to act as an electron-trapping center.

The long-lasting phosphorescence phenomenon was observed in the Tb^{3+}-doped glass sample fabricated in a strongly reducing atmosphere. This eliminated the possibility of Ln^{4+} acting as an electron-trapping center in the present case. After irradiation with the focused femtosecond pulsed laser, free electrons and holes were formed in the glass samples through multiphoton ionization, Joule heating, and collisional ionization processes [190]. The holes or electrons were trapped by defect centers, released by heat at room temperature, and recombined with electrons or holes trapped by other defect centers. The released energy, due to the recombination of holes and electrons, was transferred to the rare-earth ions and excited the electrons at the ground state to an excited state, leading to the characteristic rare-earth-ion emissions.

The probability of energy transfer between defects and rare-earth ions is proportional to the folded area of absorption, due to the transitions between the ground state and excitation state of defects and rare-earth ions; it is inversely proportional to the distance between the defects and the rare-earth ions [191]. The released energy may be in good agreement with the energy level of the rare-earth ions in Ce^{3+}-, Tb^{3+}-, and Pr^{3+}-doped glass samples, since the 5d–4f transition of Ce^{3+}, Tb^{3+}, and Pr^{3+} has a lower energy than that of other rare-earth ions. Moreover, the hole- or electron-trap depth is broadly distributed and shallow, resulting in long-lasting phosphorescence at room temperature.

Femtosecond-infrared-laser-induced, long-lasting phosphorescence in Ce^{3+}-, Tb^{3+}-, and Pr^{3+}-doped calcium aluminosilicate glasses was observed. The long-lasting phosphorescence is considered to be due to thermally stimulated recombination of holes and electrons at traps induced by laser irradiation, which leave holes or electrons in a metastable excited state at room temperature. It may be possible to selectively induce defects by using lasers with different wavelengths, pulse widths, and repetition rates. The energy due to the recombination of holes and electrons in various defects may be different and selectively excite the electrons in the ground state to an excited state of rare-earth ions, e.g., Pr^{3+}, leading to the occurrence of phosphorescence in various colors in a glass. It may also be possible by using an ultrashort-pulse laser to induce defects that are stable at room temperature and that are able to be released by another laser. This will be very important in the fabrication of rewritable three-dimensional optical memory devices with both an ultrahigh recording speed and an ultrahigh storage density [192].

3.6 Valence-State Control of Rare-Earth Ions in Glasses by Using a Femtosecond Laser and Its Application to Ultrahigh-Density Optical Memories

Laser light is monochromatic and intense and can interfere with other laser light. Moreover, laser light can be pulsed and focused to a spot of wavelength order. Therefore, lasers have been used as powerful tools to clarify elementary processes, such as excitation-energy relaxation and both electron and proton transfer on the nanosecond and picosecond time scales, which occur in a micrometer-sized area [193, 194]. Chemical-reaction mechanisms have also been elucidated for hydrogen-atom transfer, isomerization reaction, and consecutive bond breaking by means of time-resolved laser spectroscopy [195–197].

The focus here is on making microscopic modifications to transparent materials by use of a femtosecond pulsed laser (see Sects. 2.2–4 and Sect. 3.4) [5–8]. The reason for using such a laser is that the strength of its electric field can reach 100 TW/cm^2, which is sufficient to induce nonlinear optical effects in materials by use of a focusing lens when the pulse width is 100 fs and the pulse energy is 1 μJ.

In Sect. 2.3, the fabrication of permanent waveguides in various bulk glasses was demonstrated by focusing 120-fs pulses from a regeneratively amplified Ti:sapphire laser through a microscope objective lens and translating the glass samples parallel to the axis of the laser beam [5]. In Sect. 3.4, it was reported that optional three-dimensional image patterns emitting long-lasting phosphorescence in various colors could be formed inside rare-earth-ion-doped glasses after the infrared femtosecond laser was moved [6].

In this section, the observation of permanent photoreduction of Eu^{3+} to Eu^{2+} and Sm^{3+} to Sm^{2+}in glasses by an infrared femtosecond laser is reported. The mechanism of this phenomenon is also discussed.

3.6.1 Permanent Reduction of Eu^{3+} to Eu^{2+} in a Fluorozirconate Glass Produced by an Infrared Femtosecond Laser-Pulse

The composition of the Eu^{3+}-doped fluorozirconate glass sample used in this study was $0.1EuF_3 \cdot 53ZrF_4 \cdot 20BaF_2 \cdot 3.9LaF_3 \cdot 3AIF_3 \cdot 20NaF$ (mol. %). 7*N* purity-grade EuF_3, ZrF_4, BaF_2, LaF_3, AIF_3, and NaF were used as starting materials. A mixed 30-g batch of glass was melted in a glassy carbon crucible at 800°C for 60 min in an Ar + NF_3 (5 vol. %) atmosphere. The melt was then taken out of the furnace and kept at room temperature in a glovebox filled with Ar gas; a transparent and colorless glass sample was obtained. For comparison, a Eu^{2+}-doped fluoroaluminate glass sample was prepared with a composition of $0.1EuF_2 \cdot 14.9YF_4 \cdot 10MgF_2 \cdot 20CaF_3 \cdot 10SrF_3 \cdot 10BaF_2 \cdot 35AIF_3$ (mol. %) by melting the batch in a glassy carbon crucible in an Ar + H_2

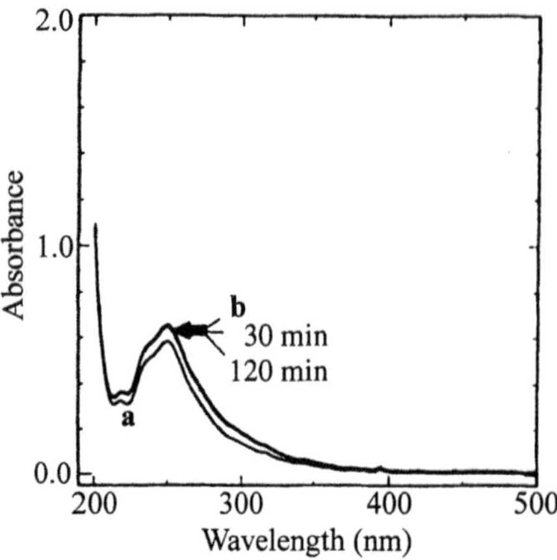

Fig. 3.28. Absorption spectra of Eu^{3+}-doped fluorozirconate glass before (*curve a*) and immediately after (*curve b*) femtosecond laser irradiation. The times shown are durations after the removal of the femtosecond laser

(5 vol. %) atmosphere at 1100°C for 60 min in a horizontal carbon furnace and quenching the melt to room temperature. A transparent and colorless glass sample was obtained. After the glass samples were annealed at the glass-transition temperature (T_g) for 1 h, they were cut and polished, and their optical properties were measured.

A regeneratively amplified 800-nm Ti:sapphire laser that emitted 120-fs, 200-kHz, mode-locked pulses was used. The laser beam, with an average power of 200 mW, was focused by a 10× objective lens with a numerical aperture of 0.30 in the interior of the glass samples with the help of an *XYZ* stage. The spot size (diameter) of the laser beam was estimated to be 3 μm.

The absorption spectra of the glass samples were measured using a spectrophotometer (Jasco V-570). The electron-spin-resonance (ESR) spectra of the glass samples were measured using an ESR spectrophotometer (Jeol FE3X). All the experiments were carried out at room temperature.

The Eu^{3+}-doped fluorozirconate glass sample was 5.0-mm thick. After irradiation with the focused infrared femtosecond laser for 1 s, a 10-μm bright spot was formed in the focus area of the laser beam in the Eu^{3+}-doped fluorozirconate glass sample, as observed through an optical microscope. The spot was considered to be the result of an increase in the refractive index at the center of the laser focus [5]. To measure the absorption spectrum of the glass sample after laser irradiation, a damaged plane of 4.0 mm × 4.0 mm was written inside the Eu^{3+}-doped fluorozirconate glass sample that consisted of damaged lines at an interval of 10 μm by scanning the laser beam at a rate of 1 mm/s. The distance of the plane from the surface of the glass sample was 1.0 mm. Figure 3.28 shows the absorption spectra of the Eu^{3+}-doped fluorozirconate glass sample before and after femtosecond laser irradiation. A small peak at 394 nm and a strong broad peak at 250 nm can be

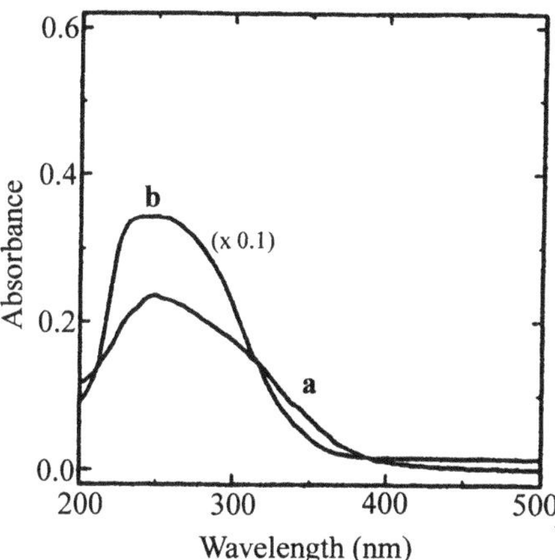

Fig. 3.29. Difference absorption spectrum of Eu^{3+}-doped fluorozirconate glass before and after the femtosecond laser irradiation (*curve a*), together with the absorption spectrum of a Eu^{2+}-doped fluoroaluminate glass sample fabricated in a reducing atmosphere (*curve b*)

ascribed to the 4f–4f transition and the charge-transfer state of Eu^{3+} [198]. No apparent increase in absorbance was observed in the 400-nm to 1-μm region, whereas absorption in the 200–400-nm region increased after laser irradiation. Moreover, no apparent variation was observed in the laser-induced absorption spectra after removal of the femtosecond laser.

Figure 3.29 shows the difference spectrum of the Eu^{3+}-doped fluorozirconate glass sample before and immediately after laser irradiation. For comparison, the absorption spectrum of the Eu^{2+}-doped fluoroaluminate glass sample is also shown. The Eu^{2+}-doped fluoroaluminate glass sample was 0.67-nm thick. By comparison with the absorption spectrum of the Eu^{2+}-doped fluoroaluminate glass sample, the broad band in the difference absorption spectrum of the Eu^{3+}-doped fluorozirconate glass sample at ~260 nm can be ascribed mainly to the absorption that is due to the 5d–4f transitions of Eu^{2+} [154].

Figure 3.30 shows the ESR spectra of the Eu^{3+}-doped fluorozirconate glass sample before and after laser irradiation. For comparison, the ESR spectrum of the Fu^{2+}-doped fluoroaluminate glass sample is also shown. No apparent signals can be observed in the spectrum of the sample before laser irradiation, whereas apparent signals similar to those of the Eu^{2+}-doped fluoroaluminate glass and two signals at approximately 3300 G (splitting coefficient, g ≒ 2.0) can be observed in the spectrum of the sample alternative.

Eu^{2+} has an f^7 electronic configuration with an $^8S_{7/2}$ ground state, which splits in a crystal field into four closely spaced doublets. In a glass, the crystal field is quasirandom from one site to the next, and so not a sharp-line spectrum but rather a broad absorption band with some sharper features at

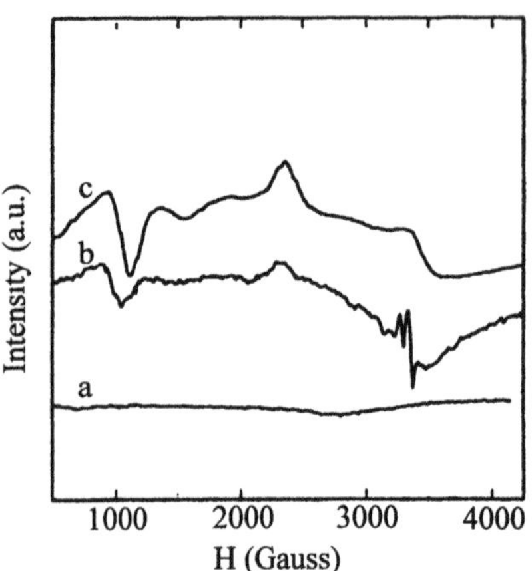

Fig. 3.30. Electron-spin-resonance (ESR) spectra of Eu^{3+}-doped fluorozirconate glass before (*curve a*) and after (*curve b*) the femtosecond laser irradiation, together with the spectrum of a Eu^{2+}-doped fluoroaluminate glass sample fabricated in a reducing atmosphere (*curve c*)

particular g values is observed [199]. In contrast, Eu^{3+} has a nonmagnetic $^7F_0$ singlet ground state that does not contribute to the ESR spectrum or to the magnetic susceptibility. The $^7F_1$ first excited state has a small thermal population at room temperature and so makes a minor contribution to the susceptibility, but any ESR signal is unobservable owing to strain broadening and fast relaxation. Therefore, the ESR spectrum was useful for examining the valence state of the Eu ions in the glasses.

The ESR spectra of Eu^{2+}-doped fluorozirconate glasses have been reported by MacFarlane et al. [199]. The spectrum of the Eu^{2+}-doped fluoroaluminate glass sample was similar in appearance to these. According to MacFarlane et al. [199], the signals in Eu^{2+}-doped fluoroaluminate glass sample can be attributed to Eu^{2+}. Therefore, some of the Eu^{3+} ions were reduced to Eu^{2+} in the Eu^{3+}-doped fluorozirconate glass after laser irradiation, allowing comparison of the ESR spectrum of laser-irradiated Eu^{3+}-doped fluorozirconate glass with that of Eu^{2+}-doped fluoroaluminate glass. In addition, the signals at $g \fallingdotseq 2.0$ can be assigned to hole-trapped V-type centers and to electrons trapped by Zr^{4+} ions, as in X-ray-irradiated fluorozirconate glasses [200].

The Eu^{3+}-doped fluorozirconate glass sample has no absorption in the wavelength region near 800 nm, and therefore photoreduction of Eu^{3+} to Eu^{2+} is most likely a nonlinear optical process. The emission spectrum of the Eu^{3+}-doped fluorozirconate glass sample was measured during femtosecond laser irradiation; emissions were observed in the 250–750-nm region, which can be attributed to the 4f–4f transitions of Eu^{3+} ions [198]. The wavelengths of the emissions were shorter than that of the excitation light. Therefore, multiphoton absorption occurred during laser irradiation. At present, the following mechanism of photoreduction is suggested: Active electrons and holes are created in the glass through a multiphoton ionization process [118]. Holes are trapped in the active sites in the glass matrix, and some electrons are trapped by Eu^{3+}, leading to the formation of hole-trapped V-type defect centers and Eu^{2+}. Efimov et al. suggested that defect centers can be induced by the short-wavelength part of a supercontinuum that is due to self-phase modulation of an ultrashort pulsed laser [201]. Further quantitative investigation is being pursued by our group. In addition, the trap levels of defect centers can be deep, resulting in stable Eu^{2+} at room temperature.

3.6.2 Permanent Photoreduction of Sm^{3+} to Sm^{2+} in Sodium Aluminoborate Glass

Room-temperature permanent photoreduction of Sm^{3+} to Sm^{2+} in various glasses was also observed, In this part, the space-selective photoreduction of Sm^{3+} to Sm^{2+} inside a sodium aluminoborate glass is introduced.

The composition of a Sm^{3+}-doped glass sample used in this study was $0.05Sm_2O_3 \cdot 10Na_2O \cdot 5Al_2O_3 \cdot 85B_2O_3$ (mol. %). Reagent grade Sm_2O_3, Na_2CO_3, Al_2O_3, and B_2O_3 were used as starting materials. A mixed 30-g batch was melted in a Pt crucible at 1250°C for 30 min in an ambient atmosphere. The melt was then poured onto a stainless-steel plate, and a transparent and colorless glass sample was obtained. For comparison, Sm^{2+}-doped glass samples with compositions of $0.5Sm_2O_3 \cdot 10Na_2O \cdot 5Al_2O_3 \cdot 85B_2O_3$ and $0.05SmF_2 \cdot 53HfF_4 \cdot 20BaF_2 \cdot 4LaF_3 \cdot 3AlF_3 \cdot 20NaF$ (mol. %) were prepared by melting the batches in glassy carbon crucibles in an Ar + H_2 (5 vol. %) atmosphere at 1250°C for 60 min in a horizontal carbon furnace and quenching the melts to room temperature. Transparent, orange glass samples were obtained. After the glass samples were annealed at the respective glass transition temperature (Tg) for 1 h, they were cut, polished, and then subjected to optical property measurements.

A regeneratively amplified 800-nm Ti:sapphire laser that emitted 120-fs, 200-kHz, mode-locked pulses was used. A laser beam with 400-mW average power was focused using a 10× objective lens with a numerical aperture of 0.30 in the interior of the glass samples with an XYZ stage.

Absorption spectra of the glass samples were measured using a spectrophotometer (Jasco V-570). Photoluminescence spectra of the glass samples were measured using a fluorescence spectrophotometer (Spex 270M) with 514.5 nm light from an Ar^+ laser as the excitation source. ESR spectra of the glass samples were measured using an ESR spectrophotometer (Jeol FE3X). All of the experiments were carried out at room temperature.

After irradiation with the femtosecond laser, the focus area in the glass sample was orange as observed in an optical microscope. Figure 3.31 shows the absorption spectra of the Sm^{3+} -doped glass sample before and after the femtosecond laser irradiation. Small peaks at 340, 350, 375, 400, and 415 nm and a strong band at 210 nm can be ascribed to the 4f–4f transitions and

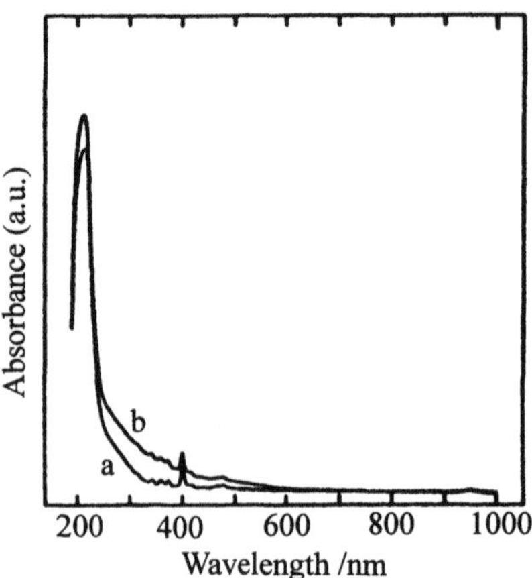

Fig. 3.31. Absorption spectra of Sm^{3+}-doped sodium aluminoborate glass before (*curve a*) and after (*curve b*) femtosecond laser irradiation

CTS of Sm^{3+} [20, 198, 202]. Absorption in the 200–600 nm region increased after the laser irradiation.

Figure 3.32 shows the differential spectrum between the absorption of the Sm^{3+}-doped glass sample after and before the laser irradiation. For comparison, the absorption spectra of the Sm^{2+}-doped fluorohafnate glass sample and the Sm^{2+}-doped sodium aluminoborate glass sample are also shown. A broad band peaking at approximately 320 nm can be observed in the differential absorption spectrum. By comparison with the absorption spectra of the Sm^{2+}-doped glass samples fabricated in a reducing atmosphere, the broad band in the glass sample after the laser irradiation can be mainly ascribed to the absorption due to the 5d–4f transitions of Sm^{2+} [20, 202].

Figure 3.33 shows the photoluminescence spectra of the Sm^{3+}-doped glass sample before and after the laser irradiation. The emissions at 560, 600, 645, and 705 nm in the unirradiated glass sample can be attributed to the 4f–4f transitions of Sm^{3+} [20,202]. The four new peaks at 683, 700, 724, and 760 nm observed in the photoluminescence spectrum of the laser-irradiated glass sample can be attributed to the 4f–4f transitions of Sm^{2+} [20, 202]. Similar to the absorption spectra, the photoluminescence spectra showed that a part of Sm^{3+} was converted to Sm^{2+} after the laser irradiation. At present, the exact quantum yield of the reaction cannot be calculated due to space-resolution limitations in the photoluminescence measurement system. A precise analysis is currently being performed.

What exactly is the mechanism of the photoreduction of Sm^{3+} to Sm^{2+} after femtosecond laser irradiation? The Sm^{3+}-doped glass sample has no absorption in the 700–900 nm region, so the photoreduction of Sm^{3+} to Sm^{2+} should be a multiphoton reduction process. Figure 3.34 shows the ESR spectra of the Sm^{3+}-doped glass sample before and after laser irradiation. No

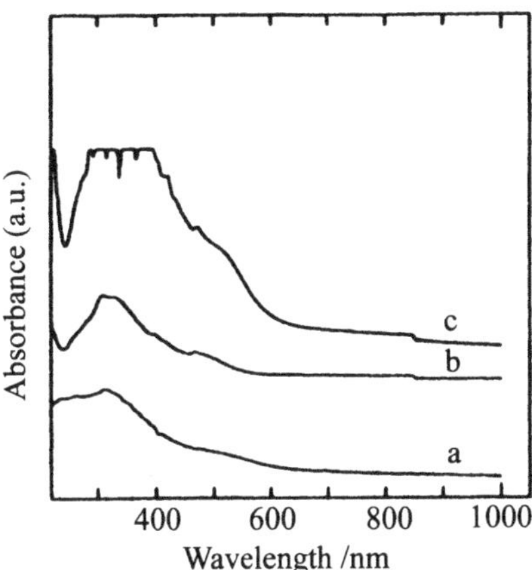

Fig. 3.32. Differential spectrum between absorption of Sm^{3+}-doped sodium aluminoborate glass after and before femtosecond laser irradiation (*curve a*), as well as the absorption spectra of Sm^{2+}-doped fluorohafnate (*curve b*) and Sm^{2+}-doped sodium aluminoborate (*curve c*) glass samples fabricated in a reducing atmosphere

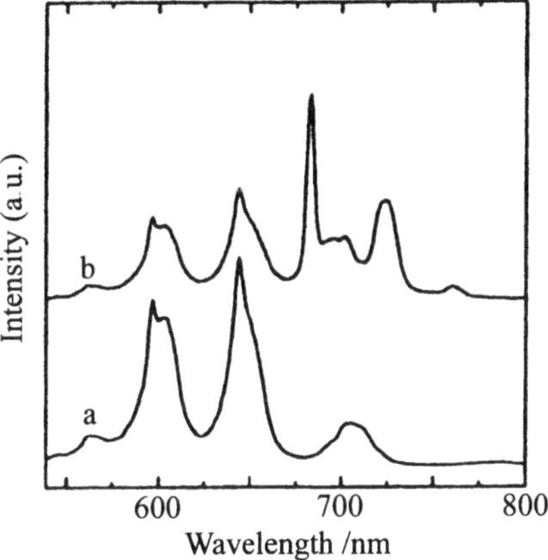

Fig. 3.33. Photoluminescence spectra of Sm^{3+}-doped sodium aluminoborate glass before (*curve a*) and after (*curve b*) femtosecond laser irradiation. Excitation was from an Ar^+ laser at 514.5 nm

apparent signals can be observed in the spectrum of the laser-unirradiated glass sample, while strong signals at approximately $g = 2.0$ can be observed in the spectrum of the laser-irradiated glass sample. The signals can be assigned to the defect centers of holes trapped by nonbridging oxygen ions and tetrahedral coordinated boron atoms and electrons trapped by the quasi-F-centers as in γ-ray-irradiated sodium borate glasses [203].

Although the mechanism of photoreduction is not fully clear at present, the following is our interpretation of the results: After irradiation with the focused femtosecond laser, active electrons and holes were created in the

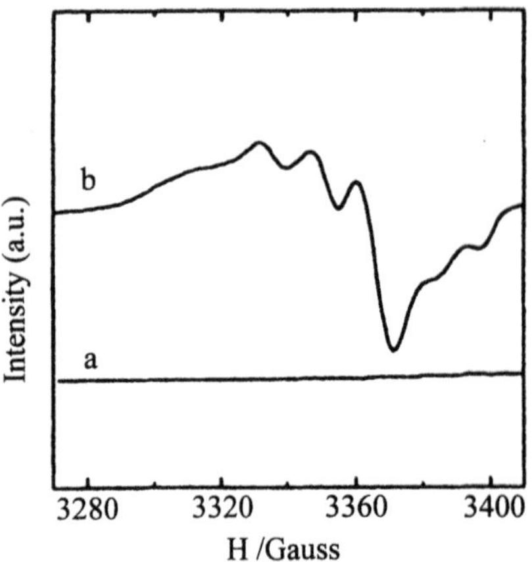

Fig. 3.34. ESR spectra of Sm^{3+}-doped sodium aluminoborate glass before (*curve a*) and after (*curve b*) femtosecond laser irradiation

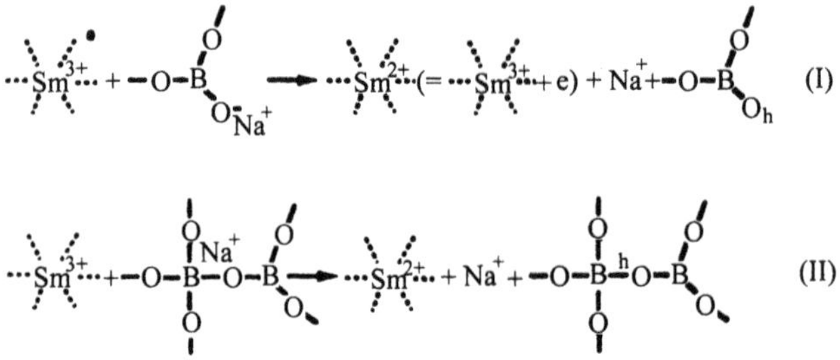

Fig. 3.35. Mechanism of photoreduction of Sm^{3+} to Sm^{2+} in Sm^{3+}-doped sodium aluminoborate glass after femtosecond laser irradiation

glass through multiphoton ionization, Joule heating, and collisional ionization processes [118]. Holes were trapped by nonbridging oxygen ions as well as by tetrahedral coordinated boron atoms, while some of the electrons were trapped by Sm^{3+}, which led to the formation of Sm^{2+} . The reactions are shown as I and II in Fig. 3.35.

The trap levels of defect centers may be deep, resulting in stable Sm^{2+} at room temperature. In this regard the thermal stability of the photoreduction product, Sm^{2+}, was examined. The results showed that Sm^{2+} was stable at room temperature. When the temperature exceeded Tg, Sm^{2+} was reconverted to Sm^{3+}, indicating that reverse reactions of I and II (Fig. 3.35) occurred at a temperature above Tg.

Permanent photoreduction of Eu^{3+} to Eu^{2+}, and Sm^{3+} to $Sm^{2+}$by a focused infrared femtosecond pulsed laser was observed. The results demonstrate the possibility of selectively inducing a change of valence state of Eu^{3+} and Sm^{3+} ions at a micrometer scale inside a glass sample by use of a focused nonresonant femtosecond pulsed laser. Whereas a three-dimensional optical memory has an approximately 10^{13} bits/cm^3 storage density, which means that data information can be stored in the form of a change in refractive index in a spot, optical memory using a valence-state change of rare-earth ions in a spot may have the same storage density and may allow one to read out data in the form of luminescence, thus providing the advantage of a high signal-to-noise ratio. Therefore, the present technique will be useful in the fabrication of three-dimensional optical memory devices with high storage density. Moreover, Sm^{2+}-doped glasses exhibit a photochemical spectral hole burning memory property [20, 202]. The microspot induced by a focused femtosecond laser inside a glass sample can be further used to store data information via the irradiation of laser light with different wavelengths. As a result, the data information can be read out in the form of spectral holes. Sm^{2+}-doped glasses will become very good optical memory devices with an ultrahigh storage density. In addition, since the optical properties of Eu^{2+}-doped glass, for example, the magneto-optical property, are significantly different from those of Eu^{3+}-doped glass, it may be possible to prepare a waveguide in which the valence state of Eu is Eu^{2+}, whereas the valence state of Eu remains Eu^{3+} outside the waveguide, by controlling the conditions of laser irradiation [5]. Therefore, the observed phenomenon is also inferred to be useful in the fabrication of waveguide-type micro-optical devices.

Part 2

Analyses of Induced Structures in Glasses

4. Development of Analytical Methods for Induced Structures

4.1 Introduction

In Part 1 of this book, external electromagnetic field induced structures in glasses and other materials and promising applications in various fields such as integrated optics and optical communications were introduced. From the viewpoint of material design, it is important to clarify the formation mechanism of the induced structures. In this chapter a novel method for the direct observation of excited-state absorption of rare-earth ions is introduced [203]. The valence state and chemical bond state of rare-earth ions in glasses showing room-temperature spectral hole burning and photostimulated luminescence were examined by using X-ray absorption fine structures (XAFS) [205]. Microscopic Raman scattering spectroscopy was used to study the focused femtosecond infrared laser induced structural change in SiO_2 glass in Sect. 4.4.

4.2 Direct Observation of Excited-State Absorption Using Laser-Flash Pump-Probe Spectroscopy

Rare-earth ions can convert the wavelength of incident light to a shorter wavelength via a multiphoton absorption process. There is great interest in such phenomena because of the possibility of infrared-pumped visible lasers and visible or ultraviolet (UV) light amplifiers. So far, considerable research has been carried out on Er^{3+} and Ho^{3+} glasses [22, 206, 207]. These ions can effectively convert 800-nm near-infrared, or 645-nm red light into green emission near 550 nm.

Thulium(III) ions have stable excited levels suitable for emitting 365-nm UV and 450- and 480-nm blue upconversion fluorescence. Recently, it was reported that a blue upconversion fluorescence of Tm^{3+} was discovered in fuorozirconate glass by co-pumping at both 676.4 and 647.1 nm using a krypton ion laser [208] or by single wavelength pumping at 650 nm [209]. In addition, it was found that both UV and blue upconversion occurred in Tm^{3+}-doped glasses [210].

It is thought that the dominant mechanism of UV and blue upconversion fluorescence of Tm^{3+} by nearly 650-nm single wavelength excitation is excited

Table 4.1. Compositions of the glasses prepared in the present study

Glass	Composition (mol. %)	Abbreviation
Fluoroindate	38InF3·19BaF2·19ZnF2·10PbF2·10SrF2·2AlF3·2GdF3	IBZPS-AG
Fluorozirconate	44ZrF4·6AlF3·6YF3·3LaF3·19BaF2·6NaF·6LiF·10PbF2	ZBLYAN-LP
Germanate	60GeO2·30BaO·10ZnO	GBZ
Tellurite	60TeO2·30BaO·10ZnO	TBZ

Tm^{3+}concentration: 1 mol. % for ESA measurement, 0.1 mol. % for fluorescence measurement.

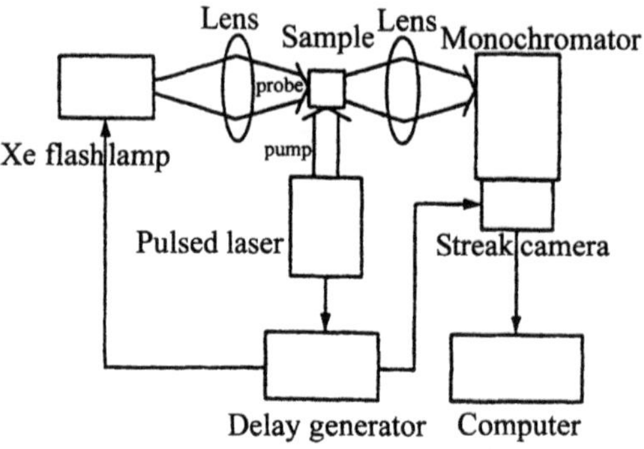

Fig. 4.1. Experimental setup for pump–probe spectroscopy

state absorption (ESA). However, little is known about the ESA spectra of Tm^{3+}.

In this section, the direct measurement of the ESA of Tm^{3+} is introduced. A new two-wavelength pumped efficient upconversion system of Tm^{3+} is proposed.

The glasses selected for this study are listed in Table 4.1. Glasses were prepared by using reagent-grade powder as the starting materials and were melted and annealed in a glovebox filled with N_2. Then, glass samples were cut and ground into a $5 \times 5 \times 5$-mm^3 cube and polished with a CeO_2 slurry. The detailed preparation technique of the glass samples is described elsewhere [211].

The upconversion fluorescence spectra were measured using a fluorescence spectrophotometer (Hitachi, type 850). A DCM dye laser (SpectraPhysics Model 375 B) pumped by an argon-ion laser (Coherent Inc. Innova 70) was used as the upconversion excitation source. The GSA spectra were measured using a conventional spectrophotometer (Jasco V570).

The experimental setup of the ESA measurement is shown in Fig. 4.1. This resembles the setup previously reported by Zemon et al. [212]. However, we employed the pump–probe method to take advantage of its time-resolving ability (Fig. 4.2).

A nanosecond pulsed laser (Coherent Inc. Infinity 40-100 and Lambda Physics Scanmate OPPO) tuned to 785 nm was employed as the pump beam

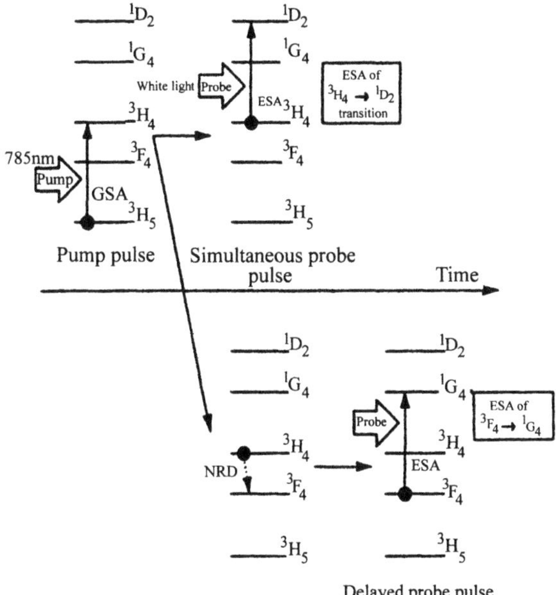

Fig. 4.2. Basic concept of the excited-state-absorption (ESA) measurement by pump–probe spectroscopy

in a configuration perpendicular to the probe beam. The output energy of the pulsed laser was up to 5 mJ per pulse. This is convenient for optical alignment and to prevent the monochromator from optical damage caused by accidental exposure to the reflected pump beam. The probe beam of a sub-microsecond xenon flash lamp (Hamamatsu L2435 Xenon Flash Lamp with C4479 Power Supply) was synchronized with the pump pulse. The transmitted probe beam was collimated and focused into a monochromator (Hamamatsu C5095). The dispersed beam was resolved by a streak camera (Hamamatsu C5680) and detected while the pump beam was turned on. In order to remove a scaling factor, another scan was conducted without the pumping, separately. The ESA spectra were obtained by determining the difference in transmission of a probe flash lamp beam when the pump laser beam was turned on and off.

The upconversion fluorescence spectra of Tm^{3+}-doped glasses using the DCM dye laser as a pumping source are shown in Fig. 4.3. The excitation wavelength was selected to be 650 nm and the excitation power was fixed at 100 mW. The upconversion fluorescences at approximately 360, 450 and 480 nm are assigned to the $^1D_2$–$^3H_6$, $^1D_2$–$^3F_4$ and $^1G_4$–$^3H_6$ transitions of Tm^{3+}, respectively. The corresponding energy level diagram is also shown in Fig. 4.3.

The upconversion mechanism of 650-nm single wavelength pumping is thought to be as follows: Thulium(III) ions in the ground state ($^3H_6$) absorb a 650-nm photon and are excited to the $^3F_{2,3}$ level. The electron on the $^3F_{2,3}$

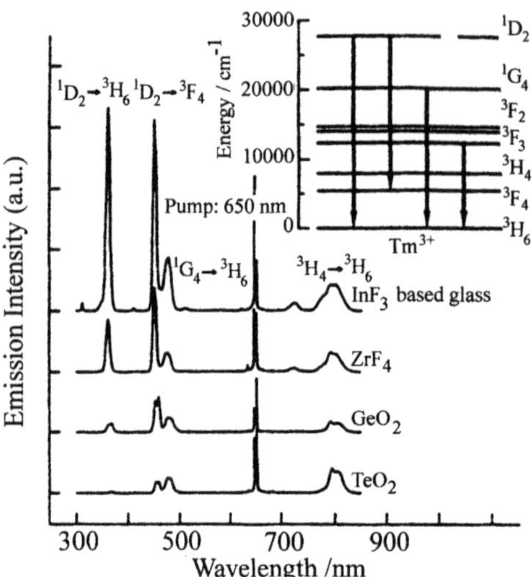

Fig. 4.3. Upconversion emission spectra of Tm^{3+}-doped glasses. The excitation wavelength was 650 nm, and the power was 100 mW. Details of the compositions of the glasses are given in Table 4.1

level falls on the $^3H_4$ level and then the $^3F_4$ level by a nonradiative decay (NRD) process. Then, the $^1D_2$ and the $^1G_4$ levels are excited from the $^3H_4$ and the $^3F_4$ levels respectively by other 650-nm photons (ESA processes). The spontaneous emission from the $^1D_2$ and the $^1G_4$ levels is observed as upconversion fluorescence. The $^3H_4$ level is the intermediate level for UV and 450-nm blue upconversion fluorescence, and the $^3F_4$ level is that for the 480-nm blue upconversion fluorescence.

In this study, pump–probe spectroscopy was adapted for the measurement of ESA spectra as follows. The 785-nm ground-state-absorption (GSA) band corresponds to the $^3H_6$–$^3H_4$ transition. When the Tm^{3+} ion is irradiated by the probe pulse, the photons whose energy correspond to the ESA from the $^3H_4$ level are absorbed. Therefore, only ESA from the $^3H_4$ level can be detected by the monochromator.

When the $^3H_4$ level is fed directly by the pump pulse, the time of maximum population on the $^3F_4$ level is delayed compared with that on the $^3H_4$ level. So, delayed irradiation of the probe pulse will give the ESA spectra of the $^3F_4$–$^1G_4$ transition.

The time dependence of the ESA spectra can be obtained by sweeping the delay time between the pump and the probe pulse. Therefore, the ESA spectra from different lower levels can be selectively detected. This is the strong point of the pump–probe method applied to the ESA measurement compared with the lock-in method etc.

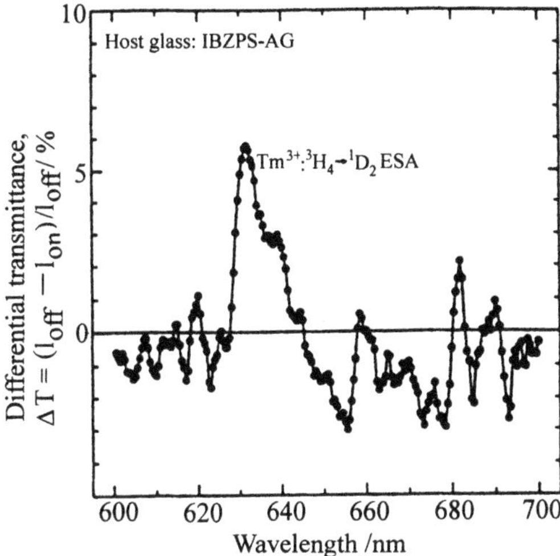

Fig. 4.4. ESA spectrum of the $^3H_4$–$^1D_2$ transition of Tm^{3+} in IBZPS-AG glass

Evidence for ESA was shown only in fluoroindate and fluorozirconate glasses. Unfortunately, in germanate or tellurite glasses, no ESA peak was obtained because of their low signal-to-noise ratio.

Figure 4.4 shows the ESA spectrum in fluoroindate glass. The intensity of the transmitted probe beam, $\Delta T = (I_{\text{off}} - I_{\text{on}})/I_{\text{off}}$ was plotted as a function of wavelength. To our knowledge, this is the first report of the direct observation of the ESA in Tm^{3+}-doped glass. Positive ΔT means a decrease in the transmission caused by ESA of the $^3H_4$–$^1D_2$ transition. ESA of the $^3H_4$–$^1D_2$ transition corresponds to a wavelength of about 630 nm.

All attempts to detect the $^3F_4$–$^1G_4$ ESA transition, which gives 480-nm blue upconversion emission, failed for all the glass systems listed in Table 4.1.

In Figs. 4.5 and 4.6, the upconversion excitation spectra and the absorption spectrum of fluoroindate glass are shown, respectively. The intensity of UV and 450-nm blue upconversion emission are the strongest with 655-nm excitation in fluoroindate glass. In contrast, the excitation spectrum of the 792-nm emission has its intensity peak near 680 nm and has a shoulder near 660 nm, but no emission is obtained when it is excited at a wavelength shorter than 640 nm. The latter profile is almost the same as that of the $^3H_6$ –$^3F_{2,3}$ GSA transition. Furthermore, the $^3H_4$–$^1D_2$ ESA band has its peak near 630 nm.

In short, the best wavelength for single wavelength excitation is ~655 nm; however, it is not the peak wavelength for both GSA and ESA. These results lead to the conclusion that ~655 nm is not the best wavelength for either GSA or ESA, although it is the most suitable wavelength for single wavelength excitation.

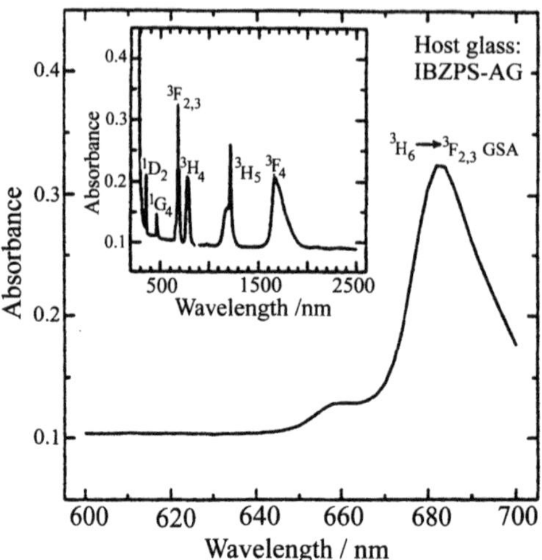

Fig. 4.5. Upconversion excitation spectra of Tm^{3+}-doped IBZPS-AG glass

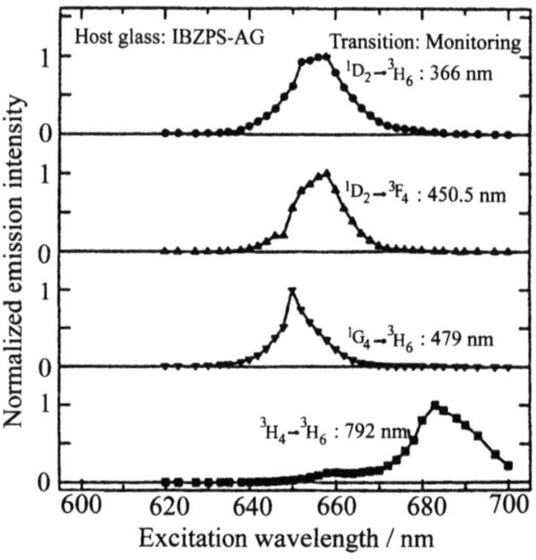

Fig. 4.6. Absorption spectrum of Tm^{3+}-doped IBZPS-AG glass near the $^3H_6$–$^3F_{2,3}$ GSA band

A similar tendency is observed in fluorozirconate glass. While ~655-nm excitation gives the strongest UV and 450-nm blue upconversion emission, the GSA and ESA transitions have their peak absorption values at ~680 and ~635 nm, respectively.

Thus, single wavelength excitation is not the best way to obtain higher upconversion intensity, because of the mismatch in the peak wavelength of the GSA and ESA transitions. A two-wavelength excitation system, that is, the choice of excitation wavelength is matched to GSA and ESA, is necessary to improve the intensity of upconversion emission. Therefore, it is possible to obtain a UV and blue upconversion laser with high efficiency when two-wavelength excitation systems are employed, with wavelengths of ~680 or ~785 nm for GSA and ~630 nm for ESA. The excitation system proposed here has the advantage that the excitation system can be simplified, as high-power laser diodes of these wavelength are now available.

In several glasses, no ESA peak was found. The reason why the ESA transition was not detected in some transitions and some glasses is as follows: First, the perpendicular configuration of the pump beam and the probe beam made the region in which the two beams overlapped small. Next, the pump-beam density was low, because a bulk specimen was employed. Therefore, considerable improvement is expected by using a collinear configuration and an optical fiber specimen. Attempts are in progress to detect the $^3F_4$–$^1G_4$ ESA transition which gives 480-nm blue upconversion emission and to find glasses in which the ESA transition is not observed.

4.3 Determination of Local Arrangement by X-ray Absorbtion Fine-Structure Analysis

Glasses doped with reduced rare earth-ions possess altered optical properties. Room-temperature persistent spectral hole burning has been observed in Sm^{2+}-doped borate glasses using the photochemical reaction $Sm^{2+} \rightarrow Sm^{3+} + e^-$ [20, 202, 213]. Photostimulated luminescence phenomena have been observed in Ce^{3+}- and/or Eu^{2+}-doped glasses (see Sect. 3.3) [108, 154]. These optical properties are assumed to be closely related to the local structure around reduced rare-earth ions. X-ray-absorption fine-structure (XAFS) analysis is a method used to investigate the local structure around particular ions in multicomponent glasses. Especially in the case of rare-earth ions, the peak of X-ray-absorption near-edge-structure (XANES) spectra assigned to the 2p–5d transition are separated by the valence of rare-earth ions. In this section, the change in the local structure of Sm^{2+}-, Ce^{3+}- and Eu^{2+}-doped borate glasses is described as a function of alkali content by XAFS analysis using synchrotron radiation. The relation between these optical properties and the local structure around reduced rare-earth ions is analyzed.

A number of $(100 - x)B_2O_3 \cdot xNa_2O$ ($x = 10, 15, 20, 25$) glasses (BN10, BN15, BN20, BN25) doped with 1 mol. % rare-earth oxide (Sm_2O_3, Eu_2O_3, CeO_2) were prepared by quenching melts. Reduced rare-earth doped borate glasses were prepared by remelting the borate glasses in a reducing atmosphere furnace. Batched composition of glass samples are listed in Table 4.2.

X-ray absorption spectra were measured in a transmission mode using an Si(111) double-crystal monochromator at BL-7C or BL-12C at the Photon Factory of the National Laboratory for High Energy Physics (BEK-PF), with an electron-beam energy of 2.5 GeV and a maximum stored current

Table 4.2. Chemical composition of examined glasses

Sample	Composition (mol. %)
BN10	$90B_2O_3 \cdot 10Na_2O \cdot xSm_2O_3$
BN15	$85B_2O_3 \cdot 15Na_2O \cdot x(Sm_2O_3$ or Eu_2O_3 or $CeO_2)$
BN20	$80B_2O_3 \cdot 20Na_2O \cdot x(Sm_2O_3$ or Eu_2O_3 or $CeO_2)$
BN25	$75B_2O_3 \cdot 25Na_2O \cdot x(Eu_2O_3$ or $CeO_2)$

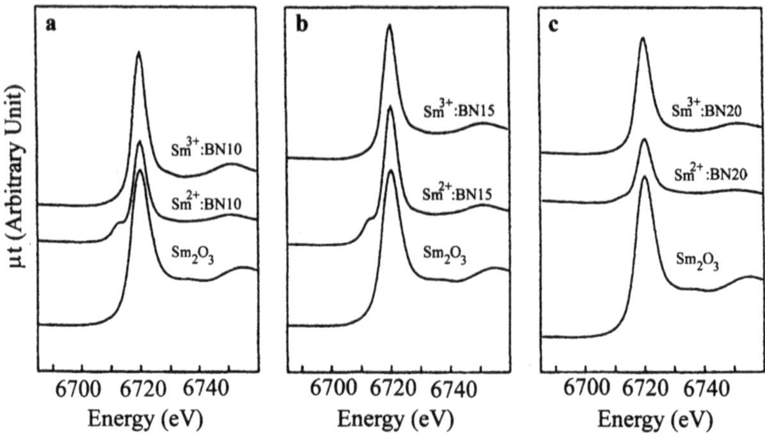

Fig. 4.7a–c. XANES spectra of Sm^{2+}- and Sm^{3+}-doped $B_2O_3 \cdot Na_2O$ glasses with that of crystalline Sm_2O_3. (**a**) BN10 glasses, (**b**) BN15 glasses and (**c**) BN20 glasses. Abbreviations are explained in Table 4.2

of 400 mA. X-ray absorption data in the neighborhood of the Sm L_{III} edge (6717 eV) and of the Eu L_{III} edge (6981 eV) were collected at 348 energies ranging from 6217 eV to 7287 eV and at 437 energies ranging from 6480 eV to 7600 eV, respectively. Harmonies were rejected by detuning the monochromator. The I_0 ionization chamber was filled with nitrogen gas, and the I ionization chamber was filled with a mixture of nitrogen (85%) and argon (15%). X-ray absorption data around the Ce L_{III} edge (5723 eV) were collected at 519 energies ranging from 5222 eV to 6157 eV. In this case, harmonics were rejected by a grazing incidence mirror. The I_0 ionization chamber was filled with a mixture of nitrogen (75%) and argon (25%) and the I ionization chamber with a mixture of nitrogen (85%) and argon (15%). Absorption data for crystalline Sm_2O_3, Eu_2O_3, EuF_3, EuF_2, CeO_2 and CeF_3 were also measured as references.

Figure 4.7 shows Sm L_{III} XANES spectra for Sm^{2+}- and Sm^{3+}-doped $B_2O_3 \cdot Na_2O$ glasses. Two white lines of 6712 eV and 6720 eV are seen in Sm^{2+}-doped samples. These peaks can be assigned to the 2p–5d transition in Sm^{2+} and Sm^{3+} in the Sm^{2+}-doped samples, respectively. Only one white line at 6720 eV is seen in crystalline Sm_2O_3 and Sm^{3+}-doped glasses.

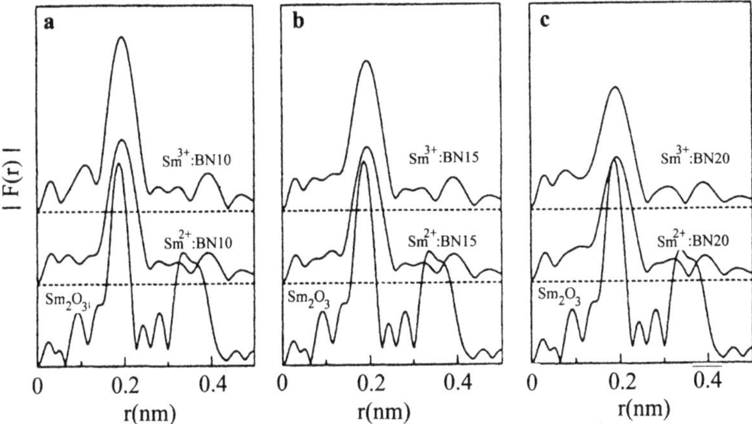

Fig. 4.8a–c. Radial structure functions of Sm^{2+}- and Sm^{3+}-doped $B_2O_3 \cdot Na_2O$ glasses with that of crystalline Sm_2O_3. (**a**) BN10 glasses, (**b**) BN15 glasses and (**c**) BN20 glasses

The EXAFS oscillation curve, $\chi(k)$, where k is the wave number of the photoelectron, is obtained after subtraction of the smooth background and normalization. Values of $\chi(k)$ weighted with the factor k^3 were Fourier transformed over the range from 27.1 to 104.2 nm^{-1} in k. The radial structure function $|F(r)|$ for Sm^{2+}- and Sm^{3+}-doped $B_2O_3 \cdot Na_2O$ samples are shown in Fig. 4.8. The first peak of each $|F(r)|$ curve corresponds to the nearest Sm–O bonds. Since the phase shift parameter and the correction for the inner potential energy were not included in these calculations, the peaks in $|F(r)|$ curves are observed at distances about 0.05 nm shorter than those in the actual structures. The first peaks of the $|F(r)|$ curves were inversely transformed to get values of $k^3\chi_1(k)$. The values of $k^3\chi_1(k)$ obtained were analyzed by a curve-fitting method, adopting the theoretical values for the phase shift and the amplitude parameters. The inner potential energy, E_0 and the mean free path for photoelectron, λ, were experimentally determined from the EXAFS data for Sm_2O_3 by a curve-fitting method. The first interatomic distances, coordination numbers, and temperature factors were obtained by fitting the calculated and observed $k^3\chi_1(k)$s. In this calculation, the parameters of Teo and Lee [214], the weighted averages of the parameters for cerium and gadolinium, were employed. The results for Sm^{2+}- and Sm^{3+}-doped $B_2O_3 \cdot Na_2O$ samples are shown in Table 4.3.

Europium L_{III} XANES spectra for Eu^{2+}- and Eu^{3+}-doped $B_2O_3 \cdot Na_2O$ samples are shown in Fig. 4.9 with those of reference samples. XANES spectra for Eu^{2+}-doped samples have a main white line at 6972 eV and a smaller white line at 6980 eV. These small white lines are assumed to occur from residual Eu^{3+} ions because XANES spectra for Eu^{3+}-doped samples have only one white line at 6980 eV.

Table 4.3. Results of curve-fitting analysis for Sm^{2+}- and Sm^{3+}-doped $B_2O_3 \cdot Na_2O$ glasses. N: coordination number; r: Sm-O bond length; σ: Debye-Waller factor; R: residual. The estimated standard deviation is given in parentheses

Sample	N	r (nm)	σ (nm)	R (%)
Sm_2O_3	6.0	0.234	0.0054 (13)	1.7
Sm^{2+}:BN10	6.8 (2)	0.244 (1)	0.0062 (20)	4.4
Sm^{3+}:BN10	8.3 (2)	0.243 (1)	0.0061 (24)	3.5
Sm^{2+}:BN15	6.3 (2)	0.243 (1)	0.0062 (20)	4.3
Sm^{3+}:BN15	7.2 (2)	0.243 (1)	0.0068 (21)	5.2
Sm^{2+}:BN20	5.5 (2)	0.242 (1)	0.0065 (23)	7.3
Sm^{3+}:BN20	5.4 (2)	0.241 (1)	0.0080 (24)	9.7

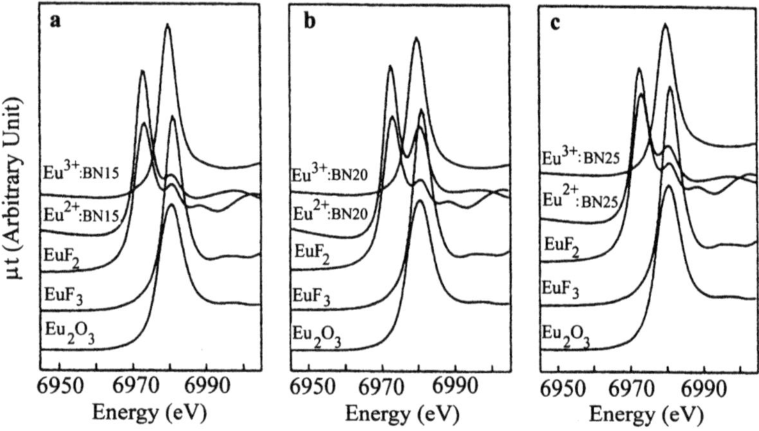

Fig. 4.9a–c. XANES spectra of Eu^{2+}- and Eu^{3+}-doped $B_2O_3 \cdot Na_2O$ glasses compared with those of crystalline Eu_2O_3, Eu_2F_3 and EuF_2. (**a**) BN15 glasses, (**b**) BN20 glasses and (**c**) BN25 glasses

The EXAFS analysis was performed for the Eu^{2+}- and Eu^{3+}-doped samples, in the same way as with the Sm^{2+}- and Sm^{3+}-doped samples. The Fourier transformation region was from 29.2 to 102.2 nm^{-1} in k. The radial structure function $|F(r)|$ for Eu^{2+}- and Eu^{3+}-doped $B_2O_3 \cdot Na_2O$ glasses are shown in Fig. 4.10. The peak areas corresponding to Eu–O bonds in Fig. 4.10 are decreased by the reduction. Therefore we applied the curve-fitting method only to the Eu^{3+}-doped $B_2O_3 \cdot Na_2O$ samples. The results are shown in Table 4.4.

Cerium L_{III} XANES spectra for Ce^{3+}- and Ce^{4+}-doped $B_2O_3 \cdot Na_2O$ glasses are shown in Fig. 4.11 with those of crystalline CeO_2 and CeF_3. It was difficult to resolve the EXAFS data for 1 mol. % CeO_2-doped glasses because the X-ray absorption coefficients of the samples were large in this energy range. Therefore information could not be obtained on the atomic arrangement around Ce ions in Ce^{3+}- and Ce^{4+}-doped $B_2O_3 \cdot Na_2O$ glasses.

Table 4.4. Results of curve-fitting analysis for Eu^{3+}-doped $B_2O_3 \cdot Na_2O$ glasses. N: coordination number; r: Eu–O bond length; σ: Debye-Waller factor; R: residual. The estimated standard deviation is given in parentheses

Sample	N	r (nm)	σ (nm)	R (%)
Eu_2O_3	6.0	0.234	0.0050 (16)	2.9
Eu^{3+}:BN15	6.5 (2)	0.243 (1)	0.0080 (20)	4.3
Eu^{3+}:BN20	6.4 (3)	0.241 (1)	0.0098 (24)	8.9
Eu^{3+}:BN25	5.9 (2)	0.239 (1)	0.0099 (22)	2.1

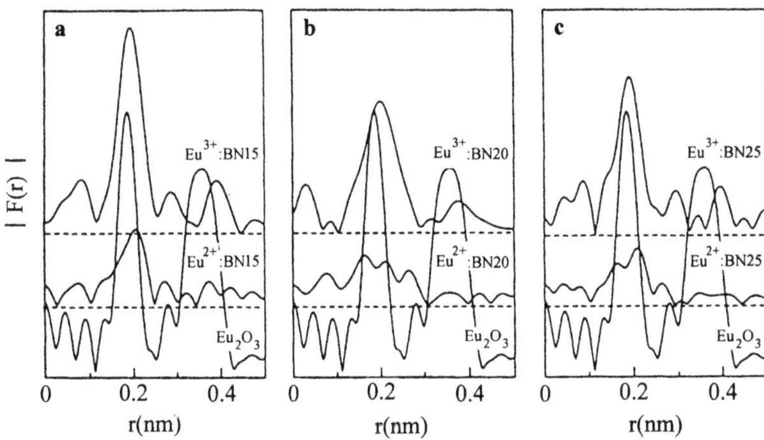

Fig. 4.10a–c. Radial structure functions of Eu^{2+}- and Eu^{3+}-doped $B_2O_3 \cdot Na_2O$ glasses compared with that of crystalline Eu_2O_3. (**a**) BN15 glasses, (**b**) BN20 glasses and (**c**) BN25 glasses

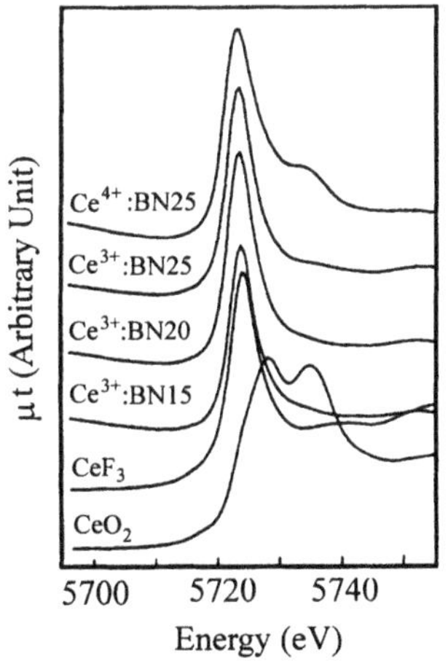

Fig. 4.11. XANES spectra of Ce^{3+}- and Ce^{4+}-doped $B_2O_3 \cdot Na_2O$ glasses compared with those of crystalline CeO_2 and CeF_3

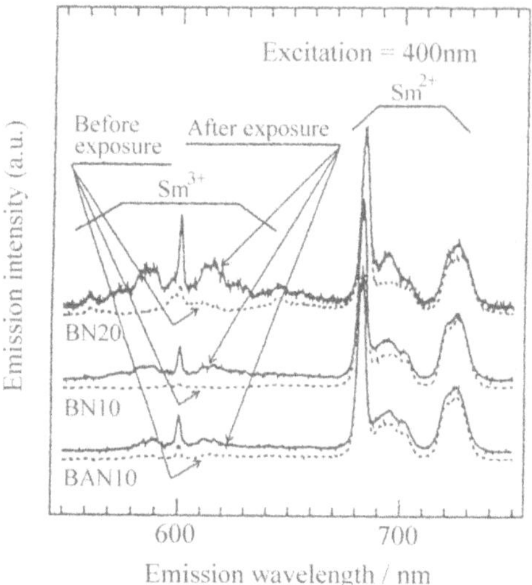

Fig. 4.12. Fluorescence spectra of Sm^{2+}-doped BAN10 ($85B_2O_3 \cdot 5Na_2O \cdot 10Al_2O_3$), BN10 and BN20 glass before (*dotted line*) and after (*solid line*) X-ray irradiation. These spectra show an increase in emission peak intensities due to Sm^{3+} compared to Sm^{2+} after the X-ray irradiation. The excitation wavelength was 400 nm

In the XANES spectra of the Sm^{2+}-doped samples (Fig. 4.7), not only is the 2p–5d transition in Sm^{2+} apparent, but also in Sm^{3+}. Cho et al. [215] investigated the X-ray irradiation effect on the fluorescence spectra of Sm^{2+}-doped $B_2O_3 \cdot Na_2O$ samples. For example, the fluorescence spectra of Sm^{2+}-doped BN10 and BN20 samples change before and after the X-ray irradiation, as shown in Fig. 4.12. The authors indicated that emission peak intensities due to Sm^{3+} increase in comparison with those due to Sm^{2+} after X-ray irradiation. The Sm^{3+}/Sm^{2+} ratio after X-ray irradiation of BN20 is larger than that of BN10. This tendency is in good agreement with that of the Sm^{3+}/Sm^{2+} ratio of XANES spectra in Fig. 4.7. Therefore, the change of valence, $Sm^{2+} \rightarrow Sm^{3+} + e^-$, is considered to be triggered by X-ray irradiation during the XAFS measurement.

As shown in Table 4.3, the average coordination number of samarium in Sm^{3+}-doped $B_2O_3 \cdot Na_2O$ samples decreased with increasing Na_2O content. In the $B_2O_3 \cdot Na_2O$ glass systems, three-coordinated boron atoms are changed to fourfold-coordinated atoms with an increase in Na_2O content up to 30 mol. %. This change of the coordination number of the boron atom may consume oxygen atoms around the Sm^{3+} ion, which causes the change in the coordination number of the samarium ion in Sm^{3+}-doped $B_2O_3 \cdot Na_2O$ samples. In the Sm^{2+}-doped $B_2O_3 \cdot Na_2O$ samples, which were prepared by remelting Sm^{3+}-doped $B_2O_3 \cdot Na_2O$ samples in a reducing atmosphere, the average coordination number of samarium ions also decreased with an increase in Na_2O content. However, the nearest neighbor Sm-O distances in both Sm^{2+}- and Sm^{3+}-doped samples are almost the same irrespective of the charge of the samarium ions and the Na_2O content; the distance is longer than that of crystalline Sm_2O_3 by 0.01 nm. This fact indicates that some of the oxygen-coordinated samarium ions are removed without a change in the valence of the samarium ion during the remelting process in a reducing atmosphere.

The change in the coordination number of the boron atom may also affect the reduction process. The differences between Sm^{2+}-doped and Sm^{3+}-doped $B_2O_3 \cdot Na_2O$ samples with the same Na_2O content decreased with an increase in the Na_2O content, and in the BN20 sample, the coordination numbers of samarium ions for both Sm^{2+}- and Sm^{3+}-doped samples are nearly the same. As mentioned above, the oxygen coordination number of samarium ions in Sm^{3+}-doped $B_2O_3 \cdot Na_2O$ samples at the highest Na_2O content becomes small; therefore, it might be possible that an oxygen ion coordinated to another atom is taken away in the reduction process. This removal may change a fourfold boron atom to a threefold boron atom.

In the case of Eu^{2+}-doped fluoride glasses [154], the change of valence, $Eu^{2+} \rightarrow Eu^{3+} + e^-$, due to X-ray irradiation is visually observed in XANES spectra after X-ray irradiation. Therefore, the change of valence of the Eu ion during X-ray irradiation is considered to be slower than that of the Sm ion. This difference is the reason why the main white lines at 6972 eV of Eu^{2+}-doped samples are observed in Fig. 4.9.

As mentioned above, the peak areas of the components due to Eu–O bonds are decreased by the reduction (Fig. 4.10). In particular, the peak of the Eu^{2+}-doped BN20 sample almost disappeared (Fig. 4.10b). Oxygen around the rare-earth ion is also removed in the case of the Eu^{2+}-doped sample. As shown in Table 4.4, the change in the average coordination number as a function of Na_2O content is smaller than that of Sm^{3+}-doped $B_2O_3 \cdot Na_2O$ samples (Table 4.3). In addition, the decrease in the peak area corresponding to the first Eu–O bonds of $|F(r)|$ is not dependent upon Na_2O content. These tendencies show that the intensity of photostimulated luminescence is dependent upon Na_2O content.

Being different from those for Sm_2O_3 and Eu_2O_3 (Fig. 4.7 and Fig. 4.9, respectively), the XANES spectra for CeO_2have two main white lines; the Ce valence in CeO_2 is the intermediate valence. In contrast, the XANES spectra for Ce^{4+}-doped BN25 resemble those for Eu^{2+}-doped $B_2O_3 \cdot Na_2O$ samples (Fig. 4.9). CeO_2 is known to be an oxidizing agent in the melting process. Therefore, most of the Ce valence in Ce^{4+}-doped BN25 becomes trivalent. Only one white line, located at 5724 eV, is seen in the XANES spectra of Ce^{4+}-doped $B_2O_3 \cdot Na_2O$ samples. The Ce ion was reduced in the reducing process.

In conlusion:

- Under X-ray irradiation, reduced rare-earth ions change their valences. Especially the reaction $Sm^{2+} \rightarrow Sm^{3+} + e^-$ occurs in the case of Sm^{2+}-doped samples.
- In Sm^{3+}- and Eu^{3+}-doped samples, the nearest-neighbor Sm–O and Eu–O distances are 0.005–0.01 nm longer than those of the corresponding rare-earth sesquioxide.
- In Sm^{2+}- and Eu^{2+}-doped samples, oxygen around the rare-earth ion is removed during a remelting process in a reducing atmosphere.
- In a Ce^{4+}-doped sample most Ce^{4+} changed to Ce^{3+} during melting in air; the change to Ce^{+3} is completed during the remelting process in a reducing atmosphere.

4.4 The Study of Induced Structures by Microscopic Raman Scattering

The phenomenon of refractive-index alteration in SiO_2 glass due to ultraviolet light irradiation has recently gained great interest among researchers. It is well known that Bragg-grating writing in a GeO_2-doped silica optical fiber using refractive-index alteration is induced by UV light irradiation and so on [14, 76, 216]. Recently, it has become clear that this refractive-index alteration can also be induced by focusing an ultrashort-pulse laser beam at a wavelength that cannot be absorbed in a one-photon process (see Sects. 2.2 and 2.3) [4, 5]. This is done through a microscope objective, and it has become evident that permanent refractive-index alteration on the order of 10^{-2}–10^{-3} can be induced inside SiO_2 glass. With ultraviolet irradiation, it is difficult to selectively make only the glass inside a high refractive index. This is because the 5-eV absorption band, which originates from the oxygen defect in the glass, is directly excited by the one-photon process. Furthermore, it has also been confirmed that an increase in the refractive index on the order of 10^{-2} can be induced in both Ge-doped and pure SiO_2 glass. However, the mechanism of how the refractive-index alteration is induced by the ultrashort-pulse laser is still unknown. It is difficult to measure this phenomenon because the refractive-index alteration is limited to the microscopic region.

Confocal microscopic Raman spectroscopy is a powerful tool in this respect, because it has a high spatial resolution and sensitivity to structural change. The purpose of this section is to investigate the confocal microscopic Raman scattering for the photoinduced refractive-index alteration found in SiO_2 glass and to reveal the mechanism behind this phenomenon.

An experimental apparatus for inducing a high-refractive-index region in glass has been described elsewhere [4]. The apparatus used 120-fs laser pulses, 800-nm in wavelength and at 200 kHz, that were generated by a laser system comprising a mode-locked Ti:sapphire laser (Coherent Inc. Mira 900F) and a regenerative amplifier (REGA 9000). A specimen of pure SiO_2 glass with

Fig. 4.13. Microscope photograph of photowritten optical waveguides in silica glass

a thickness of about 1 mm was translated through laser irradiation that was focused by a 10× microscope objective. The refractive-index changes were induced along the path traversed by the focal point; in this way, the waveguides were written inside the SiO_2 glass. These photowritten waveguides are shown in Fig. 4.13.

A schematic of an experimental setup for measuring confocal microscopic Raman spectra is shown in Fig. 4.14. To probe the Raman scattering, a sample with a high-refractive-index region was attached to a holder that could move precisely. The cw laser (Uniphase μ-green laser, 532 nm, 50 mW) was focused through a spatial filter (pinhole) and a 20× microscope objective. In order to measure the Raman spectra, the scattered light focused using the same objective was led by a beam splitter to the entrance slit of a single polychromator (Spex 270M). This was done with a holographic notch filter that could reject strong Rayleigh scattered light and was detected using an intensified charge coupled detector (Princeton ICCD). In order to remove light from the nonfocal position of the scattered light, a spatial filter was placed in the confocal position.

First, it was necessary to confirm whether the spatial resolution of the equipment was sufficient. For this purpose, a sample that had waveguides spaced with a 25-μm interval was prepared. Then, the Raman spectra were measured for two cases: focused and not focused on the waveguide. The results are shown inm Fig. 4.15. There is a lot of noise in this measurement since the exposure time is too short, but from these results it is clear that we can obtain a Raman spectrum that is in proportion to the existing waveguide separation. Thus, in place of the waveguide, the features emphasizing the 490-cm^{-1} D_1 band were reproduced. Using these results, the Raman spectra were measured by exposing the features for a number of hours.

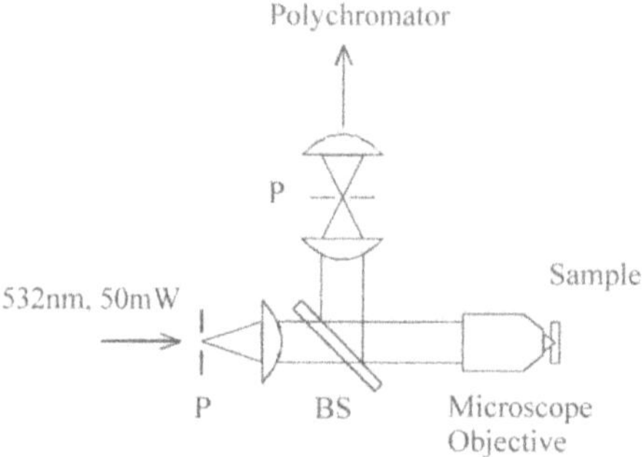

Fig. 4.14. Schematic of the experimental setup. BS: beam splitter; P: pinhole

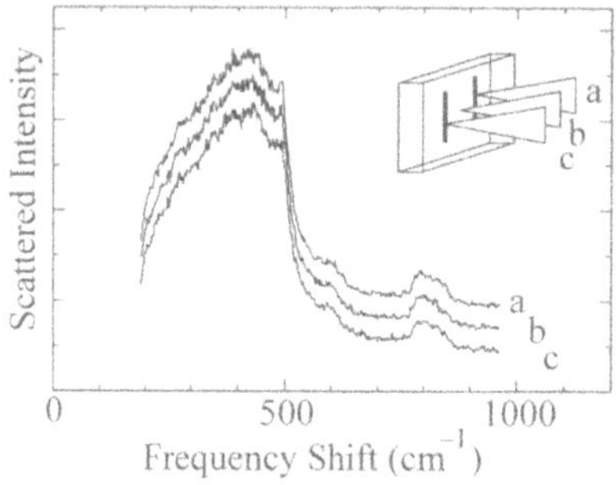

Fig. 4.15. Confocal microscopic Raman spectra in SiO_2 glass describing waveguides with a 25-μm interval induced by an ultrashort-pulse laser

Figure 4.16 shows the Raman scattering spectra of the unirradiated region and the waveguide region in SiO_2 glass. In order to evaluate the ω_1 band center value, the reduced Raman scattering spectra according to [217] are shown. The reduced Raman spectra, I_{red} are calculated from the direct spectra $\mathrm{I}(\omega_{\mathrm{L}}, \omega_{\mathrm{s}})$ according to

$$I_{\text{red}}(\omega) \equiv \frac{I(\omega_{\mathrm{L}}, \omega_{\mathrm{S}})}{(\omega_{\mathrm{L}} - \omega)^4} \frac{\omega}{n(\omega) + 1}, \tag{4.1}$$

where ω_{L} is the frequency of the incident laser light, and $\omega_{\mathrm{S}} \equiv \omega_{\mathrm{L}} - \omega$ is the frequency of the scattered light. Thus, ω is the phonon frequency, while $-\omega$ is the Raman shift for the Stokes spectrum. Here,

$$n(\omega) \equiv \frac{1}{\exp(\hbar\omega/k_{\mathrm{B}}T) - 1} \tag{4.2}$$

is the Bose–Einstein occupation number for the sample temperature. In both spectra in Fig. 4.16, the features of the pure SiO_2 glass spectrum are evident, including a shoulder near the 490-cm^{-1} D_1 band. The broad band around 430 cm^{-1} is attributed to V_{S} (Si–O–Si), the symmetrical stretching vibration mode, and is called the ω_1 band. It is clear that the ω_1 band of the

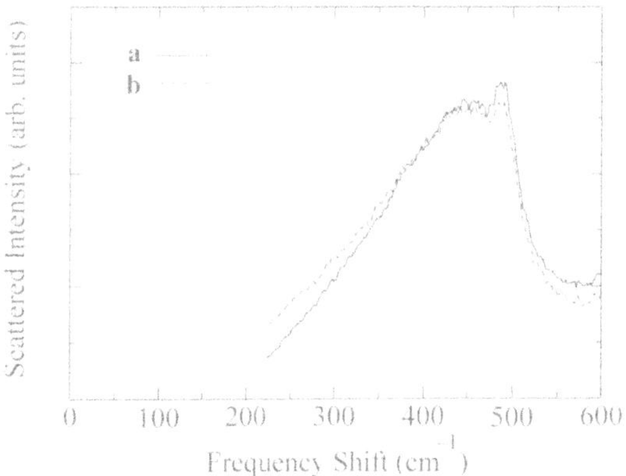

Fig. 4.16. Confocal microscopic reduced Raman scattering spectra of unirradiated region (*curve a*) and waveguide region (*curve b*) in SiO_2 glass

high refractive-index region shifted to the high-energy side and narrowed. In contrast, the intensity of the D_1 line has increased slightly. The D_1 line has been interpreted by Galeener [217] to correspond to the symmetric stretching vibration of oxygen in a tetrasiloxane ring structure. Thus, it is evident that the fourfold planner ring defect increased from the ultrashort-pulse laser irradiation.

First, the energy shift of the ω_1 band is discussed. In this study, the shift quantity of the ω_1 band in the high-refractive-index region was found to be 3–5 cm^{-1}. In order to show the relationship between the density and the Raman spectrum of SiO_2 glass, the Raman spectrum of densified SiO_2 glass was measured. By applying hydrostatic pressure, it was found that its density is 10% greater than ordinary glass. The results are shown in Fig. 4.17. These results prove that the ω_1 band shifts to the high-energy side when densified and that the energy position of the D_1 band does not shift. Devine defined the frequency data for the lattice vibrations for SiO_2 glass [218] that has various densities. From those results, it was found that the ω_1 band of the SiO_2 glass shifts in proportion to the density. Thus the shift of about 4% in the ω_1 band seems to correspond to the increase in density of about 1%.

The relationship between density and the refractive index of the material is known as the Lorentz–Lorenz formula [219], which is as follows:

$$\frac{n^2+1}{n^2+2}\frac{M}{\rho}=\frac{4\pi N\alpha}{3}\,, \tag{4.3}$$

where M is the molecular weight and $N\alpha$ is the molar polarizability. A refractive-index change of about 0.3% of the SiO_2 glass corresponds to a density increment of 1%. Although a detailed study of the refractive index of the sample used in this study was not performed, previous measurement results show it is equivalent to the expected refractive index when the laser-irradiation condition is considered. This fact indicates that the refractive

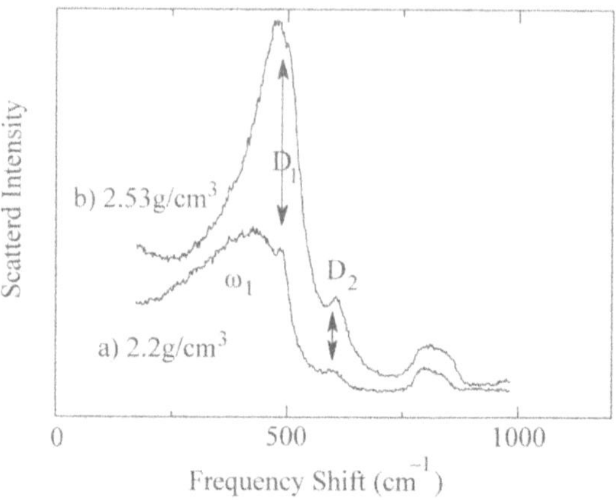

Fig. 4.17. Raman scattering spectra in ordinary SiO_2 glass (a) and in densified SiO_2 glass (b)

index generates the densification through ultrashort-pulse laser irradiation and that a high refractive index occurs.

Miura et al. [5] carried out an atomic force microscope (AFM) observation of a surface in a region where laser-induced refractive-index alteration had occurred. Their research showed that the volume decreases in the region that generated the refractive-index change, which is consistent with this study. Although in a photo-induced, high-refractive index region a defect that cannot be detected by Raman scattering may also be formed, there is also a possibility of refractive-index alteration in the local electronic polarizability. This can be seen in the shape of the ω_1 Raman band. The width of the ω_1 band originates from the variation of the bond angle between Si–O bonds, and is caused by the reflecting features of the amorphous glass.

According to the simplified central force model, the relation between ω_1 and the bond angle, θ, of the Si–O bonds is $\omega_1^2 = (\alpha/m_0)(1 + \cos\theta)$. The ω_1 band spectrum in Fig. 4.14b shows that the low-energy side is low-lying compared to the region not irradiated with the laser and that the bond angle between Si and O is small in the laser-irradiated region.

Next, the increase in the intensity of the D_1 line is considered. The D_1 line is a vibration that originates from the symmetrical motion of the oxygen that is localized in the fourfold ring structure. This is clear based on the results of the Raman spectrum found by using the isotope substitution of Galeener et al. [217]. These rings are illustrated in Fig. 4.18. Recently, using an ab initio approach to study cluster calculation, Uchino et al. [220] found that when silica glass is cooled rapidly from a thermal excitation condition, a threefold and fourfold ring structure (which is a local stable structure) is formed. Furthermore, they also suggested that the formation of such a local structure prevents atom rearrangement in the cooperative crystallization

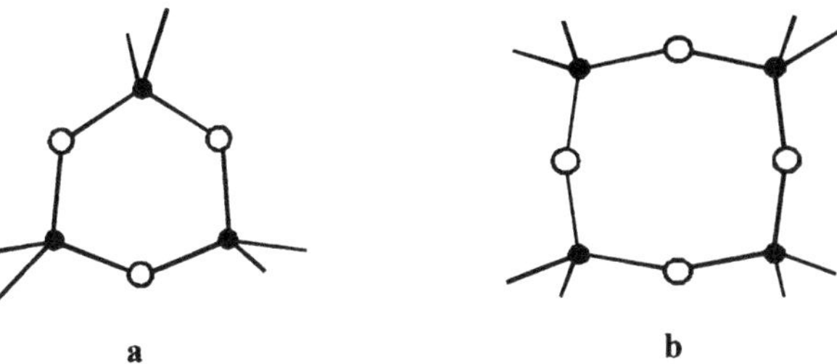

Fig. 4.18. Planar ring structures: (**a**) threefold ring and (**b**) fourfold ring. *Open circles:* oxygen; *closed circles:* silicon

process. It is possible that ultrashort-pulse laser irradiation can also be used to reconstitute an atomic arrangement and that the local stable structure remains like that of a quenching cycle. Actually, detailed research in femtosecond time-resolved spectroscopy using laser irradiation is necessary to determine whether high densification arises. Although there is no proof yet, atomic rearrangement may occur because of the electronic excitation and/or thermal excitation that causes the Si–O bond angle to narrow and the ring defects to freeze.

5. Computer Simulation of Induced Structures

5.1 Introduction

Silica (SiO_2) has various polymorphs; quartz, cristobalite, tridymite, stishovite, coesite and an amorphous one [221]. Experimental [222–226] and theoretical [227–243] studies have been performed on the crystal forms of SiO_2 to determine their electronic structure. It is well known that amorphous SiO_2 is very common and useful materials in microelectronic devices: optical fibers, semiconductor transistors, etc. Although there has been less theoretical work on amorphous SiO_2 [238,244–249] than on crystal [227–243], theoretical quantum-mechanical calculation has proven valuable to the understanding of the detailed electronic structure of amorphous SiO_2.

Photonic crystals are microstructured materials in which the dielectric constant is periodically modulated on a length scale comparable to the desired wavelength of operation. These materials, called photonic crystals, have been the subject of much research effort and many applications have been proposed.

In the previous chapters, photoinduced ultrafast structures and permanent structures in glasses by ultrashort laser pulses were introduced. In this chapter, theoretical analysis of the induced structures by computer simulation is described. Simulation of photoinduced electronic structures in SiO_2 glass using discrete variational (DV)-Xα will be described in Sect. 2 [250]. In Sect. 3, the design of photonic crystals fabricated using gold-nanoparticle-doped glasses is discussed; the photoinduced refractive-index alteration of the latter was described in Sect. 1.4.

5.2 Simulation of Photoinduced Electronic Structures in SiO_2 Glass Using Discrete Variational (DV)-Xα

In Sect. 5.2.1, the molecular dynamics calculation of amorphous SiO_2 at room temperature is introduced. The molecular orbital (MO) calculation of electronic structures of the amorphous SiO_2 is described in Sect. 5.2.2. The affect of a uniform electric field on the density of states (DOS) and the partial density of states (PDOS) is calculated and described in Sect. 5.2.3.

5.2.1 Making an Amorphous Structure

Knowledge of the atomic structure of a glass is needed to study its electronic structures by the quantum-mechanical method. It is impossible to know the structure of glass used in experiments, which only inform us of the short-range order from the radial distribution function. Therefore, in order to obtain the atomic structure using the classical mechanical method, we employed Kawamura's MXDORTO [251] was employed, which is a calculation program using the molecular-dynamics method. MXDORTO can work even on a PC, and is written in FORTRAN. This code enabled calculation of the liquid or glass structure by using the crystal and molecular-dynamics method with a two-body central force. It is especially suitable for ionic, liquid and solid analyses. It also enables utilization of the three-body-force model. The following parameter variations are available: adjustment of particle velocities, scaling of the basic cell, adjustment of temperature and pressure by the expansion of the method of Nosé [252, 253] and Anderson [254]. Quasiclassical MD (quantum correction) [255] was also available. It was possible to carry out a calculation near room temperature.

The cooling process was traced in a computer to obtain the atomic positions in solid amorphous SiO_2. The glass was first brought to a liquid state in the computer and then it was cooled. The initial velocities and initial positions of each particle were decided by random-number generation. However, the limitations of interparticle distances were considered in constructing a meaningful structure, and the particle speeds were set in proportion to the 4000-K starting temperature. There were 400 Si atoms and 800 O atoms contained in a unit cell. By imposing the periodic boundary condition in this cell, the cell boundaries had no affect on the calculation [256]. The 1200 particles constituted an ensemble whose particle number, pressure, and temperature were constant. Sufficient relaxation was necessary in this initial stage, because the structure was artificially constructed with random numbers. The partial ionization of the electric charge was set by estimating the charges to be 600% of the formal charges. In addition, the Morse term was introduced to describe the interaction in Si–O bonds. Every step in the calculation corresponded to 2 fs in real time. A relaxation process of 105 050 steps was calculated to obtain the 4000-K melt state under this condition. Thereby, the glass structure of 4000-K melt state was obtained.

Cooling this liquid was the next step. The cooling speed was -0.1 K/step. It was possible to cool the liquid to 3500 K in 5000 steps. In total, 200 000 steps were calculated to achieve the 3500 K equilibrium state. We repeated the same cooling procedure to obtain a glass at room temperature, with $\sim$1 000 000 steps. The glass constructed at room temperature (300 K) using molecular-dynamics calculation (MXDORTO) is shown in Fig. 5.1a. As shown in this figure, there are some vacancies. The pair correlation functions of atomic distances were calculated, to show that the average adjacent atomic distance between Si and O was 1.60 Å and that between O and O was 2.60 Å.

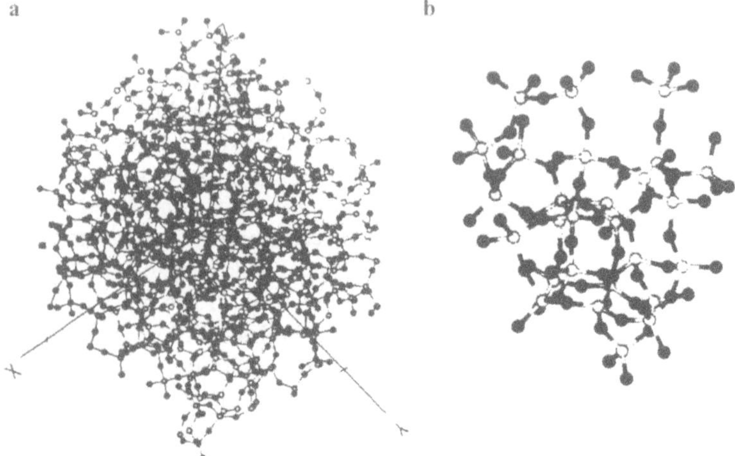

Fig. 5.1. (**a**) Amorphous SiO_2 made using a molecular-dynamics calculation (MXDORTO). It consists of 400 Si atoms and 800 O atoms. (**b**) $Si_{27}O_{72}$ cluster. *Light gray spheres* show silicon and *dark gray spheres* show oxygen. The central Si atom in each figure is the same atom

There were two peaks on the atomic distance between Si and Si, at 3.00 and 3.14 Å. These two peaks have been observed in real-space radial distributions obtained from neutron diffraction measurements; this shows that the model glass was similar to a real glass. By detailed analysis of the glass obtained, irregular coordination numbers could also be seen; there exist two, three and five configurations of Si, and one and three configurations of O. It seemed that the ratio of the numbers of two-, three-, four- and five-coordinated Si and one-, two- and three-coordinated O under the present calculation was more than that in reality, even though these irregular combinations seem to exist in glass.

5.2.2 Molecular Orbital Calculation

The structure of the glass was obtained using a computer by classical calculation with MXDORTO; therefore, study of the electron structures in amorphous SiO_2 by the quantum method was possible. Discrete variational (DV)-Xα [257] (derived from [258]) is a computation coding of the Hartree–Fock–Slater method which uses first-principles MO calculations. DV-Xα uses numerical atomic orbital functions to calculate the Xα method and execute the discrete numerical integration. DV-Xα has the following three features: (a) Linear combinations of atomic orbitals (LCAO) are used as atomic orbital functions. It is possible to obtain the numerical atomic orbital when the atomic Schrödinger equation is solved. (b) Matrix elements are calculated using the numerical integration. (c) Slater exchange potential is used, so that the calculation can be performed in a time, regardless of atomic type, that is short compared with the time for the general Hartree–Fock method. Therefore, DV-Xα has been widely used for MO calculations with inorganic molecules and metallic materials [259].

The exchange and correlation energies are calculated by the potential

$$V_{XC\uparrow}(r) = -3\alpha[(3/8\pi)\rho_\uparrow(r)]^{1/3} , \tag{5.1}$$

where $\rho_\uparrow(r)$ is the local charge density of the up spin electron. The parameter α is fixed at 0.7. MOs were constructed with LCAO which were numerically generated.

A total of 1200 atoms existed in one cell of the amorphous glass at room temperature obtained by the MO method. It was impossible to calculate all of these atoms by the quantum method because of the limitation of computer memory and the limitation of calculation time. A cluster was taken from this cell using the following conditions: (a) the center of the cluster is an Si atom, (b) all Si atoms in the cluster combine with 4 O atoms, (c) the boundary atoms of the cluster are O atoms. The cluster obtained is shown in Fig. 5.1b. 27 Si atoms and 72 O atoms are in this cluster. The central Si atom of the $Si_{400}O_{800}$ cluster in Fig. 5.1a is coincident with the center of the $Si_{27}O_{72}$ cluster by the parallel translation using a periodic boundary condition. In calculating electron structures with DV-Xα, the atoms of the remainder of the cluster outside were replaced by a formal charge (that of an Si atom is +4, and that of an O atom is −2), and the Coulomb potential of these charges was calculated with the Ewald method [256]. All atoms considered in molecular dynamics were effectively introduced into the MO method by the Madelung potential. The 27 Si atoms were classified into three types by their distance from the center; the 72 O atoms were also classified into three types so that the calculation time could be decreased. The electrons belonging to atoms which were classified into the same atomic type enter the same kind of atomic orbitals. Basis functions of Si and O were 1s–3d and 1s–2p atomic orbitals, respectively. Self-consistent charge calculations were made to accomplish the self-consistent-field calculation with the degree of convergence of the Mulliken charge within 0.1%.

The parallel electric field was made by a pair of 10×10 nm parallel boards, whose separation was 10 nm, on which 21×21 negative and positive point charges were arrayed.

5.2.3 Density of States and Partial Density of States

Figure 5.2 shows the calculated DOS and PDOS for the central Si atom and the four O atoms around it, where the constituents were reduced to SiO_2. The black lines in Fig. 5.2 show the (P)DOS under no electric field, and the gray ones show those under an electric field of ~10 MV/cm. These spectra can be compared with experimental X-ray photoemission (or absorption)

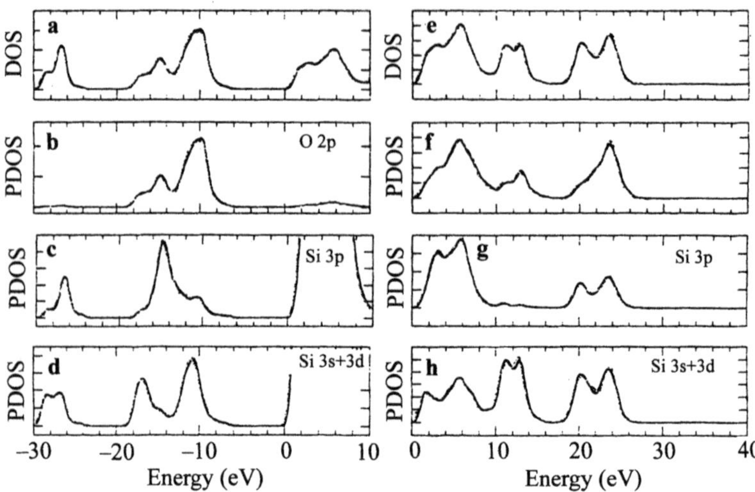

Fig. 5.2a–h. Calculated density of states (DOS) and partial density of states (PDOS). (**a–d**) Valence band (P)DOS; (**e–h**) onduction band (P)DOS. *Black lines* show (P)DOS and *gray lines* show (P)DOS affected by a ~10 MV/cm electric field

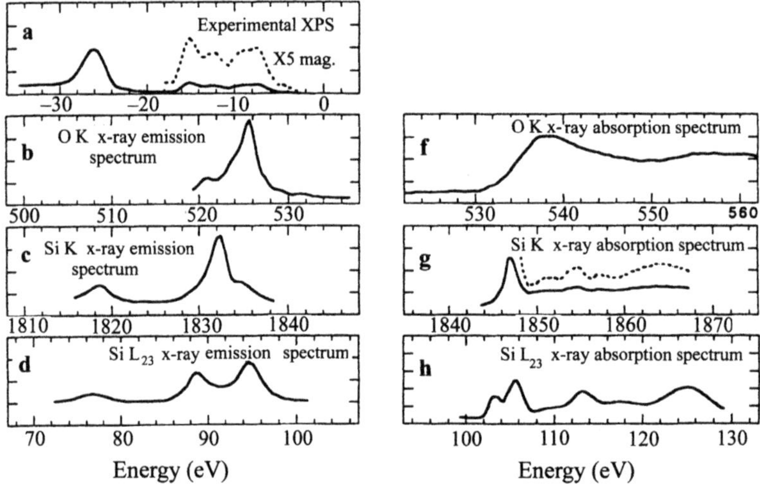

Fig. 5.3. Experimental spectrum for α-quartz. Data corresponds to the calculated (P)DOS in Fig. 5.2. For the sake of convenience, (**e**) is not shown. XPS: X-ray photoemission spectrum

spectra. Figure 5.3 shows the experimental data for α-quartz. The calculated (P)DOS were obtained by simply broadening the MO levels of each with a Lorentzian function with a full width at half maximum (FWHM) of 1.0 eV, where photoemission cross-sections were not considered. The origins of the energy in Fig. 5.2 are the calculated energies.

Table 5.1. Net charge of every species of atom (an increase and decrease in charge can be seen)

	Net charge
Central Si	+2.227
Middle Si	+2.403
Outer Si	+2.536
Inner O	−1.079
Middle O	−1.116
Outer O	−1.714

Figure 5.2a corresponds to the XPS (X-ray photoemission spectrum) measurements [224] in Fig. 5.3a. The difference in the intensity ratio between experimental results and calculated DOS originates from the difference in the photoemission cross-section of the 2s and 2p atomic orbitals. Figure 5.2b and f showing O 2p PDOS correspond to the O–K X-ray emission ($E < 0$) [226] and absorption ($E > 0$) spectra [260] in Fig. 5.3b and f, respectively. Figure 5.2c and g of Si 3p PDOS correspond to the Si–K X-ray emission ($E < 0$) [226] and absorption ($E > 0$) spectra [261] in Fig. 5.3c and g, respectively. Figure 5.2d and h of Si 3s + 3d PDOS correspond to the Si–L_{23} X-ray emission ($E < 0$) [226] and absorption ($E > 0$) spectra [261] in Fig. 5.3d and h, respectively. These figures show that the features of the experimental α-quartz X-ray spectra were approximately reproduced by the calculated PDOS of amorphous SiO_2. The fine structures in the SiO_2 experimental data were reproduced smoothed because our SiO_2 was amorphous.

The effects of an electric field can be seen in the (P)DOS in Fig. 5.2a–d, which it was suspected to be the source of the second harmonics, although changes in the (P)DOS were small. It is worthy to note that the biggest change in the PDOS was seen in O 2p around −10 eV. The electrons in the O 2p orbital may contribute to second harmonic generation. The PDOS of Si 3p on the valence band was not affected by the electric field. Therefore, the electrons in O 2p orbitals may play an important role in second harmonic generation.

The valence electrons calculated in each of the atomic orbitals are shown in Table 5.1. The electron of the Si atom inside the cluster is the smallest; the electrons become larger nearer to the outside; in contrast, the electrons of the O atom become smaller nearer the outside. It seems not to exist in actual amorphous glass, and it is necessary to reconsider the potential function used in our calculations.

The transfer of charges by the electric field is shown in three dimensions Fig. 5.4. The white cross-hatched region shows the surfaces on which the positive and negative 21×21 charges are arrayed on the right and left surfaces, respectively; the size of these surfaces and their separation are not to scale in the figure. The light gray surfaces show a charge density under a neutral elec-

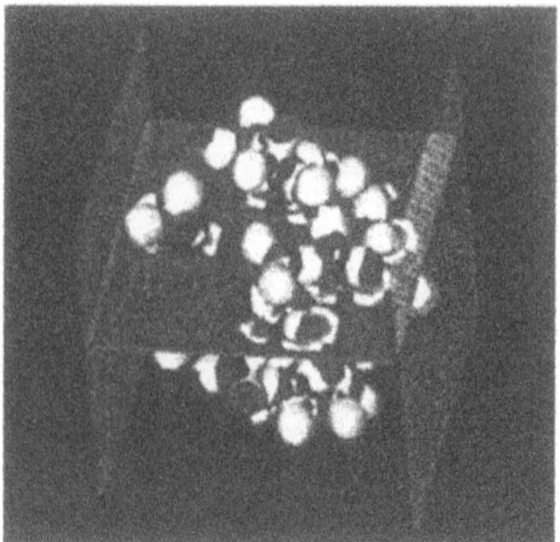

Fig. 5.4. Isosurfaces of electron densities of $Si_{27}O_{72}^{36-}$. *Light gray surfaces* show electron densities under neutral electric field, and *black* (*gray*) surfaces show those of decrease (increase) of electron densities under electric field of ~10 MV/cm. Positive (negative) point charges are arrayed on right (left) white square board, respectively; the size of the boards and their separation have been reduced in this figure

tric field, and the gray and black surfaces show the increasing and decreasing contour surfaces, respectively. The light gray square shows a slice surface.

5.3 Design and Analysis of Photonic Crystals Fabricated Using Glasses

Photonic crystals are optical materials with periodic changes in the dielectric constant, analogous to the crystal structure of a semiconductor, and band gaps can be created for certain ranges of photon energies [111, 262]. By introducing defects into the otherwise perfect crystals, very sharp defect levels can be created. Various applications are predicted, and they are expected to be realized by utilizing the defect levels inside photonic crystals; they include zero-threshold semiconductor lasers, optical waveguides with sharp bends and optical integrated circuits [111, 262–264].

Gold-nanoparticle-doped glass absorbs light around a wavelength of 530 nm due to a surface plasmon [265] (see Sect. 1.4). When a high-powered laser beam is focused on this glass, the deposited gold nanoparticles can be dissolved and the absorption suppressed. The presence and absence of the absorption cause alteration of the refractive index. In this section, the possibility of fabricating photonic crystals by using this glass is discussed.

In an investigation of the band structure of photonic crystals created using glass, the most important parameter is the refractive index (or dielectric constant) of the glass materials. First of all, the refractive index of the gold-nanoparticle-doped glass was estimated using the Kramers–Kronig method [266]. When the absorption coefficient is given for all frequencies, one can calculate the real part of the refractive index using this method. However,

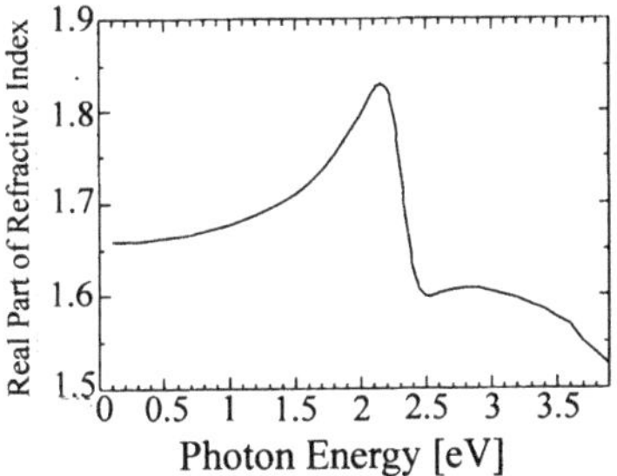

Fig. 5.5. Real part of the refractive index of gold-nanoparticle-doped glass calculated using the Kramers–Kronig method

it is not possible to integrate the absorption coefficient for all frequencies. Therefore, it was integrated for photon energies between 0 and 6 eV to obtain the real part of the refractive index. The result is shown in Fig. 5.5. This result was used as an estimation of the actual refractive index; the band calculation was performed by scanning the parameter over a certain range.

Here, for glass without absorption the dielectric constant ε_a is assumed to be $1.5^2 = 2.25$; for glass with absorption, the dielectric constant ε_b is varied such that $\varepsilon_\mathrm{b} = 2.3, 2.4, \ldots, 3.0$. First, the band diagrams of the diamond structure were calculated by using the plane-wave expansion method [267]. The parameters were assumed to be as follows: The radii of the spheres r were $0.31a$, where a is the lattice constant and $\varepsilon_\mathrm{b} = 3.0$. Figure 5.6a shows the diamond structure, and Fig. 5.6b shows its band diagram. It can be seen in Fig. 5.6b that, although there is no omnidirectional band gap due to small refractive index contrast, a band gap in the Γ-L direction (111 direction) exists. Next, the transfer-matrix method [268] was used to calculate the transmission spectra in the Γ-L direction with various dielectric constants ε_b. The results are shown in Fig. 5.6c. In Fig. 5.6c, the radii of the spheres are assumed to be 0.5 μm. Consequently, the lattice constant becomes 1.61 μm and the band gap appears near a wavelength of 2.9 μm. The band diagram of the simple-cubic structure was also calculated. Figure 5.7a and b show the simple-cubic structure and the band diagrams when radii of spheres $r = 0.5a$ and $\varepsilon_b = 3.0$, respectively. The transmission spectra in the Γ-X direction (001 direction) in Fig. 5.7c. It is also seen in this structure that the band gap appears at a wavelength near 3.0 μm. Therefore, when the radius of the laser beam is focused at 0.5 μm, the photonic band gaps are expected to be formed near a wavelength of 3 μm.

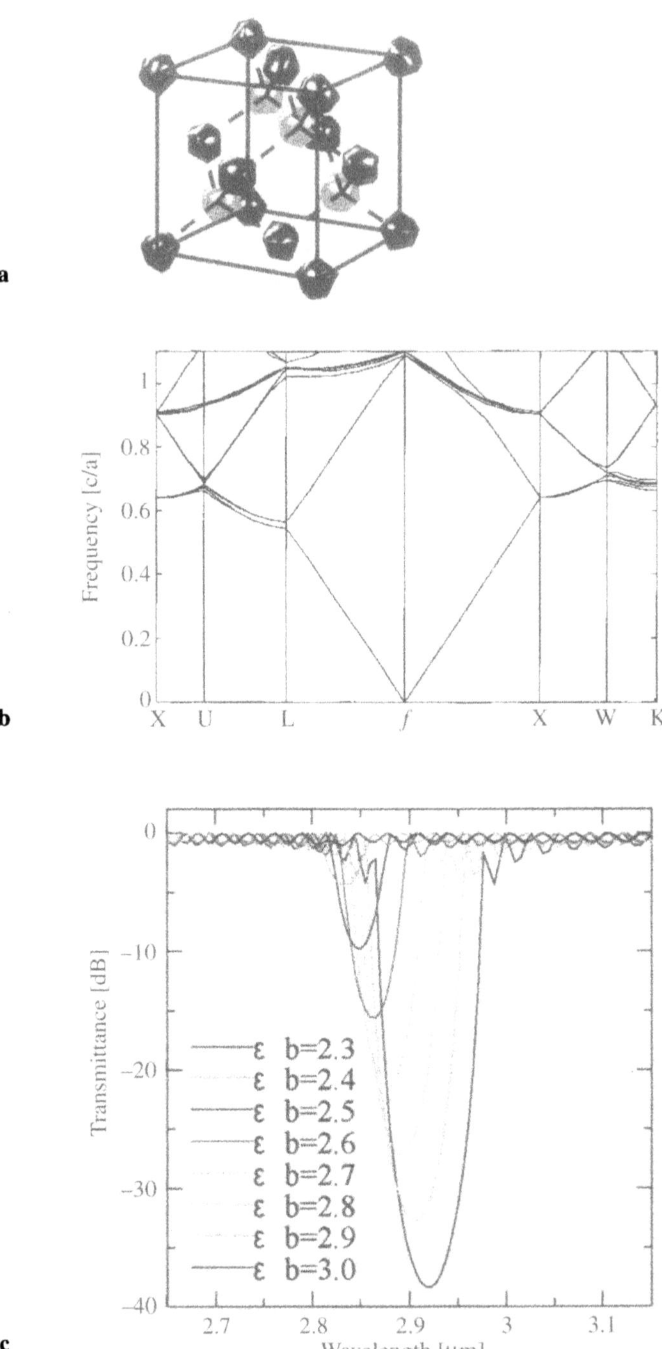

Fig. 5.6. (**a**) The diamond structure, (**b**) the band structure calculated using the plane-wave expansion method with $\varepsilon_b = 3.0$ and (**c**) the transmission spectra in the Γ-L direction calculated using the transfer-matrix method with ε_b varied from 2.3 to 3.0

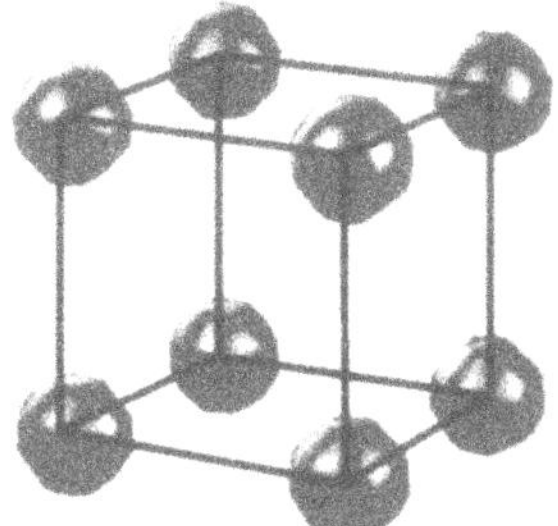

a

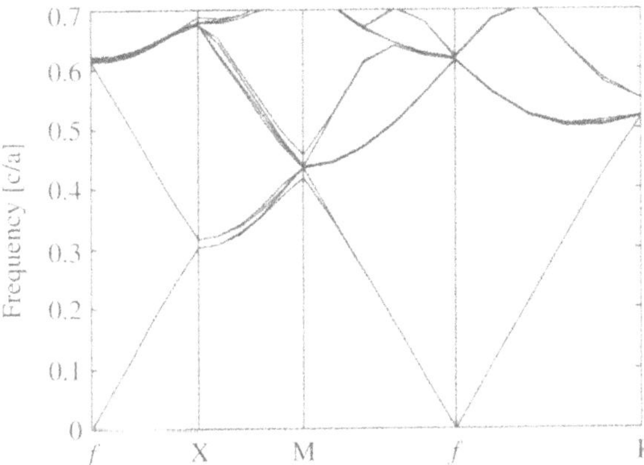

b

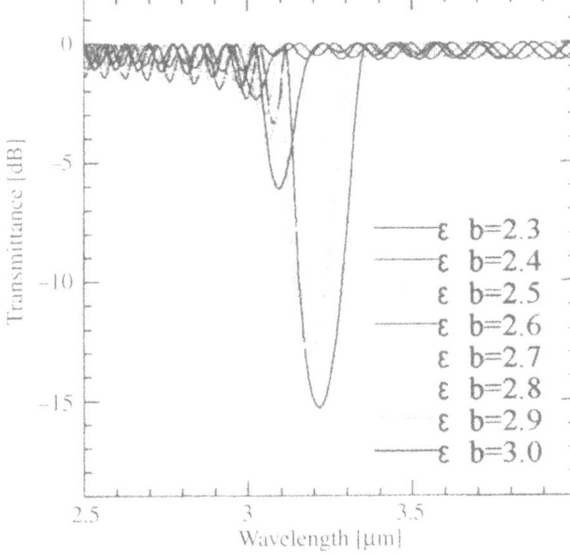

c

Fig. 5.7. (**a**) The simple-cubic structure, (**b**) the band structure calculated using the plane-wave expansion method with $\varepsilon_b = 3.0$ and (**c**) the transmission spectra in the Γ-X direction calculated using the transfer-matrix method with ε_b varied from 2.3 to 3.0

Part 3

Functional Devices Using Active Glasses

6. Active Glasses for Functional Devices

6.1 Introduction

In Parts 1 and 2, ultrafast induction of electronic structures and induction of permanent structure by ultrashort laser pulses were introduced. Three-dimensional optical waveguides were written and single-crystal-like structures were grown in glasses using a focused femtosecond laser. Various novel phenomena in rare-earth-ions-doped glasses were observed, including photostimulated luminescence, long-lasting phosphorescence and space-selective manipulation of valence state of rare-earth ions. Methods such as X-ray-absorption fine structure analysis and, microscopic Raman scattering spectroscopy were used to analyze the induced structures in glasses. Computer simulation was also performed for induced structures in glasses. In this chapter, the following functional devices using active glasses are introduced: microsphere lasers [269], rare-earth-ion-doped glasses for UV and blue upconversion lasers [270], semiconductor-microcrystal-doped films emitting electroluminescence [271], dye-doped polymers exhibiting SHG [272, 273], Faraday effect glass which can be used as a magneto-optical switch [152, 274], and long-period optical fiber gratings [275]. They vary in form from microsphere, film, bulk to fiber, and in any of the function devices, induced structure takes an important role in the realization of optical functions.

6.2 Micro-Sphere Lasers

A large number of studies has been made since about 1960 on the interaction of optical waves with spherical microparticles. The observation that a spherical microparticle can sustain high-Q resonance modes dates back to Richtmyer [276]. High-Q resonance modes, due to multiple total internal reflection in a spherical object, were called whispering-gallery modes and have several potential applications. Garrett et al. [277] were first to notice that spherical resonators for optical waves can be used as laser resonators. In this research, they observed pulsed laser oscillation in an Sm^{2+}:CaF_2 spherical crystal, which was between 1 and 2 mm in diameter. Subsequently, several studies were carried out on dye-doped polymer particles [278–280] and spherical Nd:YAG crystals, of the order of 1 mm in diameter [281]; however, little is known about the laser oscillation characteristics of spherical glasses.

Fluoride glass microspheres have been successfully made with a diameter of the order of 100 μm. Rear-earth-ion-doped fluoride glasses have high efficiency in lasing operation, and hence, the phonon energies of fluoride glasses are much less than those in SiO_2 or YAG [282]. It can safely be stated that fluoride glasses are suitable as host materials for some active laser devices. This advantage is especially effective when the shape of the fluoride glass is spherical, because the ability to sustain high power densities can be afforded by its resonant spherical properties. In addition, glass microspheres not only have the advantage of high resistance to laser damage compared with dye-doped polymers, but also allow easy-refractive index matching by the ability to vary chemical composition. In this section, the characteristics of laser oscillation in Nd^{3+} dopant ions in fluoride glasses formed into microspheres are presented.

The spherical glass specimens used were produced as follows: The raw materials were melted in a vitreous carbon crucible at 1000°C, in an induction furnace, using 20 g batches containing 53 mol. % ZrF_4, 2 mol. % LaF_3, 3 mol. % AIF_3, 20 mol. % BaF_2, 20 mol. % NaF and 2 mol. % NdF_3. The anhydrous fluoride raw materials were >99.999% pure. The molten batch was then poured in a fine stream into liquid nitrogen, and spherical glass particles which passed through a 50 mesh sieve were collected from the quenched glasses. The surface of fluoride glass spheres are easily contaminated by hydrolysis and oxidized products, such as Zr–OH and Zr–O, which are disadvantageous for lasing operation. In fact, scattering loss on the surface is the largest cause of low Q-values for spherical resonators. Therefore, the surface was etched by a chemical polishing technique. Chemical polishing was conducted using an ultrasonically agitated bath of $ZrOCl_2 \cdot 8H_2O$ dissolved in water. All the operations, except chemical polishing, were carried out in a dry nitrogen gas atmosphere. A scanning electron microscope was used to observe the surface of the glass spheres. The diameters of the spheres were measured by the contact process; the measurements were repeatable to ±0.1 μm.

The spheres, whose variation in measured diameter was less than 2 μm were used in the experiments. The laser oscillation experiment was performed using the apparatus shown in Fig. 6.1. The spherical laser was excited by a $Ti{:}Al_2O_3$ laser tuned to 800 nm, which is the wavelength corresponding to the $^4I_{9/2}$–$^4F_{5/2}$ absorption band of the Nd^{3+} ion. The pump laser was focused with a microscope objective lens and then launched into a spherical specimen which was placed on a glass plate. The pump beam was incident on a point deviating slightly from the center of the sphere. The light emitted from the spherical specimen was collected with an objective lens and then introduced into an optical fiber. The emission spectra were measured either with a monochromator equipped with a photodiode from 1000 to 1400 nm (resolution: 1.0 nm) or with a polychromator equipped with a liquid-nitrogen-cooled

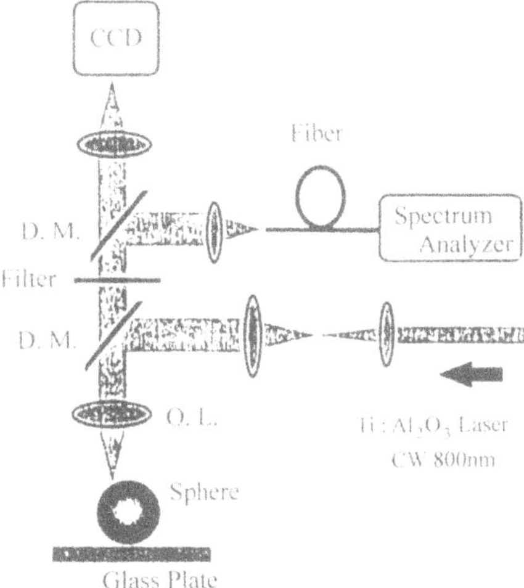

Fig. 6.1. Schematic of the experimental setup for laser oscillation of a microsphere

CCD camera from 1000 to 1100 nm (resolution: 0.1 nm). All measurements were carried out at room temperature.

Figure 6.2 shows scanning electron micrographs of the microspheres obtained in this study; the spheres of Fig. 6.2a and b were untreated and treated with chemical polishing, respectively. After chemical polishing, a significant improvement of the surface was apparent, as shown in this figure. It was found that the chemical polishing process was not only capable of modifying surface quality, but was also capable of controlling the diameter (from 30 to 500 μm) of the spheres.

A comparison is made between the emission spectra for the $^4F_{3/2}$–$^4I_{11/2}$ transition of Nd^{3+} ions obtained from a nonpolished sphere (130 μm diameter) and a polished sphere (140 μm diameter) in Fig. 6.3. The emission spectrum of the non-polished sphere is similar to the normal fluorescence spectrum of the bulk glass. In contrast, the emission spectrum of the polished sphere has several strong peaks superimposed over the broadband background. The linewidths (full-width at half maximum, FWHM) of the sharp peaks are less than the resolution of the detectors used (0.1 nm). Figure 6.4 shows the variation of the emission spectra due to the $^4F_{3/2}$–$^4I_{11/2}$ transition in a polished sphere (150 μm diameter) at various incident pump powers. It can be observed that the intensity of the sharp emission peaks are amplified with an increase in incident pump power. Further, definite thresholds existed for the sharp emission peaks. Judging from the above facts, it might reasonably be concluded that these peaks are the lasing spectra in the glass microsphere. Therefore, the observed emission spectra from the polished sphere can be regarded as an admixture of laser oscillation spectra and fluorescence

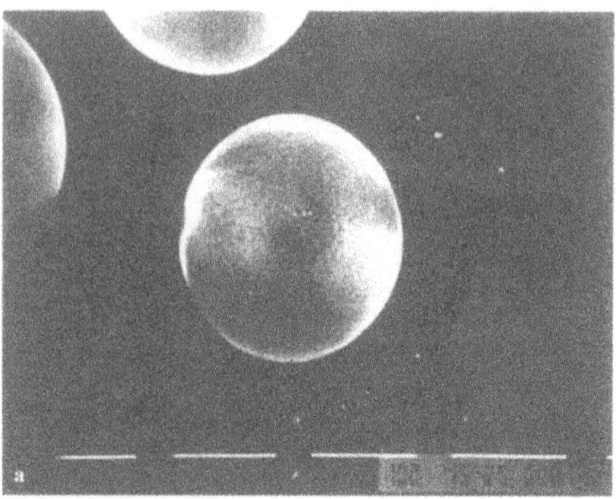

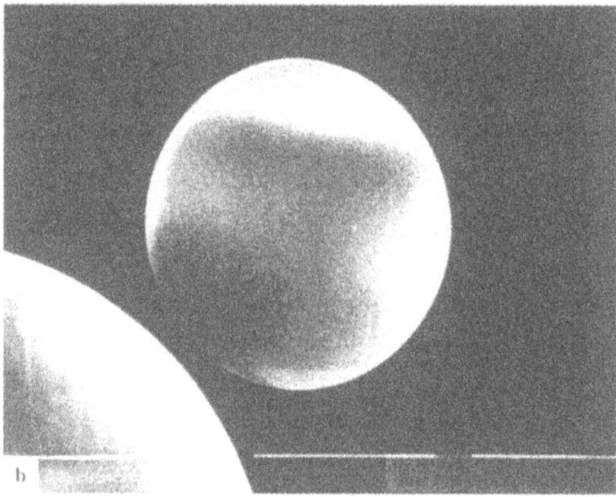

Fig. 6.2a,b. Scanning electron micrographs of two kinds of spheres. (**a**) Untreated and (**b**) treated with chemical polishing. The diameters of both spheres was ≈110 μm

spectra. Figure 6.5 shows the emission spectra around the $^4F_{3/2}$–$^4I_{11/2}$ and $^4F_{3/2}$–$^4I_{13/2}$ transitions for Nd^{3+} ions in a fluoride glass sphere (170 μm diameter). Several strong peaks of laser emission can be observed in both regions. This result proves clearly that laser oscillation on both the $^4F_{3/2}$–$^4I_{11/2}$ and $^4F_{3/2}$–$^4I_{13/2}$ transitions occurred simultaneously. The dependence of the incident pump-power on the emission peak intensity for the 1051 nm and 1334 nm peaks is shown in Fig. 6.6; the emission peak intensity is the output power for the optimum launch condition (obtained maximum output power) of the 170 μm sphere in Fig. 6.5. As shown in Fig. 6.6, the thresholds of incident pump power were found to be 5 and 60 mW for the 1051 and 1334 nm transitions, respectively. In the optimum incident condition of the pump laser, values of the emission peak intensity were in error by up to 3%. These results led to the conclusion that spherical glass lasers can be affected by a general laser diode.

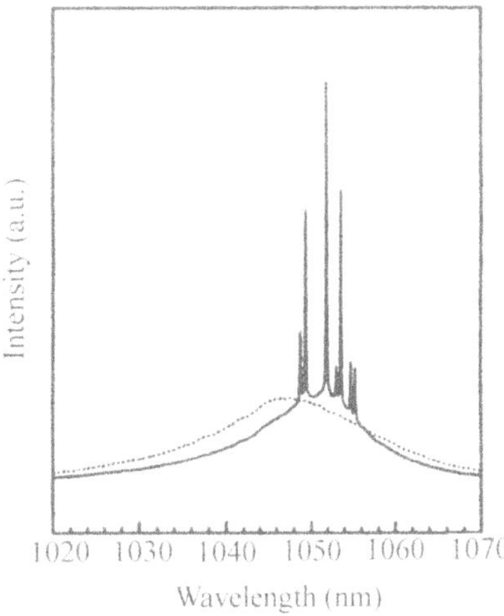

Fig. 6.3. Comparison between the emission spectra of a non-polished sphere (*broken line*) and a polished sphere (*solid line*). The spectral resolution was 0.1 nm

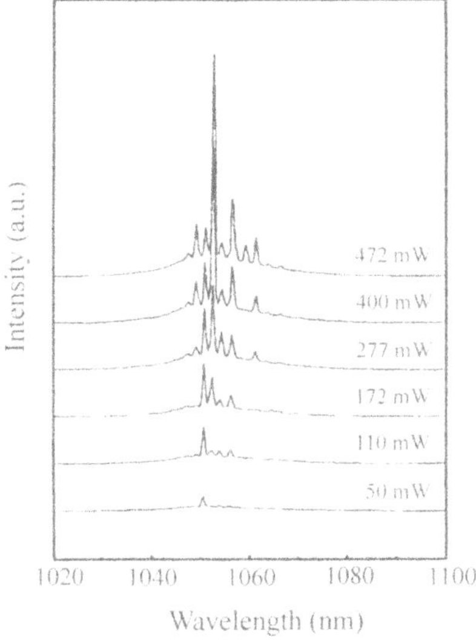

Fig. 6.4. Emission spectra due to the $^4F_{3/2}$–$^4I_{11/2}$ transition of Nd^{3+} ions in the fluoride glass microsphere at various pump powers. The spectral resolution was 1.0 nm

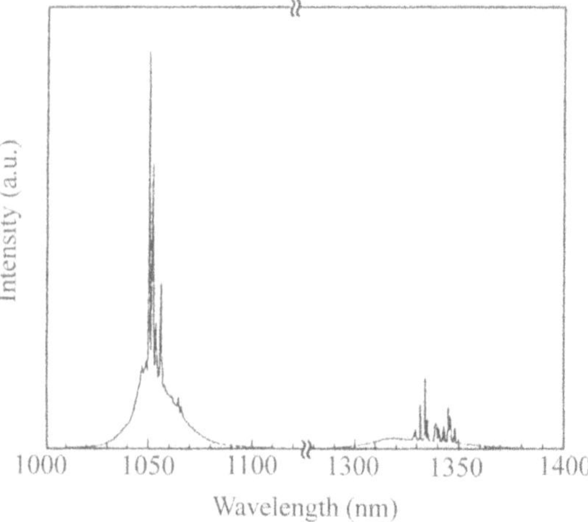

Fig. 6.5. Simultaneous laser oscillation on both the $^4F_{3/2}$–$^4I_{11/2}$ and $^4F_{3/2}$–$^4I_{13/2}$ transitions. The spectral resolution was 1.0 mm

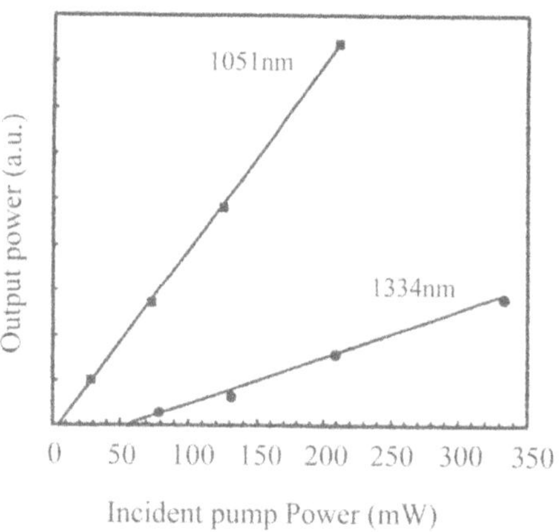

Fig. 6.6. Incident pump-power dependence on the emission peak intensity. The emission was determined at 1051 and 1334 nm. The thresholds were 5 and 60 mW at 1051 and 1334 nm, respectively. Lines are drawn as guides for the eye

Laser oscillation was observed in fluoride glass microspheres, which, to our knowledge, has never before been examined. The important point to be discussed is the assignment of resonance modes. Figure 6.7a and b show typical emission spectra for the $^4F_{3/2}$–$^4I_{11/2}$ and $^4F_{3/2}$–$^4I_{13/2}$ transitions of Nd^{3+} ions in a fluoride glass sphere (150 μm diameter), respectively. For $^4F_{3/2}$–$^4I_{13/2}$ transitions, each pair of peaks corresponds to transverse electric (TE) and transverse magnetic (TM) modes. This figure helps to define the assignment of resonance modes. The average spacing ($\Delta\lambda$) between lasing peaks were 1.8 and 2.9 nm for the $^4F_{3/2}$–$^4I_{11/2}$ and $^4F_{3/2}$–$^4I_{13/2}$ transitions, respec-

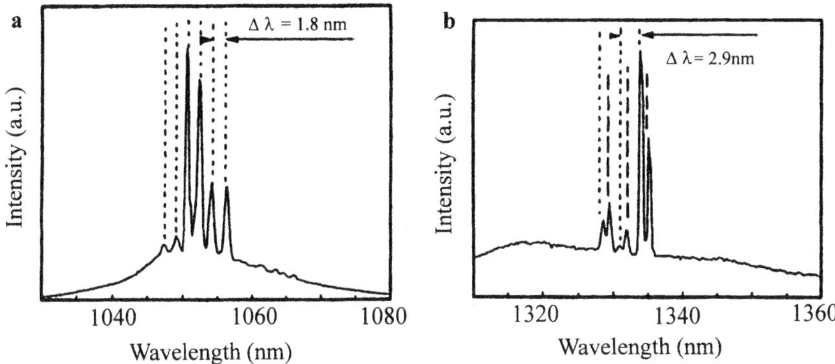

Fig. 6.7. Intensity of emission spectra for the (**a**) $^4F_{3/2}$–$^4I_{11/2}$ and (**b**) $^4F_{3/2}$–$^4I_{13/2}$ transitions of Nd^{3+} ions. The spacings between resonance peaks ($\Delta\lambda$) corresponding to each transition were 1.8–1.9 nm (**a**) and 2.8–3.0 nm (**b**). The spectral resolution was 1.0 nm

tively. For the $^4F_{3/2}$–$^4I_{13/2}$ transition, each of the pairs of peaks, denoted by the dotted and dashed lines, corresponds to TE and TM modes; however, it could not be determined which peaks are attributable to the TE mode and which to the TM mode. According to Mie scattering theory, the spacing ($\Delta\lambda$) between resonance peaks for whispering-gallery oscillation modes is approximately given by

$$\Delta\lambda = \frac{\lambda \tan^{-1}[(n_1/n_2)^2 - 1]^{1/2}}{\pi d n_2[(n_1/n_2)^2 - 1]^{1/2}} , \tag{6.1}$$

where λ is the wavelength of laser oscillation, d is the diameter of the glass sphere, and n_1 and n_2 are the refractive indices of the sphere and the surrounding medium, respectively. Thus, the wavelengths of whispering-gallery resonance peaks of the sphere depend on both the size and the refractive index of the sphere. For a glass sphere of 150 μm diameter in air, the calculated $\Delta\lambda$ based on (6.1) are 1.76 and 2.82 nm at 1050 and 1330 nm, respectively. Since a sphere annealed at 255°C was used, in this calculation the refractive index was 1.499, which was almost equal to that of the bulk glass. These values are in good agreement with the observed ones. It is concluded, therefore, that these peaks are caused by the whispering-gallery modes of the sphere. In other words, simultaneous laser oscillation of both the $^4F_{3/2}$–$^4I_{11/2}$ and $^4F_{3/2}$–$^4I_{13/2}$ transitions of Nd^{3+} ions was achieved due to multiple total internal reflection in the microsphere. In usual oxide glasses, such as silica glass, laser oscillation is very difficult near 1340 nm because the excited-state absorption of the stimulating radiation decreases the Q-value of the cavity to the extent that the lasing will not occur. Therefore, the achievement of lasing operation in the 1340 nm region using fluoride glass spheres is very significant.

It has also been observed that the incident point of the pump beam is a critical parameter in determining the oscillation wavelength, similar to the size and/or the refractive index of the sphere. This enables the oscillation wavelength to be controlled by selecting the appropriate parameters. In addition, laser oscillation at arbitrary wavelengths might be established by a combination of several rare-earth-ion dopants. Although much still remains to be done to improve the glass microsphere laser, it is no exaggeration to say that spherical glasses will be of practical use for new compact lasers.

6.3 Tm^{3+}-Doped Active Glasses for UV and Blue Upconversion Lasers

It is known that some rare-earth ions can convert the wavelength of incident light to a shorter one via a multiphoton excitation process. And now, there is still a great interest in such phenomena because of the possibility of infrared-pumped visible lasers and visible-to-ultraviolet light amplifiers. Plenty of research has been carried out on Er^{3+} and Ho^{3+} glasses [22, 206, 207]. These ions can effectively convert 800-nm near-infrared or 645-nm red light into green emission near 550 nm.

The Tm^{3+} ion also has stable excited levels suitable for emitting ultraviolet and blue upconversion fluorescence. Recently, it was reported that blue upconversion fluorescence of Tm^{3+} was found in fluorozirconate glass by co-pumping at both 676.4 nm and 647.1 nm using a krypton ion laser [208] and by single-wavelength pumping at 650 nm [209]. In addition, both UV and blue upconversion in Tm^{3+}-doped glasses was found [210].

In fluoride glasses, the maximum phonon energy is small enough to reduce the loss by nonradiative decay via multiphonon relaxation [283]. In most of studies mentioned above, fluoroaluminate or fluorozirconate glasses were employed as the host glass for the rare-earth ions, because such glasses are thermally more stable and are more easily prepared than other fluoride glasses.

However, recently, new fluoroindate glasses as stable as the conventional fluorozirconate and fluoroaluminate glasses have been reported. These glasses give doped Pr^{3+} ions a longer fluorescence lifetime than both fluorozirconate and fluoroaluminate glasses [284,285]; in other words, the fluoroindate glasses have a lower nonradiative decay rate. In this section, intense UV and blue upconversion fluorescence of Tm^{3+} in these new fluoroindate glasses is introduced.

Glass samples were prepared by using reagent-grade $BaCO_3$, GeO_2, TeO_2, ZnO, AlF_3, BaF_2, GdF_3, InF_3, LaF_3, PbF_2, SrF_2, YF_3, YbF_3, $ZnF_2 \cdot 4H_2O$, ZrF_4, Tm_2O_3, Eu_2O_3, TmF_3 and EuF_3 as the starting materials.

They were mixed thoroughly in the compositions shown in Table 6.1. For the ZBL fluorozirconate and ZABSY fluorozincate glasses, about 10 wt. % of

Table 6.1. Compositions of the glasses prepared in the study of UV and blue upconversion fluorescence of Tm^{+3}

Glass	Composition (cat. %)	Abbreviation
Tm^{3+}-doped glasses		
Fluoroindate	$99.9(38InF_3{\cdot}19BaF_2{\cdot}19ZnF_2{\cdot}10PbF_2{\cdot}10SrF_2{\cdot}2AlF_3{\cdot}2GdF_3){\cdot}0{\cdot}1TmF_3$	IBZPS-AG
Fluoroindate	$99.9(38InF_3{\cdot}18BaF_2{\cdot}19ZnF_2{\cdot}10PbF_2{\cdot}9SrF_2{\cdot}2AlF_3{\cdot}2GdF_3{\cdot}2YbF_3){\cdot}0{\cdot}1TmF_3$	IBZPS-AGYb
Fluorozincate	$99.9(40ZnF_2{\cdot}15AlF_3{\cdot}15BaF_2{\cdot}15SrF_2{\cdot}15YF_3){\cdot}0{\cdot}1TmF_3$	ZABSY
Fluorozirconate	$99.9(60ZrF_4{\cdot}33BaF_2{\cdot}7LaF_3){\cdot}0{\cdot}1TmF_3$	ZBL
Germanate	$99.9(60GeO_2{\cdot}30BaO{\cdot}10ZnO){\cdot}0{\cdot}1TmO_{1.5}$	GBZ
Tellurite	$99.9(60TeO_2{\cdot}30BaO{\cdot}10ZnO){\cdot}0{\cdot}1TmO_{1.5}$	TBZ
Eu^{3+}-doped glasses		
Fluoroindate	$95(38InF_3{\cdot}9BaF_2{\cdot}19ZnF_2{\cdot}0PbF_2\ 10SrF_2{\cdot}AlF_3{\cdot}2GdF_3){\cdot}5EuF_3$	IBZPS-AG
Fluoroindate	$95(38InF_3{\cdot}18BaF_2{\cdot}19ZnF_2{\cdot}10PbF_2{\cdot}9SrF_2{\cdot}2AlF_3{\cdot}2GdF_3{\cdot}2YbF_3){\cdot}5EuF_3$	IBZPS-AGYb
Fluorozincate	$95(40ZnF_2{\cdot}15AlF_3{\cdot}15BaF_2{\cdot}15SrF_2{\cdot}15YF_3){\cdot}5EuF_3$	ZABSY
Fluorozirconate	$95(60ZrF_4{\cdot}33BaF_2{\cdot}7LaF_3){\cdot}5EuF_3$	ZBL
Germanate	$95(60GeO_2{\cdot}30BaO{\cdot}10ZnO){\cdot}5EuO_{1.5}$	GBZ
Tellurite	$95(60TeO_2{\cdot}30BaO{\cdot}10ZnO){\cdot}5EuO_{1.5}$	TBZ

$NH_4\ HF_2$ was added into the batch to avoid inadequate oxidation. The fluoride and tellurite glasses were melted in a platinum crucible in air at 1000°C and 800°C, respectively, for 20 min; the germanate glasses were melted in an alumina crucible at 1300°C for 1 h. The crucibles were covered with a large alumina crucible to reduce volatilization loss. For the IBZPS-AG and IBZPS-AGYb fluoroindate glasses, about 10 wt. % of $NH_4\ HF_2$ was added into the batch, and these batches were melted in a gold crucible at 800°C for 1 h in a glovebox filled with N_2 to avoid oxidation [285]. The molten glasses obtained were quenched via one of three methods depending on their glass-forming ability. The oxide glasses were poured into a stainless-steel mold (13 mm in diameter and 10 mm in thickness) and cooled in air. The fluoroindate glasses were poured into a brass mold (12 mm in diameter and 12 mm in thickness), heated near to their glass-transition temperature and annealed in N_2. The fluorozirconate and fluorozincate glasses were quenched by being pressed between two stainless-steel plates.

Glass samples were annealed and then cut and ground into a shape of $5 \times 5 \times 1.5\ mm^3$, and the surfaces were polished with a CeO_2 slurry. The fluorescence spectra were measured by using a fluorescence spectrophotometer

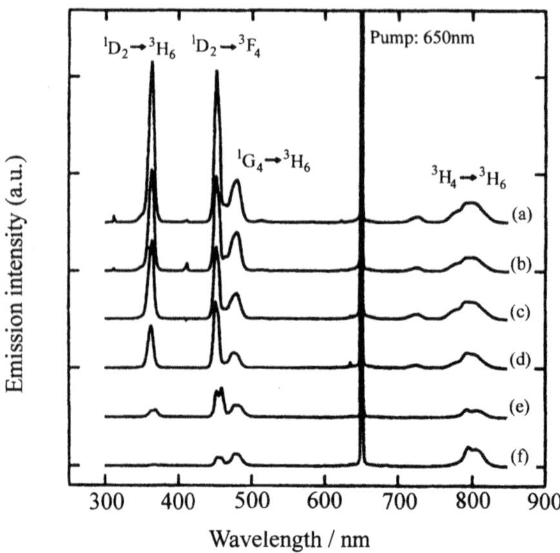

Fig. 6.8. Upconversion emission spectra of Tm^{3+}-doped glasses. The excitation wavelength was 650 nm, and the power was 100 mW. (a) IBZPS-AG, (b) IBZPS-AGYb, (c) ZABSY, (d) ZBL, (e) GBZ, and (f) TBZ. Details of glass composition are listed in Table 6.1

(Hitachi Type 850) with a built-in xenon lamp as the excitation source. The phonon sideband spectra of Eu^{3+} was measured at 12 K using a closed-cycle He refrigerator (Iwatani CRT-006-2000). A DCM dye laser (Spectra-Physics Model 375B) pumped by an Ar ion laser (Coherent Inc. Innova 70) was used as the upconversion excitation source. The setup for the fluorescence measurement has been reported elsewhere [206].

The upconversion fluorescence spectra of Tm^{3+}-doped glasses using the DCM dye laser as a pumping source are shown in Fig. 6.8. The excitation wavelength was selected to be 650 nm, and the excitation power was fixed at 100 mW. The upconversion fluorescence at approximately 360 nm, 450 nm and 480 nm are assigned to the $^lD_2$–$^3H_6$, $^1D_2$–$^3F_4$ and $^1G_4$–$^3H_6$ transitions of Tm^{3+}, respectively. The corresponding energy-level diagram and the proposed upconversion mechanism [286] are shown in Fig. 6.9.

The excitation spectra of the upconversion fluorescence are shown in Fig. 6.10. The intensity of the upconversion fluorescence is plotted as a function of the excitation wavelength, keeping the power at 100 mW.

The phonon sideband spectra were taken for the fluorescence excitation spectra Eu^{3+} around the pure electron transition $^7F_0$–$^5D_0$ and the higher-energy side (Fig. 6.11). Eu^{3+} was adopted to obtain the phonon sideband spectra because of its simple electronic level structure. In other words, the electronic level structure of Tm^{3+} is too complex to observe the phonon sideband spectra. From Fig. 6.11, the phonon energy, $\hbar\omega$, is calculated as the

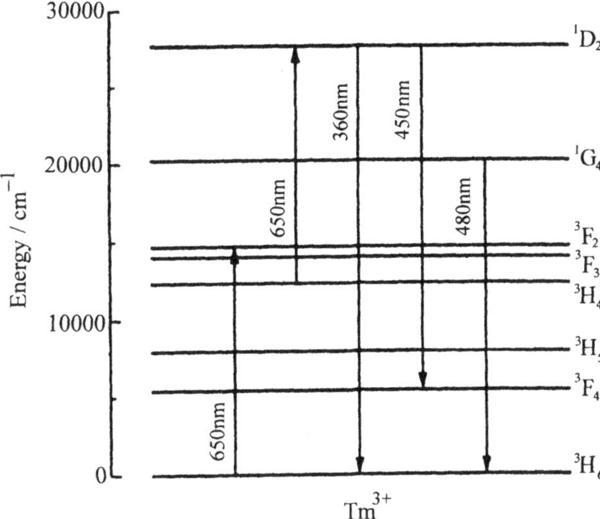

Fig. 6.9. Energy level diagram and the proposed upconversion mechanism of Tm^{3+}

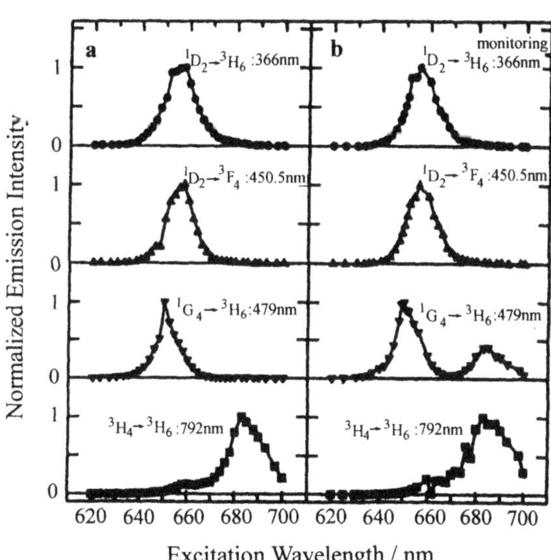

Fig. 6.10a,b. Upconversion fluorescence intensity as a function of the excitation wavelength. The excitation power was held as 100 mW. (**a**) IBZPS-AG, and (**b**) IBZPS-AGYb

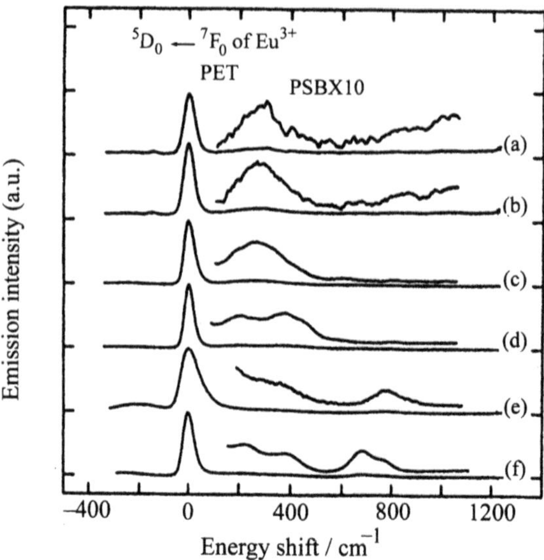

Fig. 6.11. Phonon sideband spectra related to the $^7F_0$–$^5D_0$ transition of Eu^{3+} at 12 K by monitoring the $^5D_0$–$^7F_0$ emission. (a) IBZPS-AG, (b) IBZPS-AGYb, (c) ZABSY, (d) ZBL, (e) GBZ, and (f) TBZ

energy difference between the peak of the pure electronic transition and that of the phonon sideband.

The compositional dependence of the upconversion fluorescence intensity for each emission is shown in Fig. 6.12. As seen in Fig. 6.12, more intense upconversion fluorescence is observed in fluoride glasses than in oxide glasses. For the glasses investigated here, the fluoroindate glass without Yb^{3+} (IBZPS-AG) shows the strongest upconversion fluorescence.

The intensity of fluorescence is dominated by the fluorescence lifetime of the related excited levels. For the case of upconversion fluorescence, the related levels are the upper level of the upconversion fluorescence and the intermediate levels for multistep excitation. The fluorescence lifetime of an excited level is the reciprocal of the sum of the probabilities for spontaneous emission and nonradiative relaxation, and it is described as follows [287]:

$$1/\tau = \sum A_{ij} + \sum W_{\mathrm{NRD}} = \sum A_{ij} + W_{\mathrm{MP}} + W_{\mathrm{ET}} + \dots , \qquad (6.2)$$

where A_{ij} is the spontaneous emission probability, W_{MP} and W_{ET} are the probabilities of nonradiative relaxation due to multiphonon relaxation and energy transfer to the neighbor ions, respectively. In this study, the concentration of rare-earth ions (0.1 at. % as Tm^{3+}) is low enough to ignore W_{ET}, so (6.2) can be rewritten as

$$1/\tau = \sum A_{ij} + W_{\mathrm{MP}} \, . \qquad (6.3)$$

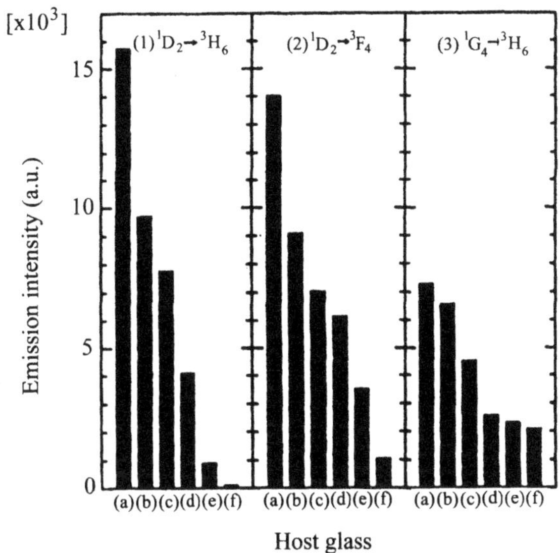

Fig. 6.12. Dependence of the upconversion fluorescence intensity on the host glass composition. The excitation conditions are the same as those of Fig. 6.8. (1) the ~360-nm UV upconversion, $^1D_2$–3H6 transition; (2) the ~450-nm blue upconversion, $^1D_2$–$^3F_4$ transition; and (3) the ~480-nm blue upconversion, $^1G_4$–$^3H_6$ transition. (a) IBZPS-AG, (b) IBZPS-AGYb, (c) ZABSY, (d) ZBL. (e) GBZ, and (f) TBZ

The multiphonon relaxation rate at temperature T(K), $W_{\rm MP}(T)$, is expressed as follows [288]:

$$W_{\rm MP}(T) = W_{\rm MP}(0)(n+1)^p \ , \tag{6.4}$$

$$W_{\rm MP}(0) = W_0(0)\exp(-\alpha\Delta E/\hbar\omega) \ , \tag{6.5}$$

$$\alpha = ln(p/g) - 1 \ . \tag{6.6}$$

Here, n is the statistical average number of vibrational quantum numbers, that is,

$$n = [\exp(\hbar\omega/kT) - 1]^{-1} \tag{6.7}$$

The other terms are defined as follows: p is the number of phonons consumed for the relaxation, ΔE is the energy gap to the next lower level, $\hbar\omega$ is the phonon energy of the host, $W_0(0)$ is decay rate at $\Delta E = 0$ and $T = 0$, and g is the electron–phonon coupling strength.

These equations indicate that $W_{\rm MP}(T)$ increases exponentially with increasing $\hbar\omega$, that is, the phonon energy of the host glass. Therefore, the fluorescence lifetime, and thus the fluorescence intensity, decreases with increasing phonon energy. Figure 6.13 shows the relation between the intensity of the upconversion fluorescence and the phonon energy estimated from the phonon sideband shown in Fig. 6.11. It can be seen that the upconversion flu-

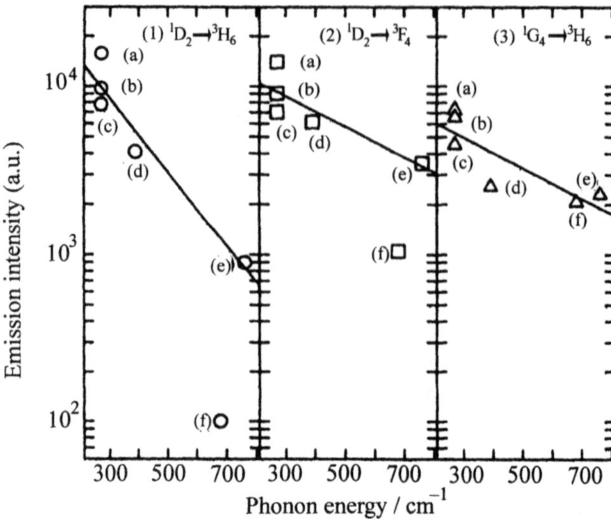

Fig. 6.13. Relation between upconversion fluorescence intensity and phonon energy of the host glass. The excitation conditions are same as those of Fig. 6.8. (1) the ~360-nm UV upconversion, $^1D_2$–$^3H_6$ transition; (2) the ~450-nm blue upconversion, $^1D_2$–$^3F_4$ transition; and (3) the ~480-nm blue upconversion, $^1G_4$–$^3H_6$ transition. (a) IBZPS-AG, (b) IBZPS-AGYb, (c) ZABSY, (d) ZBL, (e) GBZ, and (f) TBZ. The lines are drawn as only a guide to the eye

orescence intensity decreases with increasing of the phonon energy, although there are some exceptions for the tellurite and the germanate glasses.

Although tellurite glass shows approximate intensity dependence for the ~480-nm emission, assigned to the $^1G_4$–$^3H_6$ transition, the emission intensity of the $^1D_2$–$^3H_6$ (~360 nm) and $^1D_2$–$^3F_4$ (~450 nm) transitions in tellurite glass is extremely weak. This is because the absorption edge for tellurite glass (~480 nm) and the emissions of the $^1D_2$–$^3H_6$ and $^1D_2$–$^3F_4$ transitions overlap. A similar phenomenon of rather weak UV upconversion is observed in germanate glasses because the $^1D_2$–$^3H_6$ band and the absorption edge (~380 nm) overlap. The absorption edge wavelength for the other glasses is short enough not to overlap with the $^1D_2$–$^3H_6$ band.

As seen from Fig. 6.13, the fluorescence intensities of the two fluoroindate glasses are higher than that of the fluorozincate glass; nevertheless, these three glasses have the same phonon energy values. It may safely be assumed that the reasons for this behavior are as follows: the fluorescence lifetime of the intermediate level ($^3H_4$ level)is longer in fluoroindate glasses than in fluorozincate glass; the spontaneous emission probability of UV and blue emission is larger in fluoroindate glasses; and the overlap between ground-state absorption (GSA, corresponding to the $^3H_6$–$^3F_{2,3}$ transition) and excited-state absorption (ESA, corresponding to the $^3H_4$–$^1D_2$ and $^3F_4$–$^1G_4$ transitions) is larger in fluoroindate glasses than in fluorozincate glass because the popu-

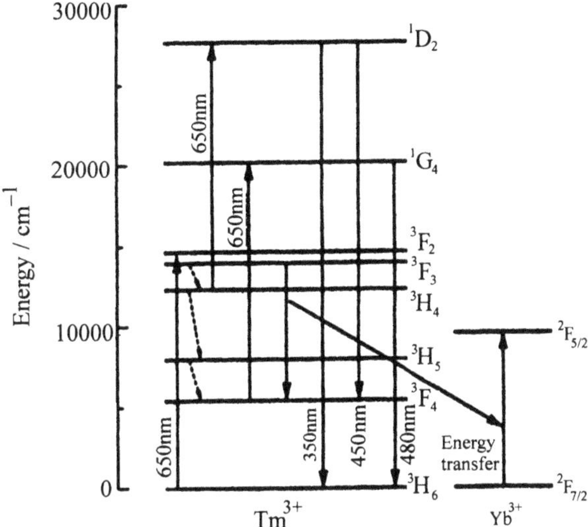

Fig. 6.14. The quenching pathway of Tm^{3+} via the energy transfer from Tm^{3+} to Yb^{3+}. The $^3F_4$ level was sensitized by this energy transfer; therefore, the second excitation peak in the $^1G_4$–$^3H_6$ emission of IBZPS-AGYb glass appears

lation of the upper level of the upconversion emission is determined by the product of probabilities of GSA and ESA. Further investigations to obtain the ESA spectra are in progress.

From a comparison of the fluorescence intensities of the two fluoroindate glasses, co-doped with Yb^{3+} or not, Tm^{3+}-doped (without Yb^{3+}) glass shows more intense upconversion fluorescence. Because of their similar compositions, these two glasses are believed to have the same phonon energy, spontaneous emission probability and wavelength for maximum excitation.

Figure 6.10 shows that there is a second peak in the $^1G_4$–$^3H_6$ emission of Yb^{3+}-codoped glass, identical to the peak excitation wavelength of the $^3H_4$–$^3H_6$ emission, while no $^1G_4$–$^3H_6$ emission from the Tm^{3+}-doped glass was observed at the peak excitation wavelength of the $^3H_4$–$^3H_6$ emission. This is evidence for the energy transfer of Tm^{3+} ($^3F_{2,3}$–$^3F_4$) to Yb^{3+} ($^2F_{7/2}$–$^2F_{5/2}$), as shown in Fig. 6.14.

By this energy-transfer pathway, the population of the $^3F_{2,3}$ level, and hence that of the $^3H_4$ level, is decreased. As a result, the intensity of the upconversion fluorescence is weaker in Yb^{3+}-co-doped glass than in Tm^{3+}-doped glass.

As mentioned above, the upper levels of UV and blue emission are much better populated by the upconversion process in these fluoroindate glasses than in other fluoride or oxide glasses. It has been reported that fluoroindate glasses could be made into single-mode optical fibers which were not damaged at least up to a power density of 4 kW/mm^2 [284]. A blue (450 nm and

480 nm) upconversion laser has been observed using Tm^{3+}-doped fluorozirconate glass optical fiber [208]. Judging from the above, there is a high possibility for the realization of a UV and blue upconversion laser using Tm^{3+}-doped fluoroindate-glass optical fiber.

6.4 Electroluminescence from Semiconductor-Microcrystal-Doped Indium-Tin-Oxide Thin Films

Electroluminescence (EL) is one of the electron-transfer processes which occurs upon the application of an electric field to specific materials. EL has been studied for organic [289] and semiconductor-based materials [290–292]. Among these studies, Colvin et al. [292] reported EL from a heterojunction structure such as indium-tin-oxide/semiconductor poly(paraphenyl vinylene)/layered CdSe microcrystals/Mg electrode. The luminescence changed in colour from red to yellow, depending on the particle size of the CdSe microcrystals. Then, they ascribed the change of band-gap energy of CdSe, which is induced by the quantum size effect, to the colour change.

It is considered that semiconductor-microcrystal-doped conducting thin films also possibly generate luminescence of various wavelengths, which can be changed by selecting the species of semiconductor and its particle size. Further, such thin composite films are prospective because they are easily prepared by the RF-magnetron co-sputtering method, which has been used extensively in our laboratory to make microcrystal-doped glass films with large optical nonlinearity [293–295]. Matsuoka et al. [296] made CdSe-microcrystal-doped indium-tin-oxide film by the sputtering method, from which red-colour luminescence was observed during the application of a dc voltage. The associated experimental facts that there was a threshold voltage for the luminescence and that the luminescence colour was not changed if the applied voltage was changed led them to the preliminary conclusion that the luminescence was related to electron transfer between different energy states. However, their luminescence spectra, which only covered the range from 400 to ~850 nm, limited further discussion.

In this section, an extension of the previous study [296] is made; the same kind of composite film is used, but this time it includes CdSe microcrystals made intentionally larger. Measurement of the luminescence spectrum up to 1000 nm is made in order to further the discussion on the luminescence process.

CdSe-microcrystal-doped ITO (indium tin oxide) thin films were prepared by the RF-magnetron sputtering method. A CdSe (purity: 99.99%) pellet of 10 mm in diameter and 5-mm thick was mounted on an ITO plate (Sn: 5 wt. %; purity: 99.99%) of 90 mm in diameter and 5-mm thick to prepare a composite target [297]. The surface area ratio of the CdSe pellet to the ITO plate was 1.6%. The sputtering power was 200 W, and the substrate

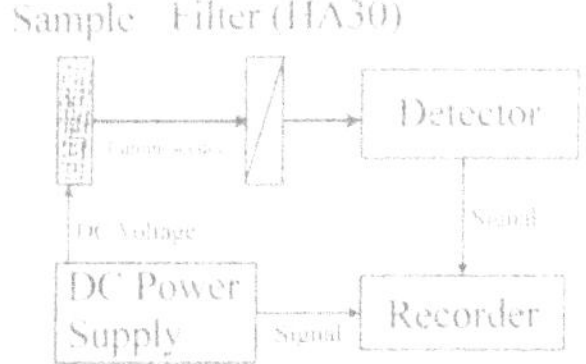

Fig. 6.15. Schematic of the setup used in the luminescence relaxation measurement

temperature was 200°C. The sputtering gas used was a high-purity argon gas (purity: ≥99.99%), and the gas pressure was set to 5.0×10^{-1} pa. The distance between electrodes was 50 mm. The adopted substrate was SiO_2 glass (Asahi Glass Corporation), and the sputtering time was 1 h.

The prepared thin films were examined with an X-ray diffraction (XRD) technique using Ni-filtered CuK_α radiation in order to characterize the included microcrystals. The measurement was conducted from $2\theta = 10—70°$ at room temperature. The chemical composition of the CdSe in the films was determined by X-ray photoelectron spectroscopy (XPS) using MgK_α radiation as an X-ray source. Xe sputtering was carried out for 30 s prior to the measurement to remove any surface contamination. The binding energy of $Cd3d_{5/2}$ and Se3d electrons, normalized to the Cls peak, was measured. The measurement of optical absorption spectra was performed from 200 to 2000 nm using a spectrophotometer (Jasco V-570) at room temperature. The luminescence spectra were measured from 550 to 950 nm at room temperature. For the luminescence measurement, two electrodes with a separation of 10 mm were attached to the film with painted silver paste; a dc voltage was applied across these two electrodes. The luminescence relaxation was measured using the system schematically illustrated in Fig. 6.15, with and without an HA30 filter (Hoya Company, Ltd.).

The XRD pattern of an as-deposited thin film prepared with a substrate temperature of 200°C, a CdSe/ITO surface area ratio of 1.6%, and a sputtering power of 200 W is shown in Fig. 6.16. The relatively broad diffraction peaks at about $2\theta = 26$ and 28° indicated by open circles could be assigned to CdSe with a zincblende-type structure. The other sharp diffraction peaks were assigned to ITO. The average particle size of microcrystals calculated using Sherrer's equation was 9 nm.

Figure 6.17a and b show the XPS spectra of $Cd3d_{5/2}$ and Se3d for the same film as that shown in Fig. 6.16. The peak position of $Cd3d_{5/2}$ corresponds to Cd in CdSe, and peaks corresponding to metallic Cd, Cd in CdO or in other oxidation states were not observed. The Se3d peak position also corresponds with Se in CdSe, and no peaks for metallic Se or Se in SeO_2 or in other oxidation states were observed.

Figure 6.18 shows the optical absorption spectra of the composite film and the pure ITO thin film prepared by the same sputtering condition. The absorption at wavelengths longer than 1000 nm in the composite film is due

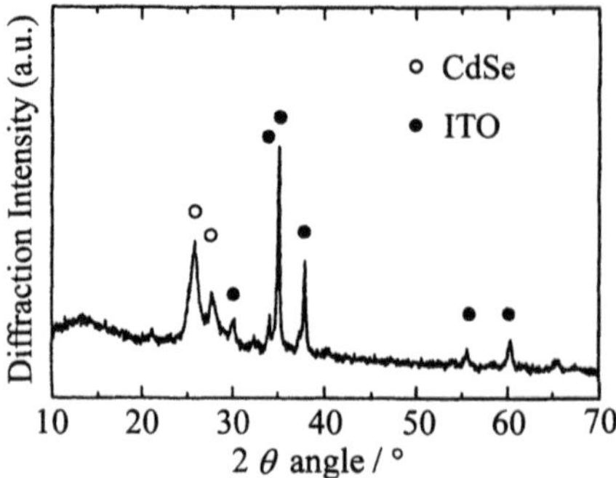

Fig. 6.16. XRD pattern of an as-deposited thin composite film prepared with a substrate temperature of 200°C, a CdSe/ITO (ITO: indium tin oxide) surface area ratio of 1.6%, and a sputtering power of 200 W

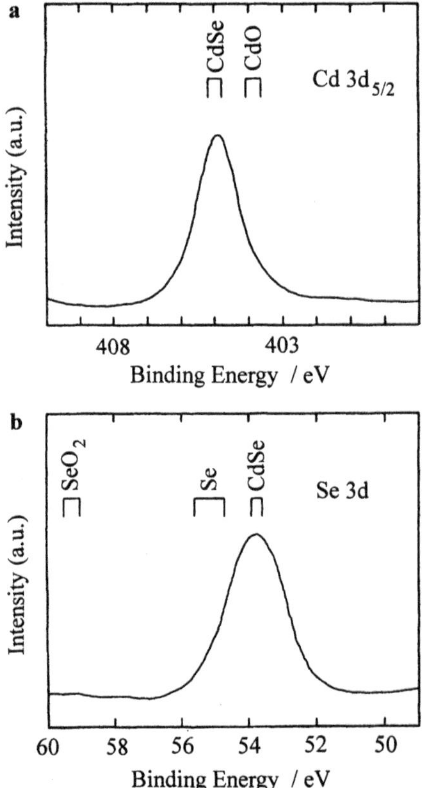

Fig. 6.17. XPS spectra of (**a**) $Cd3d_{5/2}$ and (**b**) Se3d for the CdSe-microcrystal-doped ITO film

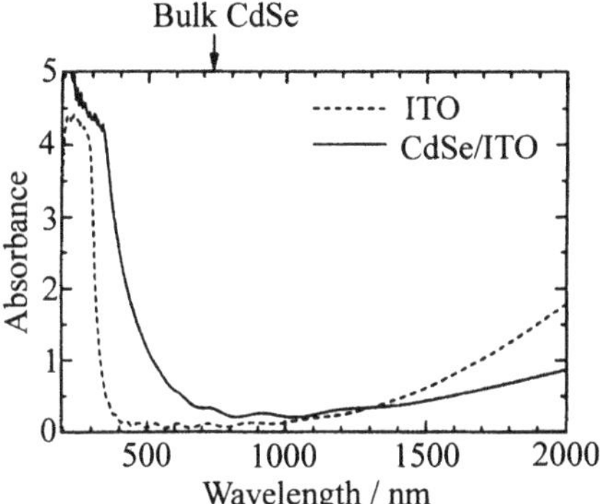

Fig. 6.18. Optical absorption spectra of the CdSe-microcrystal-doped ITO film (*solid line*) and the pure ITO thin film (*dashed line*)

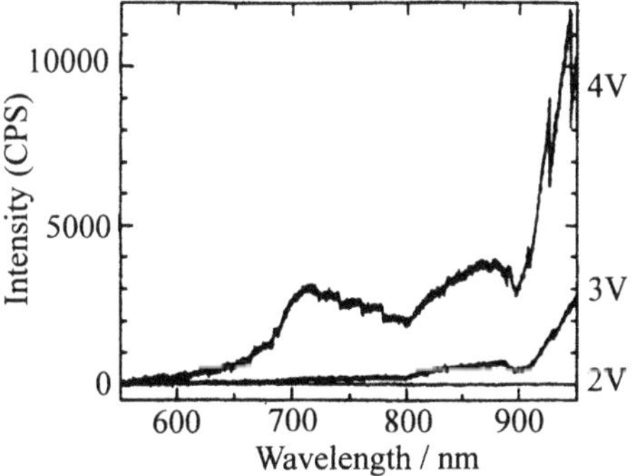

Fig. 6.19. Luminescence spectrum of the film measured under the application of a 2, 3 and 4 V/cm dc voltage

to the plasmon resonance of ITO, which is also observed in the pure ITO film. For the absorption on the short-wavelength side, the absorption edge of the composite film is at a wavelength longer than that of the pure ITO film.

The luminescence spectra of the composite film when a dc voltage of 2, 3 and 4 V/cm was applied are shown in Fig. 6.19. No luminescence was observed when 2 V/cm was applied. When 3 V/cm was applied, a weak luminescence peak appeared at 800–900 nm, but the luminescence was not visible to the naked eye. At an applied voltage of 4 V/cm, a large luminescence peak emerged at 700–750 nm; in addition, the peak at 800–900 nm became larger. The film exhibited a red colour. The peaks at ~710 and 880 nm increased in intensity almost without changing their position as the applied voltage was increased to 10 V/cm. As the applied voltage increased from 0 to 10 V, the electric current increased from 0 to 10 A; however, the resistivity of the composite film was kept almost constant at 1 Ω/cm.

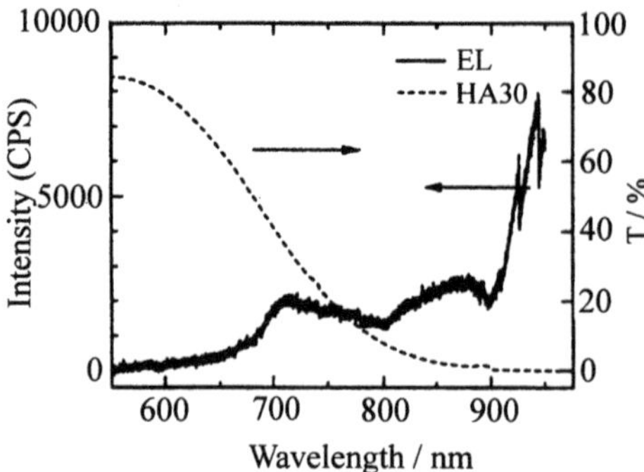

Fig. 6.20. Luminescence spectra of the film measured under the application of a 4-V dc voltage (*solid line*) and the transmittance spectrum of an HA30 filter (*dashed line*)

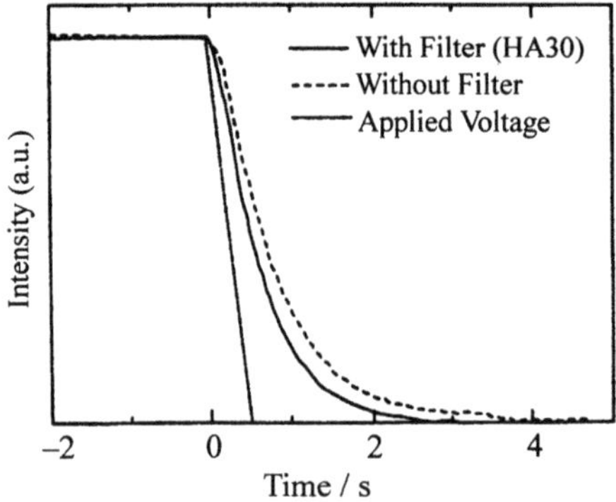

Fig. 6.21. Relaxation spectrum of luminescence under the application of a 4-V dc voltage with (*solid line*) and without (*dashed line*) the HA30 filter. The decay of the voltage is also shown (*dot-dashed line*)

The relaxation or decay of the luminescence was measured with or without using a cut-off filter; the transmission spectrum of the filter is shown in Fig. 6.20, together with the luminescence spectrum obtained at 4 V/cm. It can be seen from Fig. 6.20 that by using the filter the relaxation of the 710-nm peak can be isolated from that of the other peaks above about 800 nm. The results of the luminescence relaxation measured with and without filter are given in Fig. 6.21, in which the decay curve of the dc voltage after turning it off is also shown. It is noted that the relaxation of the luminescence peak at 710 nm measured with the filter was faster than that of whole luminescence measured without the filter, suggesting an origin for the former peak different from that of the others.

From the XRD measurement result shown in Fig. 6.16, it was found that no other crystalline species than CdSe and ITO are contained in the present composite film. On the basis of XPS results shown in Fig. 6.17, it was found

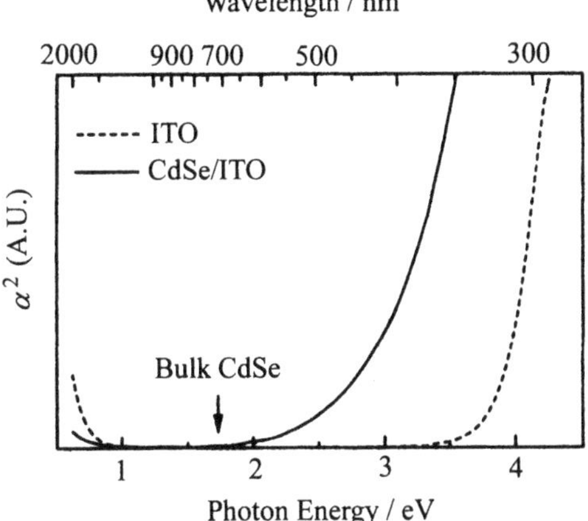

Fig. 6.22. Plots of α^2 versus the photon energy of the CdSe-microsrystal-doped ITO film (*solid line*) and the pure ITO thin film (*dashed line*) calculated using Fig. 6.18

that almost all Cd atoms are combined with Se atoms, and vice versa, as any other chemical state of Cd and Se other than that in the CdSe compound was not detected. The broadness of the XRD peak assigned to CdSe implies that the CdSe crystal size precipitated in the ITO film is as small as ~9 nm; however, the crystal size is a little larger than that in the previously prepared ITO film (~3 nm). Thus, the composite film prepared in the present work is a CdSe-microcrystal-doped ITO film in which the CdSe microcrystals are larger than those in the film previously prepared.

The absorption edge wavelength of the composite film was longer than that of pure ITO film, as can be seen in Fig. 6.18, which means that the absorption edge of the composite film corresponds to the absorption edge of the CdSe microcrystal itself. Therefore, it can be said that the absorption edge of the CdSe microcrystal is situated at ~420 nm (obtained from the α^2 versus photon energy plot [298], as shown in Fig. 6.22), or at a wavelength shorter than that of the bulk CdSe (720 nm), which is explainable in terms of the small size of the CdSe microcrystal or the quantum size effect as in the other microcrystal-doped glass films.

The observed luminescence was red in colour, in accordance with that previously reported [293]. The spectrum was a combination of visible luminescence (at 710 nm) and near infrared luminescence (at 880 nm and longer wavelengths). Unfortunately, comparison of the spectrum with the previous one was not possible because the previous one was limited only to ~850 nm or less because of the lower photosensitivity of the detector. However, a faint hump observed around 700 nm in the spectrum shown in [248] might correspond to the peak appearing at 710 nm in the present work.

In an interpretation of the luminescence observed in the CdSe-microcrystal-doped ITO film, several factors should be taken into consideration. In order to approach the question of whether ITO film itself contributes to the luminescence or not, the luminescence spectrum was measured for a pure ITO film under the same measurement conditions and at a dc voltage of 4 V. The pure ITO film exhibited no luminescence in the wavelength range from 550 to 950 nm.

A second probable source of the luminescence is the thermal effect or blackbody radiation, since the film sample is most likely electrically heated during measurements. In fact, the surface temperature of the sample was about 200°C during the luminescence measure- ment. Such a thermal effect can be deduced from the luminescence relaxation measured with and/or without the HA30 filter. Without the filter, the whole luminescence took 4 s to completely relax after the applied voltage was removed. The relaxation of the luminescence in the short-wavelength range (measured with the filter), in which the 710 nm peak is included, was faster than the whole luminescence. From these facts, it is considered that the luminescence at wavelengths longer than 900 nm may have its origin in the thermal effect or blackbody radiation and that the luminescence at 710 nm is EL.

The relaxation of the EL peak at 710 nm, however, is not sufficiently fast. If this luminescence is purely EL, it is expected to stop as soon as the applied dc voltage is turned off; in other words, the relaxation curve measured with the filter should correspond to the decay curve (Fig. 6.21) of the voltage. The slow relaxation of the 710 nm luminescence can be interpreted by considering overlapping of the tail of the slower relaxation component or blackbody radiation occurring in the longer wavelength range.

The spectrum of the blackbody radiation at 200°C, which is the surface temperature of the composite film upon application of 4-V dc voltage, is shown in Fig. 6.23. From Fig. 6.23, it is clearly seen that the blackbody radiation can explain the luminescence at wavelengths longer than ~900 nm.

It is still difficult to conclude that the luminescence peak at ~880 nm has a purely EL origin, as only one filter was used in the present work. However, considering that blackbody radiation gives rise to a monotonous luminescence profile, as shown in Fig. 6.23, and the 880-nm peak grew without changing its position as the applied voltage was increased, as did the 710-nm peak, the 880-nm luminescence is also considered to be EL.

Consequently, it is very probable that in the CdSe-microcrystal-doped ITO film there are two separated EL peaks at 710 and 880 nm overlapping the blackbody radiation. This was not clearly mentioned in the previous paper [296].

In general, the most probable origin of EL is that related to the band gap of the semiconductor. The luminescence wavelength for the present composite film is very close to the band gap of bulk CdSe (720 nm). However, in the composite film, the absorption edge of CdSe is at ~400 nm, far from that of

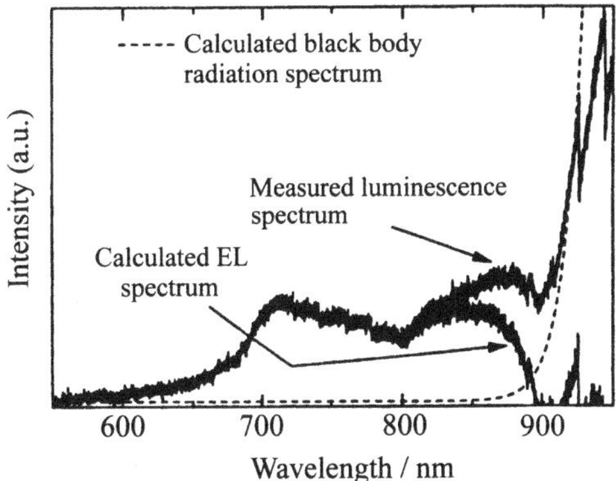

Fig. 6.23. Electroluminescence spectrum calculated by subtracting the blackbody radiation from the luminescence spectrum of the film at a dc voltage of 4 V. The blackbody radiation spectrum at the substrate temperature of 200°C was calculated by using Planck's law

the bulk CdSe; this is caused by the quantum size effect. During the application of voltage, the size of the microcrystals might happen to change because of the increase in the temperature by electric heating. If this were the case, the luminescence wavelength would become 710 nm when applied voltage was increased as the band gap energy changes with the particle size. However, from Fig. 6.19, it can be seen that the peak position of the luminescence did not change when the applied voltage was increased. Further, when the dc voltage was applied to the composition film repeatedly, the peak position of luminescence did not change. Therefore, it is suggested that the luminescence at 710 nm is not explained in terms of the band gap of the CdSe microcrystal. In this regard, the 710-nm peak may be the luminescence associated with the surface-defect energy level of semiconductor microcrystals.

Although the particle size of microcrystals in the present film is different from that in the film of the previous report [296], the luminescence colour is the same. This fact also suggests that the luminescence does not depend on the particle size of the microcrystals.

As to the origin of the peak at 880 nm, the electron transition between the conduction band of CdSe semiconductor and the valence band of the ITO matrix could be taken into consideration. If the luminescence of 880 nm is related with such an electron-transition phenomenon, the peak position of the luminescence should change for different applied voltages, because the conduction band of the microcrystals would be changed due to the quantum size effect. Therefore, the 880-nm peak has to be assigned to another origin. The electron transition associated with the surface defects of semiconductor microcrystals is also tentatively proposed as the origin of the 800-nm luminescence.

6.5 Optical Poling of Dye-Doped Polymers and its Application in Image Storage

In Sects. 2.6 and 2.7, optical poling of glass and dye-doped glass, respectively, were introduced. In this section, a polymer system is presented for all-optical poling, a thermal-crosslinked polyurethane with disperse red 19 pendant groups (DR19) (prepolymer + crosslinker → crosslinked polyurethane). Experimental results show that the photostability of the induced polar orientation of the azodye molecules was improved by the thermosetting polymer matrix. Optical image storage is also experimentally demonstrated in this film with an all-optical poling method. Optical image storage provides a micropatterning of the second-order susceptibility for polymer films which can transfer an infrared reading beam into a visible signal for optical processing. Moreover, all-optical poling of the polymer films is also performed by the coherent superposition of the 810-nm fundamental and the 405-nm second-harmonic light of a femtosecond laser.

6.5.1 Thermally-Assisted Optical Poling of Thermally-Crosslinked Polymers

Azodye-Doped Thermally-Crosslinke Polymers. A value for the second-order nonlinear optical (NLO) coefficient d_{33} as high as 70 pm/V was obtained recently in an azopolymer film by optical poling [143], which is comparable with what can be achieved with a dc electric-field poling technique. Obvious photostimulated relaxation of the induced polar orientation of the azodye molecules, however, was also observed when the film was irradiated with intense 1064-nm fundamental light [143]. This relaxation appears to be the major obstacle for the application of this new poling technique in photonic devices. In the usual electric-field poling, two kinds of polymer systems have been demonstrated to be promising for stabilizing the polar orientation of dye molecules. One is the long-side-chain polymer system with high glass-transition temperatures, in which the NLO moieties are covalently incorporated into the polymer as a pendant group [299]; the other is the crosslinkable polymer system, where the dye molecules are covalently bonded to a crosslinking polymer network by photochemical reaction or by thermal curing [300, 301]. Recently, all-optical poling of azopolyimide films with high glass transition temperature was experimentally investigated, and stable light-induced noncentrosymmetry in the thin film was achieved [147].

The thermally-crosslinked polyurethane consists of two kinds of monomers, as shown in Fig. 6.24. Monomer (a) is a prepolymer containing isocyanate groups and DR19, and monomer (b) is a crosslinker. Crosslinking can be carried out thermally through the chemical reaction between the hydroxyl (OH) groups of the crosslinker and the cyanate (CNO) groups of the prepolymer [302]. The solution of the mixture [3:2 mol of monomers (a):(b)]

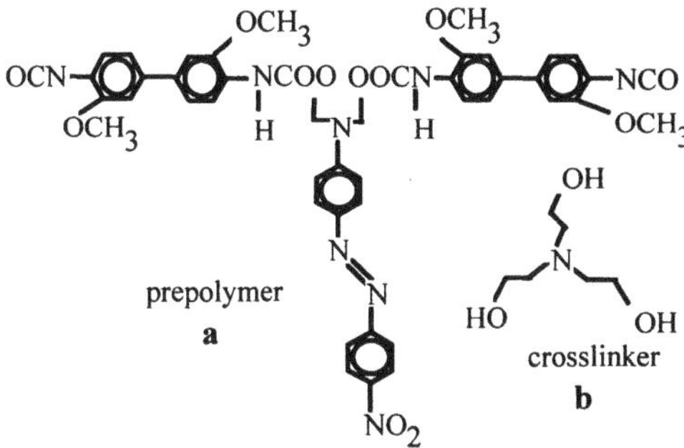

Fig. 6.24. Molecular structures of the thermally crosslinked polyurethane with DR19. Crosslinking of the polyurethane was carried out through thermal chemical reaction between the hydroxyl (OH) groups of the crosslinker and the cyanate (CNO) groups of the prepolymer

was preheated at 80°C for 0.5 h and then was spin coated onto glass substrates. The prepolymer films were dried in a vacuum for 6 h. The thickness and the transmission at 532 nm of the films were measured to be about 1.5 μm and $10^{-1.1}$, respectively.

Thermally-Assisted Optical Poling. An experimental setup similar to that shown in Fig. 2.30 was used. The light source was a Q-switched Nd:YAG laser, which emitted 3.5-ns, 1064-nm and 3-ns, 532-nm laser pulses. The repetition rate could be varied from 1 to 100 Hz. The ω and 2ω light beams (which are referred to here as the seeding beams) were used in the preparation. During the preparation process, the two collinear seeding beams were simultaneously incident upon the sample. The sample was placed in an oven with windows. The oven was controlled with a digital temperature controller. The ω beam passed through the sample, was blocked by two HA30 filters (heat-absorbing filters) placed behind the sample, which resulted in only the passage of the second-harmonic generation (SHG) signal. The light-induced second-order susceptibility of the sample was measured via SHG of the ω beam, which was detected by a photomultiplier tube (PMT), when the 2ω beam was blocked and left only the ω beam incident. The signal delivered from the PMT was observed and averaged by an oscilloscope. In addition, a shutter was set in front of the PMT to avoid possible saturation coming from the intense green seeding beam during seeding. Typically, the pulse energies were about 1 mJ for the infrared ω beam and 1 μJ for the green 2ω beam, and the beam waists ($1/e^2$ of the intensity radius) at the sample were 400 and 350 μm, respectively. In all thermally-assisted optical-poling processes, seeding was started at room temperature and then samples were heated to the poling temperature at a heating rate of 20°C/min.

When experiments were changed from ordinary optical poling into optical image storage, the experimental setup shown in Fig. 6.25 was used. First, the two seeding beams were expanded to 12-mm diameter by two beam ex-

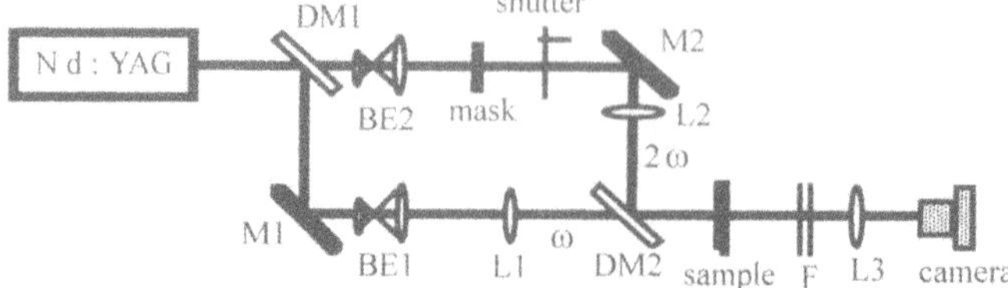

Fig. 6.25. Experimental apparatus for image storage based on all-optical poling. M1: mirror for 1064 nm; M2: mirror for 532 nm; DM1 and DM2: dichroic mirrors for 1064 nm and 532 nm; L1–L3: lenses; BE1 and BE2: beam expanders; F: filters for 1064 nm

panders, and the 2ω beam was modulated by passing it through an image mask. Then, they were introduced into the sample through two lenses 50-cm focal length. The ω beam passed through the sample and was blocked by two HA30 filters placed behind the sample, which resulted in only the passage of the SHG signal. In the seeding process, the two seeding beams were simultaneously introduced at the same spot on the sample. In the reading process, the 2ω beam was blocked by a shutter and the ω beam was used as the reading beam. The image stored in the polymer film was read using the ω beam and recorded by a camera with a macrozoom lens, where the signal was the SHG of the ω beam.

Relaxation Effects of the Light-Induced Polar Orientation of Molecules. Usually two kinds of decay processes exist in all-optical poling, an initial fast decay that occurs within a few minutes after interruption of the preparation process and a slower multiexponential decay. The fast component is attributed to the *cis–trans* isomerization, based on the decay time [146, 303]. The typical decay evolution of the light-induced SHG signal of the prepolymer (urethane) film at room temperature is shown in Fig. 6.26. Measurements of the relaxation processes were carried out in two cases: (a) the film was irradiated throughout by the intense ω light after interruption of the seeding process; and (b) the intensity of the ω light was reduced by 10% (0.1 mJ/pulse) of the light intensity for the first case, and the film was irradiated by the ω light only when the measurements were made. In this way, the photostimulated relaxation effect (in the first case) and the dark relaxation effect (in the second case) were measured. Dark relaxation is mainly determined by the orientational diffusion (free volume) of the azodye molecules inside the matrix, while photostimulated relaxation depends on many other factors, such as the intensity and the repetition rate of the ω light, as well as the orientational diffusion.

Obviously this photostimulated relaxation obstructs the application of the optical-poling technique in photonic devices. It is generally believed that the stability of the light-induced polar orientation of molecules can be improved by reducing the free volume of dye molecules. Unfortunately a decrease in the free volume will make light-induced polar orientation of azodye molecules very

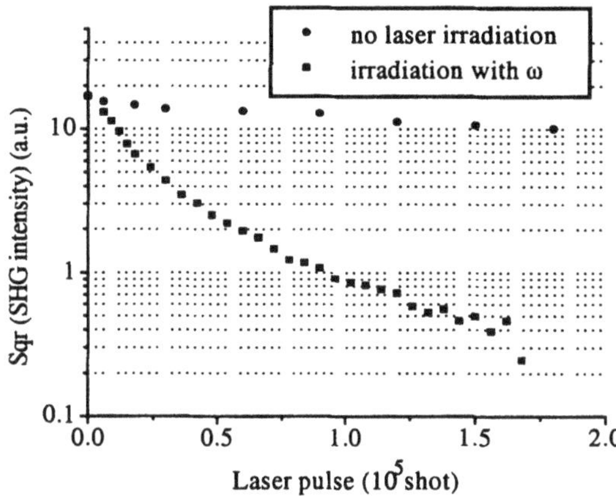

Fig. 6.26. Dark and photostimulated decays of the light-induced SHG signal of the urethane film. For photostimulated-decay measurements, the film was irradiated throughout by the intense ω light; for dark-decay measurements, the intensity of the ω light was reduced by 10% of the light intensity for the first case and the film was irradiated by the ω light only when the measurements were made

difficult. Therefore, a thermally-crosslinked polymer system for all-optical poling is presented in the following.

Thermosetting Enhancement of Photoinduced Molecular Polar Orientation Stability. A larger polar orientation degree of the azodye molecules in the azourethane film can easily be obtained by optical poling because of its larger free volume. Although the molecular orientation stability of this type of film is low, it can be improved by a thermally-crosslinked reaction. Therefore, thermal-assisted optical poling was applied to the thermal-crosslinking polyurethane. Under thermal excitation, the hydroxyl (OH) groups of the crosslinker can react with the cyanate (CNO) groups of the prepolymer to form a three-dimensional network of polyurethane with DR 19 side groups [302]. This three-dimensional network will restrict the rotational motion of the azodye molecules.

In order to investigate the influence of the crosslinking reaction on the stability of the light-induced polar orientation of the azodye molecules, the samples seeded optically at different temperatures were cooled to room temperature, and then the photostimulated decays of the polar orientation were measured. In all cases, the seeding time was set at around 30 min. The optimum temperature for the maximum of the light-induced nonlinearity was found to be about 85°C. For comparison, the results measured on the photostimulated polar orientation decays of samples seeded at 23 and 85°C are shown in Fig. 6.27. As expected, the light-induced SHG signal of the sample seeded at 23°C was unstable and decayed rapidly. For the sample seeded at 85°C, the signal almost kept constant, and no tendency to further decay was found over the period of irradiation with laser shots of 1.7×10^5.

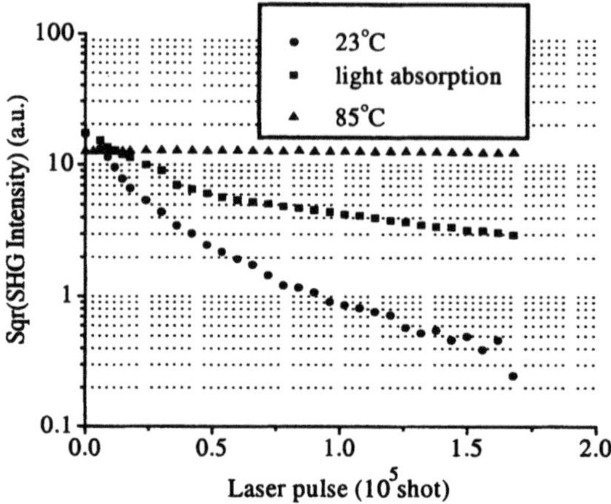

Fig. 6.27. Photostimulated polar orientation decays of the azodye molecules in thermally crosslinked polyurethane films. All measurements were performed at room temperature. Samples were seeded optically at 23 and 85°C and in the case of light absorption

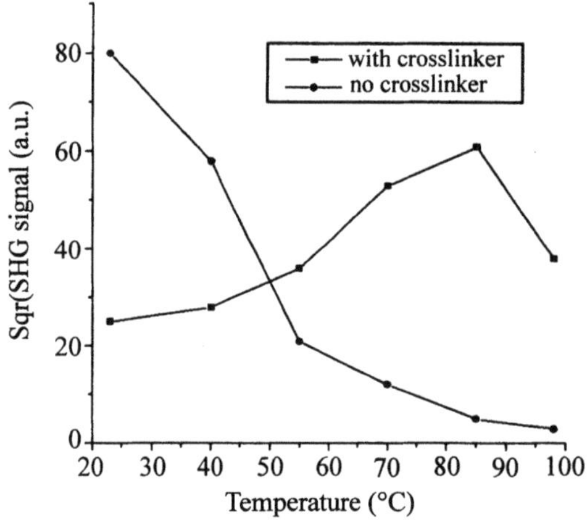

Fig. 6.28. Temperature dependence of light-induced SHG signal for both azourethane films with and without the crosslinker. The film was maintained at different temperatures while the seeding and measurement processes were carried out

The temperature dependence of all-optical poling for azourethane films both with and without the crosslinker was also measured to confirm that the improvement of the polar orientation stability of the films with the crosslinker resulted from the thermally-crosslinked reaction between the prepolymer and the crosslinker. The results are shown in Fig. 6.28. The film was maintained at different temperatures while the seeding and measuring processes were made.

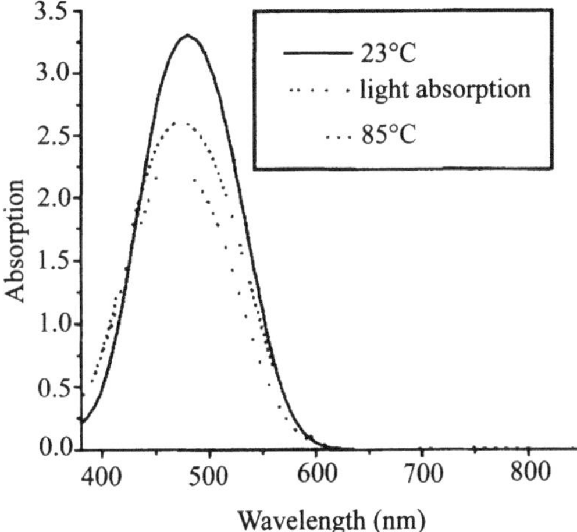

Fig. 6.29. Absorption spectra of thermally crosslinked polyurethane films. Samples were seeded optically at 23°C and 85°C and in the case of light absorption

The measurements were performed after seeding the film and the point at which the signal reached its saturation value. From Fig. 6.28, one can find that when the temperature of the film with the crosslinker is increased the light-induced SHG signal first increases, then decreases at around 96°C. In contrast, the signal for the film without the crosslinker decreases throughout with increasing temperature.

The thermally-crosslinking reaction in the sample can also be achieved by increasing the repetition rate and the pulse energy of the 532-nm seed light, because the sample is heated through light absorption. The seeding process was carried out at room temperature for 90 min. The repetition rate and the pulse energy of the 532-nm seed light were set at 100 Hz and 10 μJ, respectively. The results measured on the decay of the SHG signal in this case are also shown in Fig. 6.27. From Fig. 6.27, one can see that the polar orientation stability of the sample seeded optically in this case is situated between the curves for 23 and 85°C. The further increase in power of the seeding beam caused damage to the sample. Compared with thermally-assisted optical poling, thermally crosslinking through light absorption has some of the advantages of the optical-poling technique, such as the micropatterning of the second-order susceptibility.

The spectra of the polymer films seeded at 23 and 85°C along with that of the polymer film crosslinked thermally through light absorption are shown in Fig. 6.29. Blue-shifts of the absorption peak between the spectra of the samples after and before thermal crosslinking indicate that the improvements of the polar orientation stability are due to the thermally-crosslinking reaction, which results in a rigid three-dimensional polymeric network in the samples [302].

Constructive and destructive processes exist and play roles in optical poling. The degree and stability of the induced polar orientation of molecules are determined by an equilibrium between these processes. For example, molecular orientational diffusion is the main competing process for molecular polar alignment. When the temperature of a sample is increased, the thermosetting reaction is sped up, but a higher thermal randomization energy is also provided for the NLO moieties. Consequently, the induced polar orientation will be maintained by the thermosetting reaction on the one hand, but destroyed by the enhanced molecular orientational diffusion on the other hand. Further, the thermosetting reaction can fix the induced polar orientation, but then also can make optical poling more difficult. Thus, if the thermosetting reaction is fully achieved before poling, it will be a minus factor for the poling process. Hence, the degree and the stability of the light-induced polar orientation depend on many other factors, such as the increased rate of temperature and the final poling temperature, apart from the usual optical-poling conditions.

Measurements of the Light-Induced Second-Order Nonlinear Optical Coefficient. In order to obtain a maximum for the light-induced second-order susceptibility, we also measured the dependence of all-optical poling on different seeding conditions, such as the polarization configuration of the two seeding beams and the intensity ratio between the two seeding beams. It was found that the SHG signal with parallel polarization was larger than that with perpendicular polarization of the two seeding beams. This polarization dependence for all-optical poling can be understood by considering the physical origin of the light-induced second-order susceptibility, which is attributed to the interference of the coherent excitations by the one-photon process at frequency 2ω and the two-photon process at ω [120,304]. Different efficiencies for all-optical poling with different polarization configurations depend on the probabilities of the optical transitions in the different cases. Moreover, when the intensity ratio of the ω beam and the 2ω beam was about 1000, the SHG signal reached a maximum. This is because efficient all-optical poling of the sample requires an optimization of the contrast of the interference fringes. In fact, if the thickness of the film is smaller than the coherent length of sample, all-optical poling depends not only on the polarization configuration and the intensity ratio between the two beams, but also on the relative phase of the two beams [143].

In the optimum seeding case, we measured the induced second-order susceptibility by comparing with d_{11} of quartz ($d_{11} = 0.5$ pm/V) [305]. If the thickness of the nonlinear film is less than its coherence length and the angle of incidence is at the nonlinear Brewster angle, the second-order susceptibility of the film relative to quartz can be obtained [137] using (2.3). The second-order nonlinear optical coefficient d_{33} for the azopolyurethane film seeded at 85°C was estimated to be 12.7 pm/V.

6.5.2 Optical Image Storage Based on All-Optical Poling of Polymer Films

In order to take advantage of the usefullness of the merit of optical poling, its application in optical image storage was also experimentally investigated. In the seeding process, the repetition rate of the laser and the seeding time were set at 80 Hz and 2 min, respectively. The seeding and reading processes were performed at room temperature (23°C), and no special processing before and after storage was required. The image of the mask and the image stored in the film and read using an the infrared beam are shown in Figs. 6.30a and b, respectively. Based on the image size (4 mm $\times$ 11mm) of the mask and the 2ω beam diameter (660 μm) at the sample, the resolution of this image storage was estimated to be better than 60 μm. In fact, if the resolution is limited mainly by the optical wavelength, it can be improved further by eliminating some experimental defects, such as poor spatial distribution of laser beam, irregular sample surface, and distortion of the focused image.

In addition, the image stored in the film can be optically erased by overwriting the test spot with the 2ω seeding beam when its power is increased; the image can also be rewritten onto the test spot by rewriting with the two seeding beams. The advantage of this optical storage based on optical poling is that a visible image can be obtained even when using an infrared readout beam, which makes a photonic device possess two kinds of functions, optical storage and optical frequency doubling. At present, however, the most important problem to overcome is that the sample absorbs the SHG signal within one coherence length, which limits the efficiency of the SHG. Recently, Fiorini et al. [145] presented a new method of all-optical poling to overcome the absorption, in which a transparent polymer material was used. The origin was attributed to the simultaneous three-photon and two-photon excitations on the same electronic level.

a

b

Fig. 6.30. Image stored by all-optical poling. (**a**) image of the mask; (**b**) image stored in the polymer film and read using an infrared beam

6.5.3 All-Optical Poling of Polymer Films Using a Femtosecond Laser

SHG in the polymer films was also encoded by the coherent superposition of 810-nm fundamental and the 405-nm second-harmonic light of a femtosecond laser. The light source was a Ti:sapphire regenerative amplifier laser system, which emitted 200-fs, 810-nm laser pulses at repetition rate of 200 kHz. The average power of the laser was 960 mW. The ω seeding beam was split from the source beam, and passed through a time-delay device and a $\lambda/2$ plate to control the path length and the polarization of the beam, respectively. Another beam separated from the source beam was frequency doubled by a KDP crystal, served as another seeding beam, and is denoted as the 2ω seeding beam here. The two collinear seeding beams were introduced into the film sample through a quartz lens of 10-cm focal length. We achieved time superposition of pulses between the two seeding beams by adjusting the delay device and observing the optical Kerr effect of CS_2. During the SHG preparation, the two seeding beams were introduced simultaneously into the glass sample; during the probe, the 2ω beam was blocked by a shutter and only the ω beam remained incident. The SHG signal of the ω light was detected by a photomultiplier and observed and averaged by an oscilloscope. A 405-nm bandpass filter was placed in front the photomultiplier to allow only the SHG signal to pass through it. In addition, a shutter was set in front of the photomultiplier to avoid possible saturation coming from the intense blue seeding beam during preparation. The beam radius ($1/e^2$ of the intensity radius) at the sample and the pulse's maximum energy were approximately 300 μm and 0.75 μJ for the ω light and 250 μm and 0.01 μJ for the 2ω light, respectively.

The growth and decay processes of the second-order optical suceptibility of the film induced by a femtosecond laser were measured, which are shown in Fig. 6.31. For the preparation process the light-induced second-order optical susceptibility reached a saturation value in 2 min. This rapid growth is attributed to the higher peak power of the femtosecond laser, which increased the probability of the two-photon transition at ω. When the 2ω seeding beam was switched off, a nonexponential decay was observed. The decay rate depended strongly on the intensity of the ω light, indicating that the decay resulted mainly from the photostimulated relaxation by the ω light.

6.6 The Faraday Effect in Glasses to Obtain Magneto-Optical Switches

The Faraday effect is the phenomenon in which the plane of polarization of a light beam transmitting through a material is rotated when the material is placed in a magnetic field. Glasses with a large Faraday effect are promising materials for magneto-optical switches, modulators, nonreciprocal elements in laser gyroscopes, optical circulators, and sensors of magnetic field and electric current [306], because glasses are homogeneous and can be easily fabricated into various forms such as fibers. Therefore, to date, many investigations have been carried out on the Faraday effect in glasses [306–314]. In

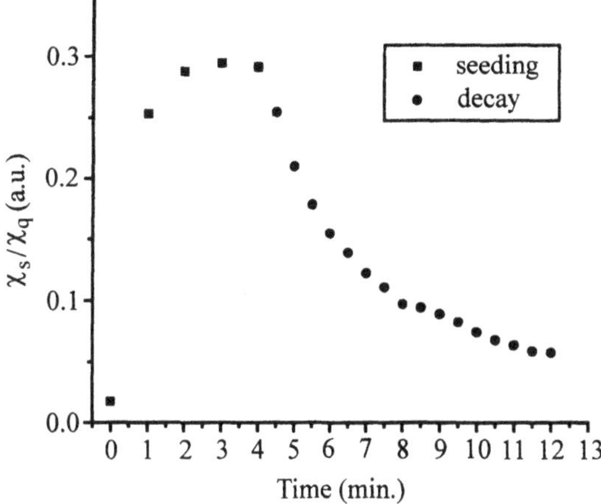

Fig. 6.31. Growth and decay of the second-order optical susceptibility of the film induced using a femtosecond laser

this section, the wavelength dispersions of the Faraday effect in chalcogenide glasses and the influence of glass matrix on the Faraday effect in rare-earth-doped glasses are discussed. Useful guidelines are proposed for the designing of a glass with a large Faraday effect.

6.6.1 Wavelength Dispersions of the Faraday Effect in Chalcogenide Glasses

The Faraday effect of diamagnetic glasses is temperature independent, while the Faraday effect of paramagnetic rare-earth-ion-containing glasses is affected by temperature [306]. Therefore, diamagnetic glasses with a large Faraday effect are expected to be potential materials in applications for optical switches and laser isolators, in which the temperature coefficient of the Verdet constant of glasses should be very small. Borrelli reported the occurrence of the Faraday effect in several oxide glasses in 1964 [307]. Glasses having Te^{4+} as the glass former were observed to have relatively high Verdet constants. The large Verdet constant of the Tl^+-containing glasses was explained to be due to the larger oscillator strengths of the s^2–sp transitions of Tl^+.

One of the chalcogenide glasses, As_2S_3, has been reported to have a large Faraday effect [307]. The value of the Verdet constant of this glass at the wavelength of 700 nm is 0.194 min/Oe/cm, which is about 18 times the value for SiO_2glass [314]. Therefore, chalcogenide glasses are expected to be potentially useful materials for such devices as magneto-optical switches. It is important to study the relationship between the Verdet constant and glass composition in order to develop glass with a large Verdet constant and other useful properties. However, there have been few reports on the wavelength dispersions of the Faraday effect and the correlation between the glass composition of chalcogenide and the Verdet constant. In this section, the wavelength dispersions of the Faraday effect in several chalcogenide glasses are reported, and the correlation between the glass composition and the Verdet constants of these glasses is discussed based on the Becquerel theory [313].

Glass compositions used in this investigation were 20As · 80S ($As_{20}S_{80}$), 20Ge · 20As · 60S ($Ge_{20}As_{20}S_{60}$), 40As · 60S ($As_{40}S_{60}$) and 40As · 57S · 3Se ($As_{40}S_{57}Se_3$) (mol. %). Five-N-grade chemicals, As, S, Ge and Se, were used as raw materials. About 50-g batches were mixed in a glovebox and placed into silica-glass ampules. A vacuum of less than 0.1 Pa was created in the glass ampules,f and the open sides of the glass ampules were then sealed. Melting of the batches was carried out in a rocking electric furnace at 850–1000°C for about 2 h. The glass samples were obtained by quenching the melts to room temperature. The samples were annealed at the glass-transition temperature for 1 h, and then ground with emery paper, and finally polished, using 1 μm alumina aqueous suspensions, to mirror smoothness. The optical properties of the specimens with a thickness of about 0.5 mm were measured. Absorption spectra of the glasses were obtained using a Jasco V-570 spectrophotometer. The wavelength dispersions of the Faraday effect for the glasses were measured using a Jasco K-250 Faraday effect measurement apparatus. The strength of the applied magnetic field was 1.5 T. An SiO_2-glass sample was used as a standard. The Verdet constant of SiO_2 glass at a wavelength of 633 nm was 3.8 rad/m/T, which agrees well with the reported value of 3.5 rad/m/T [314]. All measurements were carried out at room temperature.

Figure 6.32 shows the absorption spectra of the chalcogenide glasses. The glasses are transparent in the long wavelength region of the absorption edge. The absorption edge, λ^*, was defined as the crossing point of the two dotted lines indicated for each spectrum in Fig. 6.32. The values of λ^* for $As_{20}S_{80}$, $Ge_{20}As_{20}S_{60}$, $As_{40}S_{60}$ and $As_{40}S_{57}Se_3$ were 463, 529, 569 and 591 nm, respectively. The absorption edge of the glasses gradually increased in the following order: $\lambda^*(As_{20}S_{80}) < \lambda^*(Ge_{20}\ As_{20}S_{60}) < \lambda^*(As_{40}S_{60}) < \lambda^*(As_{40}S_{57}Se_3)$.

Figure 6.33 shows the wavelength dependence of the Faraday effect of the glasses. The Verdet constant is the rotation angle in minutes divided by the product of the applied magnetic field in oersteds and the specimen thickness in centimeters. The Verdet constant of the glasses is positive at wavelengths longer than λ^*. The values of the Verdet constants of the glasses increased in the following order: $As_{20}S_{80} < Ge_{20}As_{20}S_{60} < As_{40}S_{60} < As_{40}S_{57}Se_3$; this agrees well with the order of increase for the absorption edge.

According to Becquerel, the Verdet constant of a diamagnetic material, V, can be expressed as a function of the vibration number of light, ν, and the dispersion of the refractive index of the material, $\mathrm{d}n/\mathrm{d}\nu$ [313],

$$V = [g\nu/(2mc^2)](\mathrm{d}n/\mathrm{d}\nu)\ , \tag{6.8}$$

where g is the Lande splitting factor, m is the mass of an electron, c is the velocity of light, and n is the refractive index.

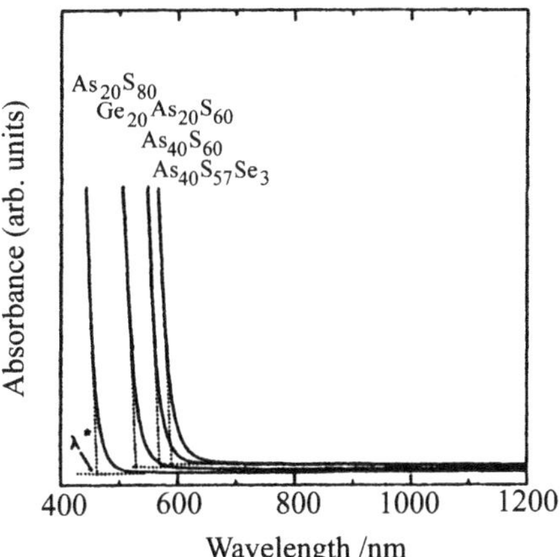

Fig. 6.32. Absorption spectra of the chalcogenide glasses. *Dotted lines* give absorbtion edge, λ^*

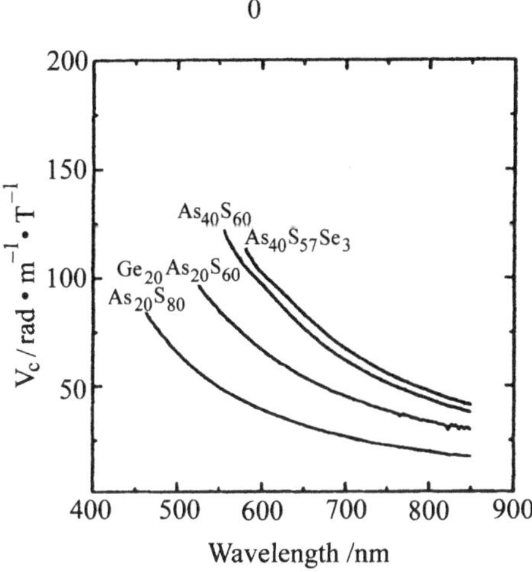

Fig. 6.33. Wavelength dispersions of the Faraday effect in the chalcogenide glasses

Equation (6.8) can be rewritten as

$$V = [-g\lambda/(2mc^2)](\mathrm{d}n/\mathrm{d}\nu) \tag{6.9}$$

using the wavelength, λ.

According to the single-oscillator Drude-Voigt equation [315], the refractive index is related to the frequency ω of light as follows:

$$n^2 - 1 = (4\pi e^2/m)[Nf/(\omega_0^2 - \omega^2)] \, , \tag{6.10}$$

where e is the electron charge, N is the number of molecules in a unit volume, f is the average oscillator strength, and ω_0 is the average resonance frequency.

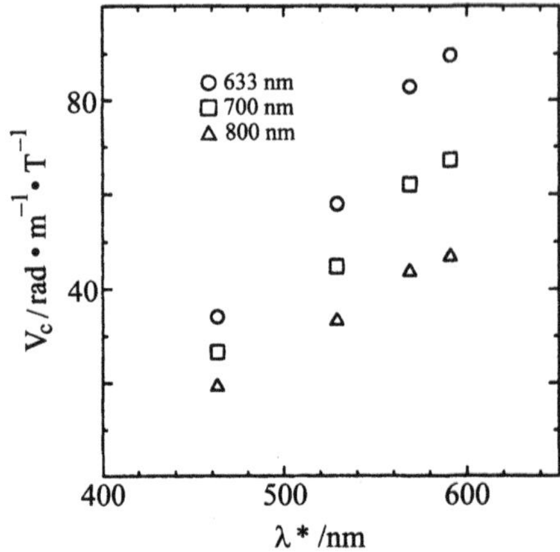

Fig. 6.34. Relationship between the Verdet constants at 633, 700 and 800 nm and the absorption edge of the chalcogenide glasses

Equation (6.10) can be rewritten in a more convenient form as

$$n^2 - 1 = (e^2 N f \lambda_0^2)/(\pi m c^2) \cdot [1 - (\lambda_0/\lambda)^2]^{-1} , \tag{6.11}$$

using the relationship of $\omega = 2\pi/\lambda$.

Using (6.9) and (6.11), V can be expressed as

$$\begin{aligned} V = {} & (e^2 N f \lambda_0^2)/(\pi m c^2) \cdot [(\lambda_0^2 \lambda^2) g/(2mc^2)] \\ & \times [1 - (\lambda_0/\lambda)^2]^{-2} \cdot \{1 + [(e^2 N f \lambda_0^2)]/(\pi m c^2) \\ & \times [1 - (\lambda_0/\lambda)^2]^{-1}\}^{-1/2} \end{aligned} \tag{6.12}$$

From (6.11), $n^{*2} - 1 \fallingdotseq (e^2 N f \lambda_0^2)/(\pi m c^2)$ can also be obtained; here, n^* is the refractive index at a wavelength far longer than λ_0.

V can be further simplified to the following equation when $(\lambda_0/\lambda^2 \ll 1$:

$$V = [(n^{*2} - 1)/n^*] \cdot [(\lambda_0^2/\lambda^2) g/(2mc^2)] . \tag{6.13}$$

Equation (6.13) indicates that the Verdet constant of diamagnetic glass is in inverse proportion to λ^2 and increases with increases in both the refractive index n^* and the absorption edge of the glass. The Verdet constant of the glasses was confirmed to be a simple function of λ^{-2} at long wavelengths, using a curve-fitting method, which agrees well with (6.13).

Figure 6.34 shows the correlation between the Verdet constant at several wavelengths and the absorption edge of the glasses. Apparently, the Verdet constant of the glasses increases with increasing λ^*. Usually a large absorption edge of the glass will give rise to a long wavelength of λ_0. Therefore, these results are also consistent with (6.13).

From the viewpoint of practical application, the magneto-optical figure of merit defined as θ/α, where θ is the Faraday rotation angle and α is the

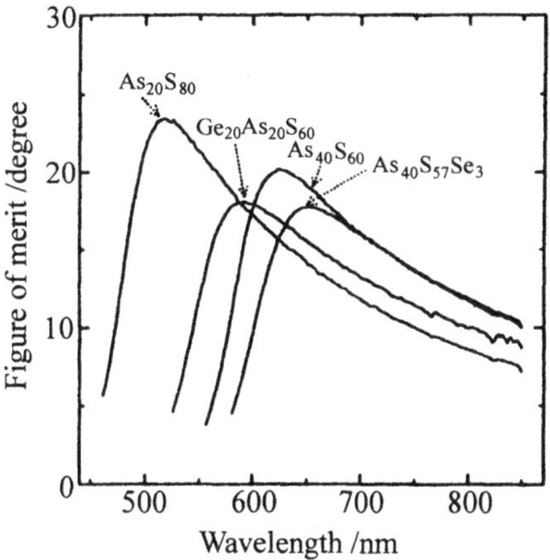

Fig. 6.35. Magnetooptical figure of merit for the chalcogenide glasses

absorbance, is an important factor. Figure 6.35 shows the magneto-optical figure of merit for the chalcogenide glasses, which was determined to be about 5 to 25° at wavelengths from 450 to 850 nm under an applied external magnetic field of 1.5 T. The magneto-optical figure of merit of the glasses increases in the following order for wavelengths longer than 750 nm: $As_{20}S_{80}$ < $Ge_{20}As_{20}S_{60}$ < $As_{40}S_{60}$ < $As_{40}S_{57}Se_3$; this agrees well with the order of the Verdet constants. The magneto-optical figure of merit of the chalcogenide glasses at 633 nm is about 1.5 and 8 times larger than that of the SF6 glass made by Schott Co., Ltd., or that of the 8363 glass made by Corning Inc. [313]. Moreover, the Verdet constant of the chalcogenide glasses is temperature independent [307]. Therefore, these glasses may become potentially useful materials for magneto-optical switches.

6.6.2 Influence of a Glass Matrix on the Faraday Effect in Eu^{2+}-Containing Glasses

Glasses doped with rare-earth ions are promising materials for lasers, optical-fiber amplifiers and spectral hole burning memory [2, 179]. There has been a considerable amount of interest focused on the basics and application of rare-earth-ion-doped glasses. Many researchers have concentrated their attention on glasses doped with trivalent rare-earth ions such as Nd^{3+}, Er^{3+} and Pr^{3+}. However, few studies have been conducted on divalent rare-earth-ion-doped glasses [181]. Perhaps this is mainly because glasses containing divalent rare-earth ions must be prepared under a strong reducing atmosphere.

Glasses containing Eu^{2+} have very interesting properties, such as a large Faraday rotation and photostimulated luminescence [154, 181, 182]. In 1966, Shafer and Suits found that Eu^{2+}-containing borate glasses have a large Verdet constant [181]. In addition, an Eu^{2+}-containing fluoroaluminate glass was found to have a larger Faraday effect than Tb^{3+}-containing glasses with the same cation concentration [182]. The reason is considered to be due to the longer wavelength of electric dipole transition between $4f^{n-1}5d$ and $4f^n$ of Eu^{2+} than that of Tb^{3+}.

To develop an Eu^{2+}-containing glass with a large Faraday effect, it is important to investigate the influence of a glass matrix on the Faraday effect of glass containing Eu^{2+}. The glass matrix may affect the electronic structure of Eu^{2+}, since the energy levels of 5d orbitals are significantly affected by the ligand field around Eu^{2+} ions, resulting in the variance of the Faraday effect in glass containing Eu^{2+}, according to the Van Vleck and Hebb theory [313]. Moreover, the diamagnetic property of a glass matrix may also affect the Faraday effect in Eu^{2+}-containing glass. However, there are currently few reports on the influence of a glass matrix on the Faraday effect in Eu^{2+}-containing glasses.

The wavelength dispersions of the Faraday effect were examined in fluoroaluminate, borate and Ga_2S_3-based glass samples containing 5 cat. % Eu^{2+}. The influence of the glass matrix on the Faraday effect in Eu^{2+}-containing glasses is discussed.

The compositions of glass samples used in the present study were $5EuF_2 \cdot 10YF_3 \cdot 10MgF_2 \cdot 20CaF_2 \cdot 10SrF_2 \cdot 10BaF_2 \cdot 35AlF_3$ (FEu), $5EuO \cdot 15NaO_{1/2} \cdot 80BO_{3/2}$ (OEu) and $5EuS \cdot 25LaS_{3/2} \cdot 20GeS_2 \cdot 50GaS_{3/2}$ (SEu) (mol. %). Detailed methods for preparing the FEu and SEu glasses have been described elsewhere [182, 309]. For the fabrication of an OEu glass sample, Eu_2O_3, Na_2CO_3 and B_2O_3 were used as starting materials. An approximately 10-g batch was melted at 1200°C for 30 min under an ambient atmosphere and then poured onto stainless steel. The obtained glass was smashed and put into a covered glassy carbon crucible. Remelting was performed at 1250°C under an Ar (95 vol. %) $+H_2$ (5 vol. %) atmosphere. The melt was quenched to room temperature to obtain glass. No emission due to the 4f–4f transitions of Eu^{3+} was observed for FEu and OEu samples upon the irradiation by 394-nm UV light. Only emissions due to the 5d–4f transitions of Eu^{2+} were observed. Therefore, Eu ions exist in a divalent state in FEu and OEu samples. The Möessbauer spectrum of SEu samples was measured. Eu ions in the sample were confirmed to be present in their divalent state.

Glasses obtained were cut and polished for the measurement of optical properties. Absorption spectrum measurements were performed using a Jasco V-570 spectrophotometer. The wavelength dispersion of the Faraday effect of these glasses were measured using a Faraday effect measurement apparatus (Jasco K-250). The relative experimental error of the Verdet constant (V_c) was less than 3%, in the wavelength region of 400 to 850 nm. The densities of glasses were measured at room temperature, using Archimedes' principle with CCl_4 as the immersion liquid. The experimental error was estimated to be ±0.001. The concentrations of Eu^{2+} ions per cm^3 were calculated from

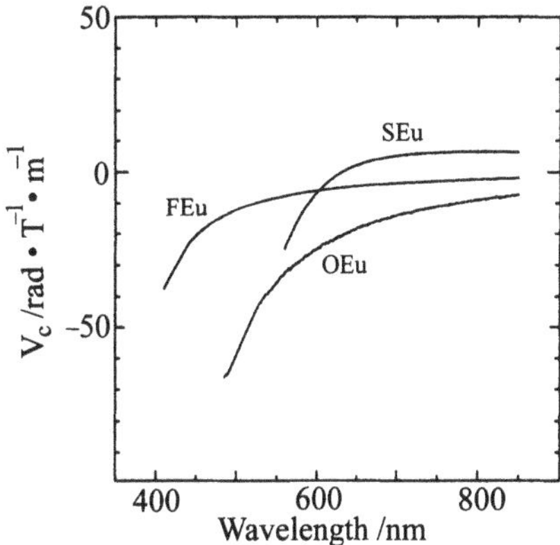

Fig. 6.36. Wavelength dependence of the Faraday effect in glasses containing 5 cat. % Eu^{2+} ions

the glass compositions and densities. All measurements were performed at room temperature.

Figure 6.36 shows the wavelength dependence of the room-temperature Faraday rotation for glasses containing 5 cat. % Eu^{2+}. V_c is determined from the rotation angle, in radians, divided by the product of the applied magnetic field, in tesla, and the specimen thickness, in meters. The V_c of FEu and OEu samples is negative, and the absolute value of V_c decreases with increasing wavelength. On the other hand, the V_c of SEu glass is negative in the short wavelength region, while it becomes positive in wavelength regions longer than 635 nm.

Figure 6.37 shows the absorption spectra of the glass samples. The wavelength of absorption edge, λ^*, is defined as shown in Fig. 6.37 by the crossing point of the two dotted lines for FEu glass. λ^* shifts to a longer wavelength in the following order: FEu < OEu < SEu.

Van Vleck and Hebb derived the following relationship between the paramagnetic Verdet constant, V_c, and the magnetic susceptibility:

$$V_c = (4\pi^2\nu^2 f\chi)/(g\beta ch) \cdot \Sigma C_n/(\nu^2 - \nu_n^2) \,, \tag{6.14}$$

where ν is incident light frequency, f is a constant with the value of 3.44×10^3 min/rad, χ is the magnetic susceptibility, g is the Lande splitting factor, β is the Bohr magneton, c is velocity of light, h is the Planck's constant, ν_n is a transition frequency, C_n is related to the transition probability, and n is an index which extends to all the quantum numbers (except the magnetic quantum numbers) of the excited states.

Equation (6.14) can be rewritten approximately as

$$V_c = (A/T)NgJ(J+1)C_t/(\lambda^2 - \lambda_t^2) \tag{6.15}$$

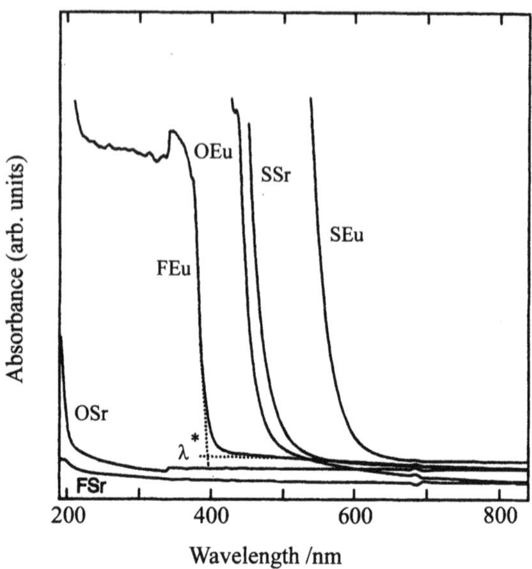

Fig. 6.37. Absorption spectra of Eu^{2+}- and Sr^{2+}-containing glasses

and

$$V_c^{-1} = (T/A(\lambda^2 - \lambda_t^2)/[NgJ(J+1)C_t] \ , \tag{6.16}$$

where A is a negative constant, T is the absolute temperature, N is the number of magnetic ions per unit volume, J is the total angular momentum quantum number of the ground state, C_t is effective transition probability, λ is the wavelength of the incident light, and λ_t is the effective transition wavelength due to the 5d–4f transitions of paramagnetic rare-earth ions. The effective transition wavelength, λ_t, can be calculated from the relationship between V_c^{-1} and λ^2 from (6.16).

Figure 6.38 shows the relationship between V_c^{-1} and λ^2 for glass samples containing 5 cat. % Eu^{2+}. Linear relations were observed between V_c^{-1} and λ^2 for FEu and OEu glasses. The values of λ_t obtained by the least-squares fitting method were 394 nm for FEu and 440 nm for OEu. However, there is no linear relation between V^{-1} and λ^2 for SEu glass, which is in conflict with the Van Vleck and Hebb theory. This contradiction is believed to be caused by the diamagnetic effect of the glass matrix, which has always been previously ignored. The Faraday effect of a glass matrix should be taken into consideration when one use the Van Vleck and Hebb theory is used to analyze the behavior of the Faraday effect in paramagnetic rare-earth-containing glasses.

Glass matrices are usually diamagnetic materials, and they give a positive V_c in the visible wavelength region. The measured V_c of glasses containing Eu^{2+} ions is therefore influenced by both the diamagnetic effect of a glass ma-

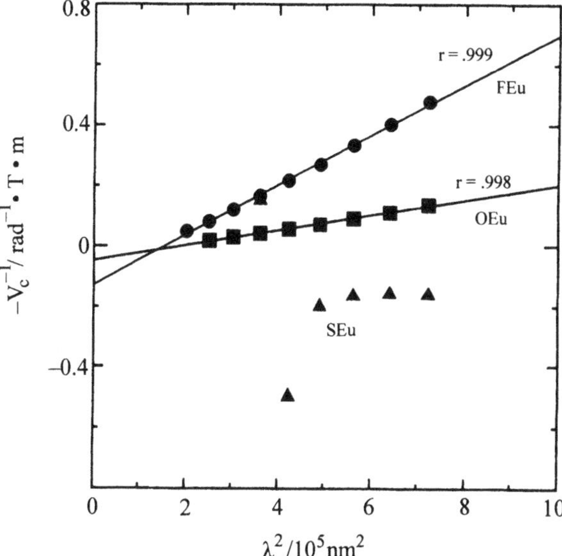

Fig. 6.38. The relationships between V_c^{-1} and λ^2 of the glasses containing 5 cat. %Eu $^{2+}$ ions. The data are fitted to the following linear functions using a least-squares method: $-V_c^{-1} = -1.28 \times 10^{-1} + 8.25 \times 10^{-7}\lambda^2$ for FEu glass and $-V_c^{-1} = -6.66 \times 10^{-2} + 2.48 \times 10^{-7}\lambda^2$ for OEu glass. The correlation coefficients (r) are given

trix and the paramagnetic effect of Eu^{2+} ions. Hence, V_c can be expressed as

$$V_c = V_m + V_{Eu}^* , \tag{6.17}$$

where V_m is the Verdet constant due to the diamagnetic properties of a glass matrix and V_{Eu}^* is the Verdet constant due to the paramagnetism of Eu^{2+} ions. Only V_{Eu}^* obeys the Van Vleck and Hebb theory.

To observe the influence of the diamagnetic effect of glass matrix on the Faraday effect in glasses containing Eu^{2+}, glasses in which Eu^{2+} was substituted by Sr^{2+} were also prepared. Sr^{2+} was chosen as a substitute for Eu^{2+} because the paramagnetic contribution of Sr^{2+} can be neglected. Moreover, the ionic radii of Sr^{2+} and Eu^{2+} are approximately the same, i.e., 1.32 nm for Sr^{2+} and 1.31 nm for Eu^{2+} [316]. As shown in Table 6.2, the concentration of Eu^{2+} and Sr^{2+} per unit volume in the glasses were also approximately the same. Therefore, the network structure of Eu^{2+}-containing glasses can be considered similar, except that the sites occupied by Sr^{2+} in the XSr (X = F, O and S) glasses are occupied by Eu^{2+} in the XEu (X = F, O and S) glasses. Glasses containing 5 cat. % Sr^{2+} therefore can be considered appropriate to describe the diamagnetic effect of the matrix on the Verdet constant of glasses containing 5 cat. % Eu^{2+}.

Table 6.2. Properties and parameters of glasses containing 5 cat.% Eu^{2+}. d: density of the glasses containing 5 cat. % Eu^{2+}; d': density of the glasses containing 5 cat. % Sr^{2+}; λ_t: effective transition wavelength; N: number of Eu^{2+} per unit volume; N':n number of Sr^{2+} per unit volume

Glass sample	d (g/cm^3)	d' (g/cm^3)	λ_t (nm)	N (10^{21}/cm^3)	N' (10^{21}/cm^3)	$N(\lambda^2-\lambda_t^2)^{-1}$ at 550 nm	$N(\lambda^2-\lambda_t^2)^{-1}$ at 600 nm	$N(\lambda^2-\lambda_t^2)^{-1}$ at 700 nm
FEu	3.910	3.752	356	1.12	1.11	6.37×10^{15}	4.80×10^{15}	3.08×10^{15}
OEu	2.765	2.532	428	2.05	2.03	1.72×10^{16}	1.16×10^{16}	0.67×10^{16}
SEu	4.274	4.031	505	0.89	0.87	1.87×10^{16}	8.48×10^{15}	3.79×10^{15}

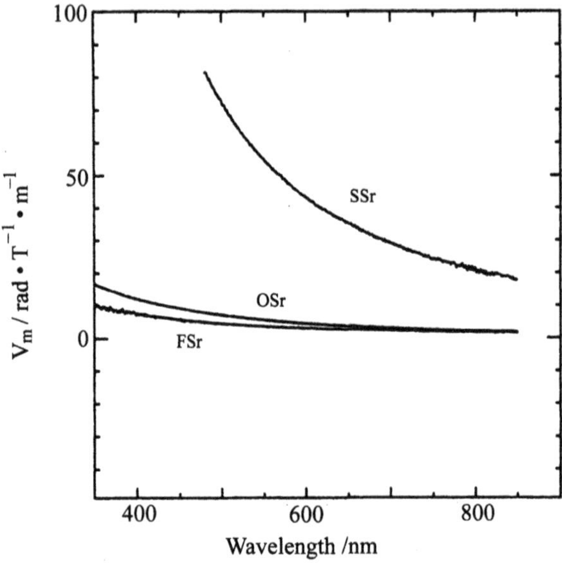

Fig. 6.39. Wavelength dependence of the Faraday effect in glasses containing 5 cat. % Sr^{2+} ions

Figure 6.39 shows the wavelength dependence of the Faraday rotation of glass samples containing 5 cat. % Sr^{2+}. It is clear that all of these glasses exhibit typical diamagnetic characteristics. V_m is positive and decreases with increasing wavelength. The magnitude of V_m increases in the following order: FSr < OSr < SSr.

Figure 6.40 shows the relationship between ${V_{Eu}^*}^{-1}$ and λ^2 in the samples containing 5 cat. % Eu^{2+}. V_{Eu}^* was calculated as $V_c - V_m$. Linear relationships were found between ${V_{Eu}^*}^{-1}$ and λ^2 for all samples. The values of λ_t obtained by the least-squares fitting method were 356 nm for FEu, 428 nm for OEu and 505 nm for SEu. The order of λ_t agrees well with the wavelength of the absorption edge, λ^*, obtained from the absorption spectra, as shown in Fig. 6.41. The effective transition wavelength of Eu^{2+} ions in the fluoride glass is shorter than those in oxide and sulfide glasses. We attribute this difference to the higher energy of the 5d orbital of Eu^{2+} in the fluoride glass

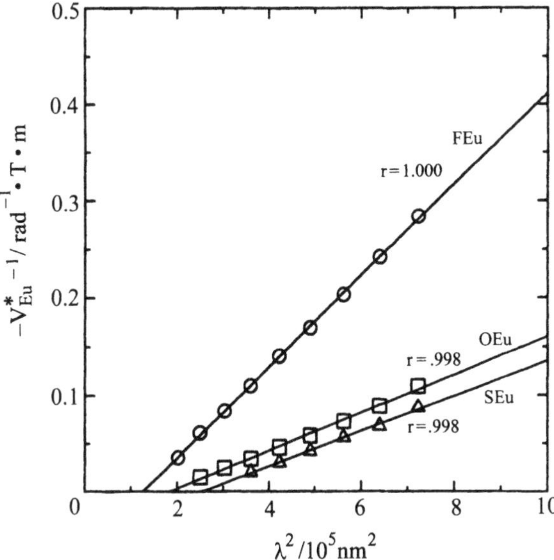

Fig. 6.40. Relationships between $V^{*\ -1}_{Eu}$ and λ^2 for the glasses containing 5 cat. %Eu $^{2+}$ ions. The data were fitted to the following linear functions using a least-squares method: $-V^{*\ -1}_{Eu} = -5.97 \times 10^{-2} + 4.71 \times 10^{-7}\lambda^2$ for FEu glass, $-V^{*\ -1}_{Eu} = 3.59 \times 10^{-2} + 1.96 \times 10^{-6}\lambda^2$ for OEu glass and $-V^{*\ -1}_{Eu} = -4.65 \times 10^{-2} + 1.82 \times 10^{-7}\lambda^2$ for SEu. The correlation coefficients (r) are given

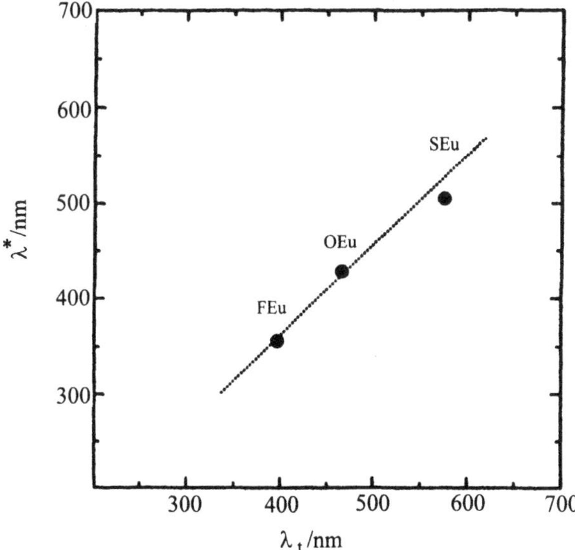

Fig. 6.41. Relation between the wavelength of the absorption edge (λ^*) and the effective transition wavelength (λ_t)

as observed for 5d levels of Ce^{3+} in various crystals [189]. V_c is rewritten as

$$V_c = V_m - A'C_t[N/(\lambda^2 - \lambda_t^2)] , \tag{6.18}$$

where A' is a positive constant.

The parameters $N(\lambda^2 - \lambda_t^2)^{-1}$ and N were calculated and are given in Table 6.2. C_t is independent of the glass composition [154]. Therefore, the borate glass sample containing 5 cat. % Eu^{2+} ions has the largest Verdet constant (absolute value); this is due to the fact that it has the largest N and the largest $N(\lambda^2 - \lambda_t^2)^{-1}$ and that the glass matrix has a relatively small absolute positive Verdet constant. The large N for the borate sample results from the small specific volume of glass-network-forming units, such as BO_3 and BO_4. In contrast, the value of $N(\lambda^2 - \lambda_t^2)^{-1}$ at 550 nm for SEu is the largest due to SEu having the longest λ_t; however, the V_c of SEu is smaller than that of OEu. This is because the glass matrix of SEu glass has a larger positive Verdet constant due to the stronger diamagnetism of the glass matrix.

The results will be useful in the material designing of glass with a large Faraday effect.

6.7 Long-Period Optical Fiber Gratings Fabricated Using a Femtosecond Laser

Fiber Bragg gratings are fiber-type optical devices that operate as Bragg reflection gratings [14,317] and band-rejection filters [318]. They can be used as wavelength division multiplexers [319,320] and dispersion compensators [321] in the telecommunications field and otherwise as temperature and strain sensors [322]. They have a periodic perturbation of the refractive index along the fiber length. Fiber gratings whose grating period is about 100–1000 μm are called long-period fiber gratings (LPFG) [323]. When the guided core mode is propagated in LPFG, the core mode couples to radiation modes of the fiber, which are effectively extinguished by leakage of light away from the fiber. LPFG are band-rejection filters and are often used as gain-flattening filters for Er-doped amplifiers [323]. Since a periodic refractive-index structure can easily be obtained by using the photorefractive effect of some Ge-doped glasses, most LPFG have been fabricated in germanosilicate optical fibers by UV-light irradiation. Irradiation of UV light causes an increase in the refractive index due to the formation of Ge-related glass defects. Therefore, the technique using UV light can be applied only to the Ge-doped fibers with the photorefractive effect. However, LPFG fabricated using UV-light irradiation have a problematic aging characteristic in that the index change relaxes even below 100°C [324]. Moreover, in order to enhance the photosensitivity, additional processes such as H_2 loading at high pressure or doping of photosensitive ions are necessary. Recently, to avoid the above problems, researchers have proposed new techniques for the fabrication of LPFG; these are residual-stress relaxation [325, 326] and direct exposure of the fiber to 10.6-μm CO_2 laser pulses [327, 328]. Since the technique of residual-stress relaxation utilizes the index change caused by local heating of the fibers, resulting from the release of the stress remaining in the core during the drawing process, LPFG can be fabricated even in those fibers which have no UV-active centers such as pure-silica-core fibers. The technique of direct exposure with CO_2 laser pulses also induces an increase in the refractive index through stress relief and/or densification of the fiber, or thermo-diffusion of dopants such as nitrogen, rather than through Ge-related defects.

Recently, there has been a great deal of interest in multiphoton processes. The special feature of multiphoton reactions is the access to a specific position within glass. Use of a one-photon reaction resonant with glass absorption results in the reaction of the entire exposed parts adjacent to the glass surface. However, it should be noted that a multiphoton reaction can induce selective reaction in the vicinity of the focal point of the beam when photon density is sufficiently high. Focused irradiation of femtosecond laser pulses at 800 nm has been found to cause a permanent refractive index increase within various glasses, and optical waveguides can be formed by inducing continuous refractive-index alteration (see Sects. 2.2 and 2.3) [4, 5]. This technique does not require a photosensitizing procedure such as H_2 loading at high pressure or doping of photosensitive ions. Recently, fabrication of LPFG by focused irradiation of infrared femtosecond laser pulses was investigated [275]. A periodic refractive-index structure was induced in the core of a single-mode fiber using femtosecond pulses at 800 nm. The core and clad glasses and a polymer (acrylic resin) coated on the clad have no intrinsic absorption at that wavelength. Most techniques for grating fabrication require polymer removal. The polymer removal process leads to a longer fabrication process and has the possibility of reducing the fiber strength due to scratching of the clad glass. Since the polymer does not absorb light at 800 nm, the possibility of forming the grating without removing the polymer exists. An attempt was made to irradiate the fiber with femtosecond pulses without removing the polymer coating. Although the laser power was weakened to such a degree that alteration of the refractive index of the core did not occur, the resin was ablated. Thus, we could not induce a refractive-index alteration in the core without damaging the resin. It seems that the photochemical reaction in the refractive-index alteration induced by focused irradiation of femtosecond pulses at 800 nm is probably related to the multiphoton process.

In this section, LPFG fabricated using focused irradiation with femtosecond laser pulses at 800 nm. A profile of induced index alteration, power dependence of refractive-index alteration of core and clad glass, and the aging characteristic of LPFG were measured to investigate the thermal decay of the index alteration. The mechanism of index alteration is discussed.

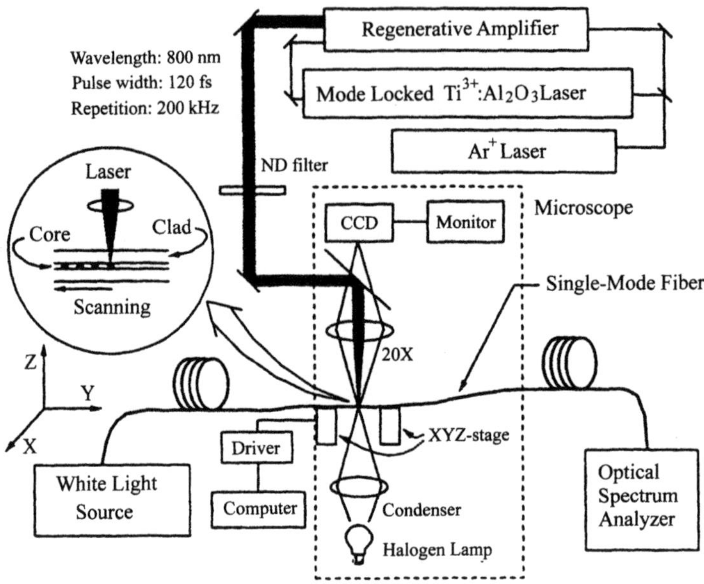

Fig. 6.42. Experimental setup for long-period fiber grating (LPFG) fabrication using focused irradiation with femtosecond laser pulses

The experimental setup for the fabrication of LPFG using focused irradiation with femtosecond pulses at 800 nm is shown in Fig. 6.42. The optical fiber used in this experimental was a non-H_2-loaded standard telecommunications single-mode fiber (NA 0.11, 9.3 ± 0.5 µm mode field diameter, 125 ± 2 µm clad diameter, 1260 ± 40 nm cutoff wavelength). The compositions of the core and clad glasses were Ge-doped silica glass and pure silica glass, respectively. Femtosecond-pulse irradiation was performed after removal of the resin coating. The laser pulses used to induce refractive-index alteration were derived from a regeneratively amplified Ti^{3+}:Al_2O_3 laser pumped by an Ar^+ laser. The pulse width was 120 fs, the wavelength was 800 nm and the repetition rate was 200 kHz. The laser beam was guided into a microscope and focused by a 20× objective (NA 0.46) into the core. The features during focused irradiation of femtosecond pulses were observed through a CCD camera mounted on the microscope. The fiber was fixed on a computer-controlled XYZ-stage and was irradiated point-by-point. An optical spectrum analyzer was used to simultaneously monitor the transmission spectra of the LPFG being fabricated. The laser power was set at 150 mW using an ND filter. The beam size before the objective was 6 mm, and the irradiation time was 10 s for each spot. Assuming the profile of the femtosecond laser beam to be Gaussian, the spot size at the focal point and Rayleigh length were estimated to be 2 µm and 3 µm, respectively. The fluence per pulse was 24 J/cm^2, and each spot was subjected to a dose of 50 MJ/cm^2. Since the total dose exposed here is almost the same as that exposed in a previous study (100 MJ/cm^2) [275], the

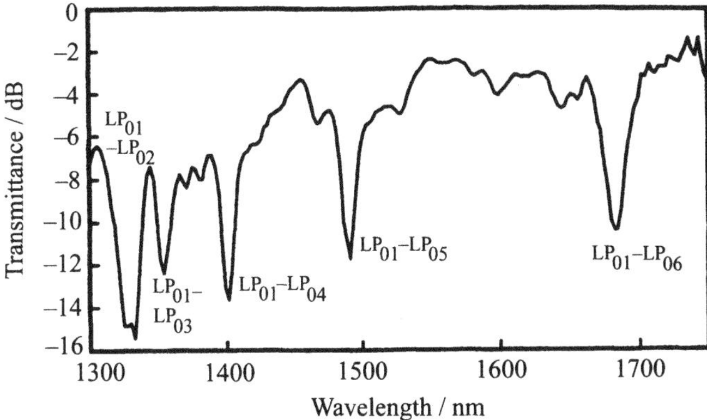

Fig. 6.43. Transmission spectrum of the 29.9-mm LPFG with a grating period of 460μm

value of the index increase can be estimated to be the same value as that in the previous study (0.01).

To measure the refractive-index alteration, we used a refractive-index profiler (York Geometry S14). This profiler can measure the refractive-index profile of the cross-section of the fiber vertical to the+ fiber length and measure the index at the fiber surface. Focused irradiation with femtosecond pulses can induce refractive-index alteration only at the focal point. Since the region of refractive-index alteration caused by focused irradiation with femtosecond pulses is too small to be able to cut the fiber just at that point, scanning irradiation was used to make an irradiated line along the fiber length at a rate of 100 μm/s. The fluence per pulse was the same as that used for grating fabrication.

To investigate the thermal decay of the induced index alteration due to the focused irradiation with femtosecond pulses, the transmission spectrum of the LPFG was measured after continuous heating at various temperatures for 480 min in an electric furnace and subsequent cooling to 20°C.

Figure 6.43 shows the transmission spectrum of the 29.9-mm LPFG with a grating period of 460 μm. The resolution of the measurement is 1 nm. Some large loss peaks, whose full widths at half maximum are about 10–20 nm, can be clearly observed. These peaks are due to couplings from the guided mode to the forward-propagating cladding modes [323]. Coupling modes are also shown in Fig. 6.43. Many small peaks can be also observed and the transmission spectral shape is complicated.

Figure 6.44 shows the index change near the focal point in the fiber after scanning irradiation with femtosecond pulses at 800 nm. The index change is obtained by subtracting the index value before irradiation from that after. Near the focal point, the refractive index increases after focused irradiation with femtosecond pulses. The maximum value of the index change is approx-

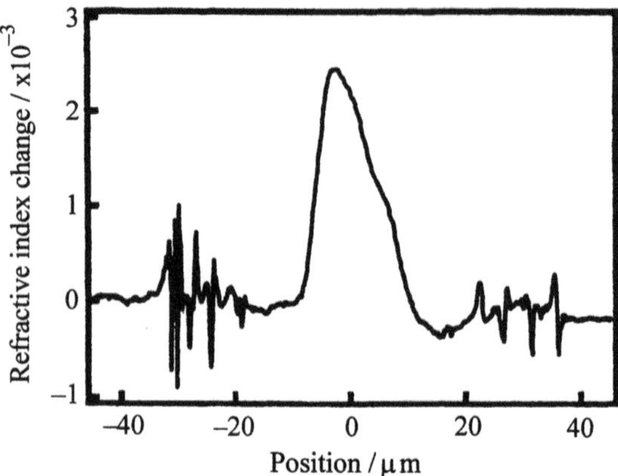

Fig. 6.44. Profile of induced index change using focused irradiation with femtosecond pulses at 800 nm. The index change is obtained by subtracting the index value before irradiation from that after

imately 0.0025, less than the estimated value (0.01). The measured value is the index change of the sample after scanning irradiation, and the estimated value is that after spot irradiation for 10 s. Since the total dose of the scanning irradiation is less than that of spot irradiation, the measured value is less than the estimated value. Since the full width of the index change region is approximately 20 μm, the size of the region of index alteration is almost the same as that of the core region.

We investigated the threshold of the index alteration for Ge-doped SiO_2 glass (core glass) and SiO_2 glass (clad glass). We determined whether index alteration occurred by using a 2000× microscope. The data are plotted as shown in Fig. 6.45a and b for Ge-doped SiO_2 glass and for SiO_2 glass, respectively. The irradiation power was controlled by using an ND filter. Focusing condition and irradiation time were the same as those for grating fabrication. The reaction related to index alteration for Ge-doped SiO_2 glass has a threshold at a dose of 10 MJ/cm^2. The threshold for SiO_2 glass was 13 MJ/cm^2, almost the same as that for Ge-doped SiO_2 glass.

Figure 6.46 shows the temperature dependence of the loss peak wavelength, λ_p, at 1.49 μm in Fig. 6.44 and the transmittance, T_p, at λ_p. This loss peak corresponds to the LP_{01}–LP_{05} coupling. It was found that between 20 and 500°C both values of λ_p and T_p recover to their initial values before heat treatment within errors. This indicates that the index alteration induced by femtosecond laser pulses at 800 nm shows no relaxation between 20 and 500°C and that the fabricated LPFG have a high resistance to thermal decay below 500°C, i.e., a superior aging characteristic is exhibited.

As shown in Fig. 6.43, the transmission spectrum of the LPFG fabricated by focused irradiation with femtosecond pulses is complicated compared to that of LPFG fabricated using UV-light irradiation. The index-alteration

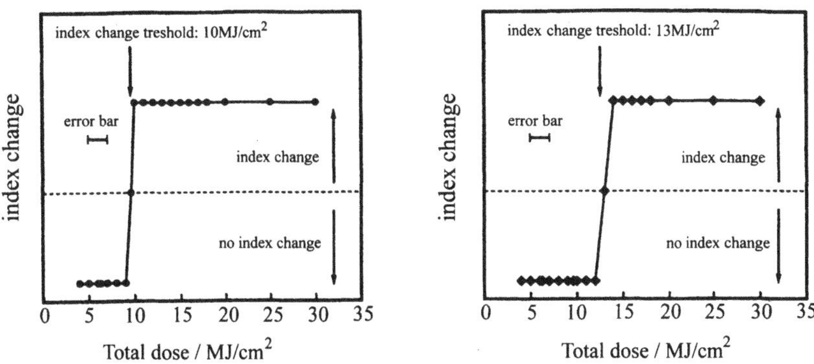

Fig. 6.45a,b. Dependence of index alteration on total incident dose when (**a**) Ge-doped SiO_2 glass and (**b**) $SiO4_2$ glass is focused upon a 20× objective

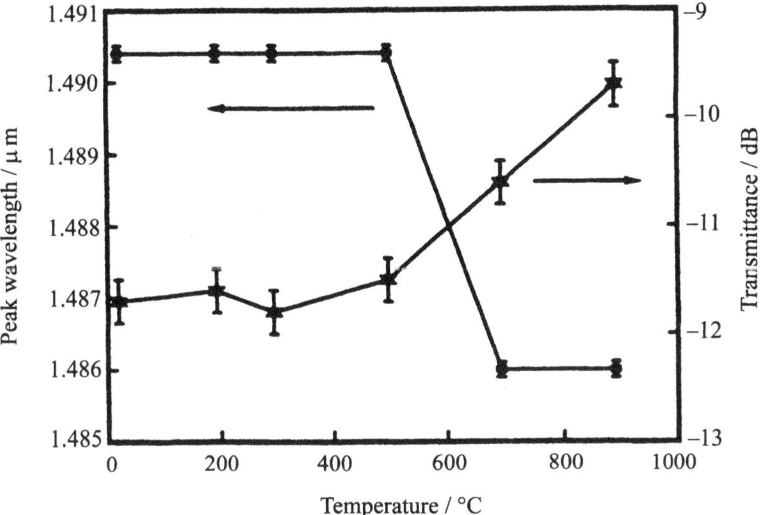

Fig. 6.46. Variations of the loss peak wavelength and the transmittance of the LPFG after heat treatment

threshold for Ge-doped SiO_2 glass is almost the same as that for SiO_2 glass (Fig. 6.45). The compositions of the core and the clad glass are Ge-doped SiO_2 glass and SiO_2 glass, respectively. This means that unless laser pulses are focused only in the core the index of the clad also changes. During fabrication of LPFG by focused irradiation with femtosecond pulses, deviation of the core position from the focal point along the X- or Z-axis in Fig. 6.42 results in an index increase in the clad and an irregularity in the region of index alteration. The irradiation technique in this study is not yet good enough to induce regular index modulation in the fiber. The complexity of the spectral shape may be attributed to the irregularity of the index modulation. The excess loss value is more than 4 dB, which is remarkably large compared with that of LPFG using UV-light irradiation (0.2 dB). The large excess loss may be caused by scattering due to some type of damage formed within the core and the clad and overlapping of the loss peaks due to the irregular refractive-index modulation. In order to reduce the spectral complexity and the large excess loss, it is necessary to produce the regular index modulation in the fiber.

Since the thermal degradation of the fiber Bragg gratings fabricated using UV-light irradiation occurs even at temperatures lower than 100°C [319], annealing of the grating at an elevated temperature for a short time, thereby removing the unstable part of the UV-induced index, is required to obtain thermal stability in the grating performance [329]. In contrast, LPFG fabricated by focused irradiation of femtosecond pulses have a high resistance to thermal decay in spite of no special stabilization. This thermal stability can be achieved because the cause of the index increase induced using focused irradiation with femtosecond pulses is different from that of the UV-induced index increase. In the case of UV-induced gratings in Ge-doped silica glass, photoexcitation of oxygen-vacancy-defect states forms paramagnetic GeE′ centers that contribute to the index change [330]. Because the defects related to GeE′ centers relax even at temperatures below 100°C, the grating performance degrades thermally. Variations of λ_p and T_p after heat treatment above 500°C indicate that the index change induced here relaxes above 500°C. Therefore, it seems that the index increase induced using focused irradiation with femtosecond pulses is not attributed to Ge-related defects, and different factors may be effective. From the observation of AFM, a local densification in glass irradiated using focused irradiation with femtosecond pulses at 800 nm has been found [326]. In addition, since the Ge-doped SiO_2 glass and SiO_2 glass samples have no absorption at 800 nm, the refractive-index alteration should be caused by a multiphoton process. A nonlinear reaction via a multiphoton process and/or conventional heating by multiphoton transition may occur during laser irradiation. According to Bloembergen [331], when the alternating electric field of light is sufficiently high, even in the low-frequency region of light which is not absorbed by solid materials, free electrons caused by a multiphoton process are accelerated by the high electric field and may cause electronic collisions, which leads to Joule resistive heating. In this study, the electric field was estimated to be 3.8×10^8 V/cm, which is high enough to cause acceleration of free electrons and Joule heating. According to Glezer [332], a void is formed in the focal area surrounded by densified material due to energy transfer from hot, high-density electron plasma created by a femtosecond laser pulse to the lattice. It is reasonable to expect that the index change in this study occurs due to a similar thermal effect. At a fluence lower than the level at which a void is created, the index increase probably results from densification of a focal point due to local melting and rapid quenching by laser irradiation. It should be noted that densification has also been observed in the case of UV irradiation. It is known that an increase in the refractive index of SiO_2 glass densified by applying high pressure with heating is stable at temperatures less than those initially applied [333]. Since densification by focused irradiation with femtosecond pulses might result from some thermal effect, it shows a high thermal stability. However, densification by UV-light irradiation results from a structural change due to electron transfer from Ge-related defects, which is not related to a thermal process. Further study is needed to clarify the mechanism causing the index alteration induced using focused irradiation with femtosecond pulses.

LPEG operate on the principle of phase matching between two modes in a fiber, with the peak wavelength λ_p of coupling being given by [323]

$$\lambda_{\mathrm{p}} = (n_{01} - n_{\mathrm{lm}})\Lambda \,, \tag{6.19}$$

where Λ is the grating period and n_{01} and n_{lm} are the effective indices of the LP_{01} and LP_{lm} modes, respectively. The temperature dependence of the peak wavelength, $\mathrm{d}\lambda_{\mathrm{p}}/\mathrm{d}T$, is given by differentiating (6.19) as follows [334]:

$$\mathrm{d}\lambda_{\mathrm{p}}/\mathrm{d}T = (\mathrm{d}\Lambda/\mathrm{d}T)\Delta n + \Lambda(\mathrm{d}\Delta n/\mathrm{d}T) \,, \tag{6.20}$$

where Δn is the difference in effective indices ($\Delta n = n_{01} - n_{\mathrm{lm}}$). The temperature dependence of the grating period, $\mathrm{d}\Lambda/\mathrm{d}T$, and the difference in effective indices (Δn), $\mathrm{d}\Delta n/\mathrm{d}T$, result from the thermal expansion coefficient, α, and the temperature dependence of refractive index of the glass, respectively. In this experiment the glass composition of the core is Ge-doped silica. In previous studies, it was found that focused irradiation with femtosecond pulses at 800 nm induces increases in refractive indices in various glasses [4,5]. Therefore, if the glass composition is selected by considering the thermal expansion coefficient and the temperature dependence of refractive index, it seems that focused irradiation with femtosecond laser pulses is capable of being used to produce any value of $\mathrm{d}\lambda_{\mathrm{p}}/\mathrm{d}T$ as desired.

7. Ultrafast Optical Switches

7.1 Introduction

All-optical switches have attracted much attention because they are key devices for high-speed optical data processing systems and optical communication systems. Nonlinear optical effects induced by ultrashort pulses at low light power levels are required for the realization of such devices. In other words, materials with a large and fast third-order nonlinear optical response have been expected to achieve all-optical switching. In Chap. 1, the third-order nonlinear optical properties of several nonlinear optical materials, such as glasses, glasses doped with metal nanoparticles, and organic materials, were described. In this chapter, two kinds of ultrafast optical switches that are demonstrated with femtosecond laser pulses are introduced: THz optical switching in glasses containing bismuth oxide [335] and ultrafast optical Kerr-shutters using metal-nanoparticle dispersed glasses [336].

7.2 THz Optical Switching in Glasses Containing Bismuth Oxide

Nonresonant-type glasses containing Bi_2O_3 were introduced in Sect. 1.2. These samples were found to have third-order optical susceptibilities, $\chi^{(3)} > 10^{-13}$ esu by third-harmonic generation (THG) measurement [19] and by optical Kerr shutter (OKS) measurement using a nanosecond laser pulse [337], and they were also found to have an ultrafast response by a degenerate four-wave mixing (DFWM) method [19]. In this section, OKS measurements alone and using THz pulse trains in the sub-picosecond time domain are reported.

7.2.1 Preparation of Glasses

A glass composed of $63.3Bi_2O_3 \cdot 32.6B_2O_3 \cdot 4.1SiO_2 \cdot 0.24CeO_2$ (molar ratio) was prepared by a melting method. The concentration of Bi_2O_3 in this glass amounts to (92 wt. %). Reagent-grade Bi_2O_3, SiO_2, B_2O_3 and CeO_2 were used as the raw materials. CeO_2 was used to suppress the precipitation of Bi metal during melting [338]. The mixtures of raw materials were melted in a

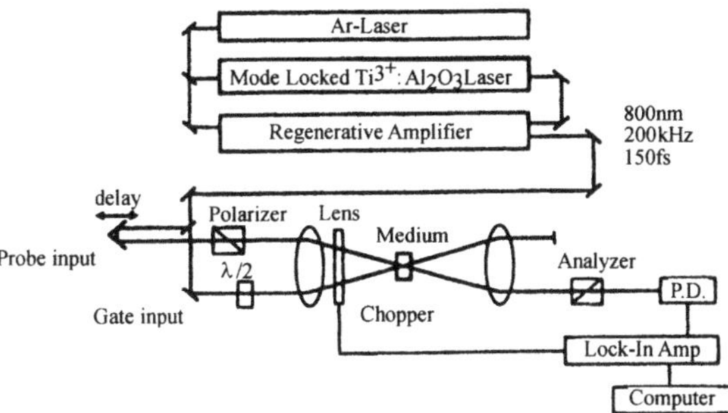

Fig. 7.1. Experimental configuration for optical Kerr shutter (OKS) measurement. PD: photodiode

Pt crucible in a SiC furnace in air at 1150°C for 1 h. The liquid was poured onto a stainless-steel plate and kept at 360°C for 1 h to remove strain in the glass and was cooled at 1°C/min to room temperature. The glass plate obtained was polished to a thickness of 0.7 mm for OKS measurements.

7.2.2 Optical Kerr Shutter Measurements

OKS measurements were performed at a wavelength of 800 nm in the noncollinear configuration, using 150-fs laser pulses derived from a regeneratively amplified Ti^{3+}:Al_2O_3 laser pumped by an Ar^+ laser operating at a 200-kHz repetition rate. The experimental configuration is shown in Fig. 7.1. The output beam from the laser was separated into two beams with a beam splitter. One of the two beams was used as a gate beam, and the other was used as a probe beam. The power ratio of the gate to the probe was 10. The two beams were focused onto the same spot by a lens of 200-mm focal length, leading to a focal diameter and a interaction length of approximately 100 μm and 1 mm, respectively. The sample was set between a polarizer and an analyzer in a cross-Nicol configuration. The polarization of the gate beam was set at $\pi/4$ with respect to that of the probe beam. The gate and probe power densities were around 3 GW/cm^2 and 80 GW/cm^2, respectively. The delay time was defined as τ. $\tau = 0$ was determined by tracing an autocorrelation second-harmonic generation (SHG). The OKS signals were detected using a photodiode interfaced to a lock-in amplifier. The probe beam was delayed with respect to the gate beam to measure the response time of the OKS switching. CS_2 and nitrobenzene poured into a 1-mm-thick quartz cell were used as a reference.

7.2.3 Optical Kerr Shutter Measurements Using 1.5-THz Pulse Trains as the Gate Beam

A light source produced by the combination of a regeneratively amplified Ti^{3+}:Al_2O_3 laser pumped by the second harmonic (SH) light of a Nd^{3+}:YLF

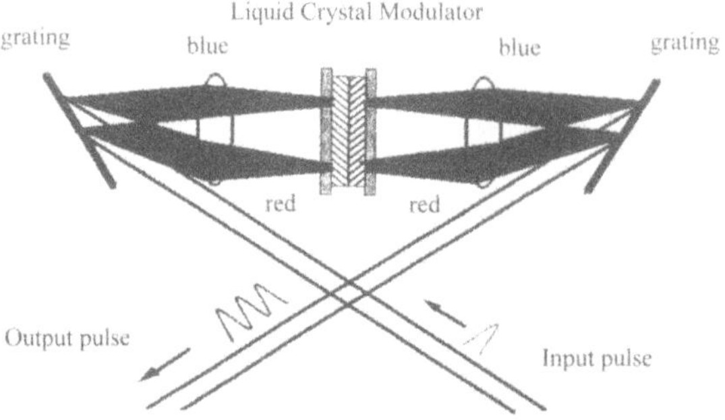

Fig. 7.2. Schematic of the new pulse-shaping apparatus. This apparatus consists of two gratings, two lenses and a single liquid-crystal spatial phase modulator (LC SPM) used as the mask patterns

laser (1.054-μm wavelength; 200-ns duration; 1-kHz repetition rate) operating at a 1-kHz repetition rate and an optical parametric amplifier was prepared. A pulse-shaping apparatus [339, 340] was utilized to generate 1.5-THz pulse trains as the gate beam. The pulse apparatus is shown in Fig. 7.2. This apparatus consisted of two gratings, two lenses and a single liquid-crystal (LC) spatial phase modulator (SPM). OKS measurements were performed using 1.5-THz pulse trains as the gate beam at a wavelength of 633 nm in the noncollinear configuration. The gate and probe power densities were 40 GW/cm^2. The OKS signals were detected using a photodiode interfaced to a boxcar averager. The probe beam was delayed with respect to the gate beam to measure the response time of the OKS switching. CS_2 poured into a 1-mm-thick quartz cell was used as a reference.

7.2.4 Properties of All-Optical Switches

Transparent glass samples were obtained for all compositions. A glass block of $100 \times 50 \times 5$ mm^3 was fabricated. Figure 7.3 shows the transmission spectra of a sample of 0.7-mm thickness and CS_2 poured into a 1-mm-thick quartz cell. There was no measurable absorption in all samples at wavelengths of 800 and 633 nm, where OKS measurements were performed.

In the OKS measurement, the probe transmittance, T, for an optical Kerr shutter is given by

$$T \propto \sin^2(2\theta_B) , \tag{7.1}$$

where θ_B is an angle between the polarization of the gate beams and that of the probe beams. The experimental result for Bi_2O_3 glass is shown in Fig. 7.4. The T obtained by OKS measurement changed according to the polarization dependence between the gate and the probe beams as given by (7.1).

When the gate beam power is sufficiently small, T is given by

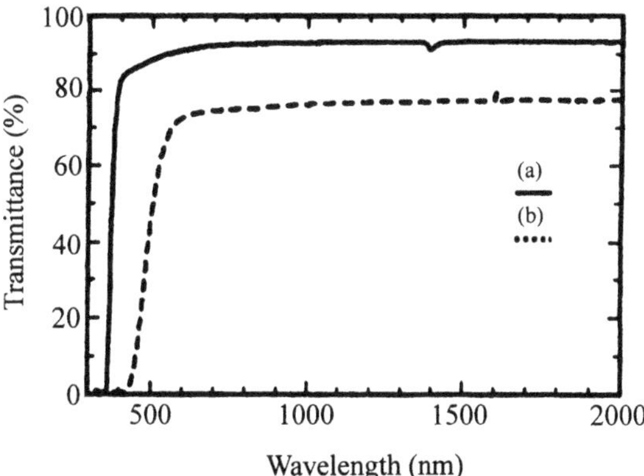

Fig. 7.3. Transmittance spectra of glasses containing Bi_2O_3 and CS_2: CS_2 is poured into a 1-mm-thick quartz cell (*curve a*) and Bi_2O_3 glass with a thickness of 0.7 mm (*curve b*)

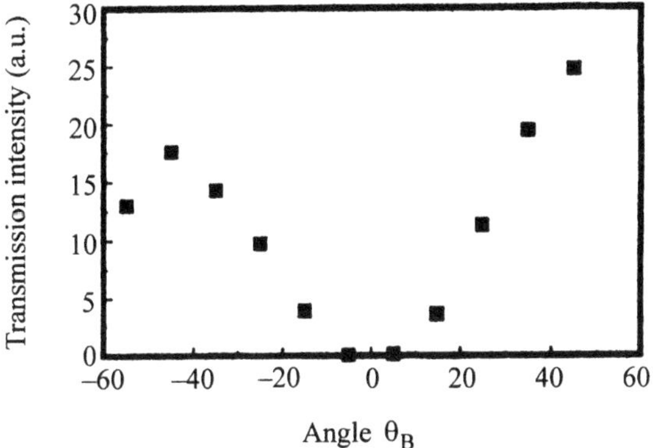

Fig. 7.4. Polarization dependence between the gate and probe beams in Bi_2O_3 glass

$$T \propto n_{2B}[\text{OKS}]^2 I_g^2 L_{\text{eff}}^2 , \tag{7.2}$$

where $n_{2B}[\text{OKS}]$ is the OKS nonlinear refractive index, I_g is the gate power, and L_{eff} is the effective medium length. Figure 7.5 shows the gate power intensity, I_g, dependence of the probe transmittance, T, for the sample and the reference material CS_2 with $\tau = 0$. The T increased in proportion to the square of intensity I_g.

Figure 7.6 shows the decay of the OKS signal in the sample, CS_2, and nitrobenzene with a gate power density of 40 GW/cm^2. Decay components in the reference materials, CS_2 and nitrobenzene, of approximately 1 ps and 30 ps were found, respectively.

For generating THz pulse trains, a pulse-shaping technique [339, 340] using two gratings, two lenses and a single LC SPM was utilized. A grating

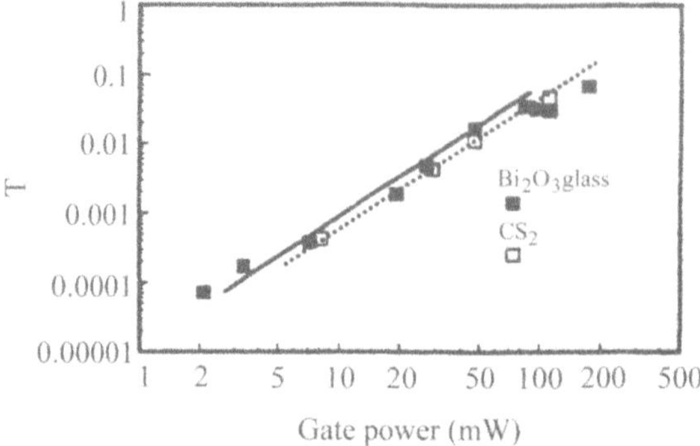

Fig. 7.5. Pump power dependence of the OKS signal intensity in Bi_2O_3 glass and CS_2 at a wavelength of 800 nm with $\tau = 0$. T is proportional to the square of the gate power, I_g, as expected from (7.2). The curves are a fit of (7.2) to the data

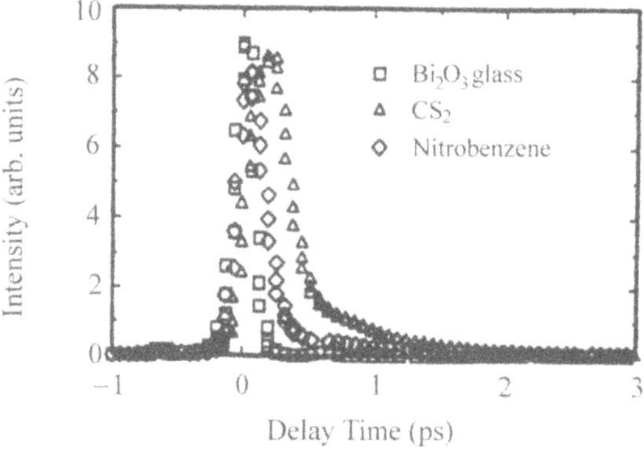

Fig. 7.6. Decay curve of the OKS signal in Bi_2O_3 glass, CS_2 and nitrobenzene

and lens were used to image the spectrum of a pulse onto spatially varying mask patterns that can retard (phase-shift) different frequency components. A subsequent lens and grating were used to combine the spectrally filtered components, producing a "shaped" waveform in the time domain. When a LC SPM is used as a programmable mask pattern, the desired waveform can be entered into a computer, which is used to calculate the necessary mask patterns and fabricate them through its interface with the LC SPM. The new pulse trains were generated from a single pulse through this apparatus. When an interval of the gate pulse was 670 fs (1.5-THz repetition rate), OKS signals in reference material of CS_2 overlapped each other because of the decay components caused by molecular orientation relaxation. Therefore, pulses could not be separated from each other in CS_2, as shown in Fig. 7.7a. However, OKS signals in the sample were completely separated pulses, as shown in Fig. 7.7b. It was found that the sample can immediately switch to the THz high repetition rate.

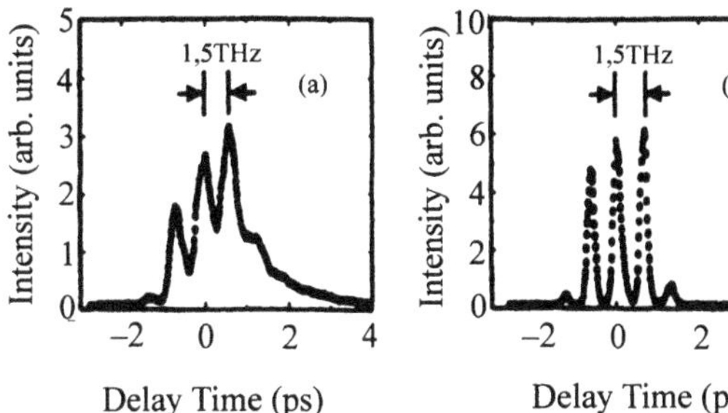

Fig. 7.7. Decay curve of OKS signals in: (**a**) CS_2 and (**b**) Bi_2O_3 glass using 1.5-THz pulse trains as the gate beam

These results of polarization dependence (Fig. 7.4) and the gate power dependence (Fig. 7.5) indicate that the switching operation in the sample was driven by the optical Kerr effect that originated from third-order optical nonlinearity. If the thermal effect was the cause of the switching operation, the probe transmittance, T, would not have such a dependence on θ_B or I_g.

When the probe transmittance of the sample was compared with that of CS_2 at the same gate power (Fig. 7.5), it could be seen that the probe transmittance of the sample was 1.3 times larger than that of CS_2 with $\tau = 0$. From (7.2) the OKS nonlinear refractive index $n_{2B}[\text{OKS}]$ is evaluated by comparing T with the reference materials at the same gate power. As a result we estimate $n_{2B}[\text{OKS}]$ of the sample to be 1.7 times larger than that of CS_2 at a wavelength of 800 nm in the sub-picosecond time domain with $\tau = 0$.

It can be seen that the signal maxima of the sample and CS_2 are different. As the molecular orientation effect was not simultaneous with the 150-fs laser pulse, the maximum of the CS_2 signals was delayed. This is the result of molecular orientation relaxation [37]. In contrast, the OKS signals in the sample existed only during the time the probe beam was overlapped with the gate beam. Therefore, it is assumed that the response time of OKS measurements in the sample was <150 fs.

7.3 Ultrafast Optical Kerr Shutters Using Metallic Nanoparticles Dispersed in Glasses

In Sect. 1.4, the temporal behavior of the nonlinear response of gold nanoparticles embedded in a SiO_2 glass matrix was described; it consists of two response times: the faster one within a few picoseconds, and the slower one over 100 ps. The nonlinear response was explained in terms of the thermalization process between the electron and the lattice temperatures and the thermal diffusion process from a gold nanoparticle to a host matrix. It was considered that the nonlinear response time is on the order of picoseconds. In this section, the femtosecond nonlinear response in the gold nanoparticle system is presented. The OKS method is applied to measure the ultrafast response of the system. The correlation time of the Kerr signal was found to be as short as 240 fs. The ultrafast nonlinear response is discussed, taking account of the generation of the quasi-equilibrated hot electron system that induces the transient index change.

Gold nanoparticles embedded in an SiO_2 glass matrix were prepared by a sputtering method. The SiO_2 and gold layers were constructed alternately on an SiO_2 base glass plate. After an annealing treatment, gold nanoparticles were precipitated and dispersed in the SiO_2 glass matrix. Details have been reported elsewhere [46]. The mean diameter of the particles was 7.6 nm, with a deviation of 2.4 nm. The sample was 480 nm thick and the volume fraction of gold was 0.027. This high volume fraction is a special feature of this method.

In the femtosecond OKS experiment, the output pulse from an optical parametric amplifier (OPA) was used. The OPA was pumped by a Ti:Al_2O_3 regenerative amplifier. The typical pulse energy of the output pulse was 50 nJ, and the repetition rate was 200 kHz. The full width at half-maximum (FWHM) of the incident pulse width obtained by the SHG autocorrelation trace was 500 fs at the position of the sample. Since the OPA had a wide tunability for the wavelength of the pump pulse, the wavelength was set to the peak wavelength of the surface-plasmon resonance. The typical energy density of the excitation pulse was 33 $\mu J/cm^2$ which corresponds to the power density of 80 MW/cm^2. As a probe pulse, we used part of the output pulse from the OPA. The polarization plane of the pump beam was rotated by $\pi/4$ from that of the probe beam. The nonlinear medium was placed between a polarizer and an analyzer in a cross-Nicol configuration, meaning that the probe beam could not pass through the analyzer without the pump beam. Third-order nonlinearity induced by the pump and probe pulses generated a Kerr signal that passed through the analyzer. The Kerr signal was detected by a photomultiplier tube. To improve the signal-to-noise ratio, the pump and probe beams were chopped in each frequency, $f1$ and $f2$, and the Kerr signal was detected at the sum frequency ($f1 + f2$). All experiments were executed at room temperature (301.5 K).

Figure 7.8 shows an optical density (OD) spectrum of an Au/SiO_2 composite thin film at 301.5 K (solid curve). An absorption peak can be recognized at 2.33 eV along with a slightly increasing background. The origin of the peak is assigned to surface-plasmon resonance. The dotted curve indicates the spectrum of the incident laser pulse used in the experiment. From the spectrum width, the field correlation time of the pulse is determined to be 170 fs, assuming a Gaussian spectrum shape.

Figure 7.9 shows a temporal change of the optical density (ΔOD) at the peak of the surface-plasmon band. ΔT is the time separation between the pump and probe pulses. The temporal behavior is decomposed into a fast

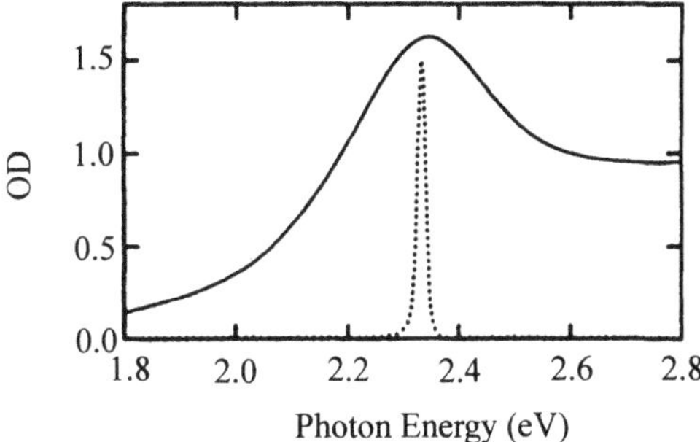

Fig. 7.8. Absorption spectrum (*solid curve*) of the Au nanoparticles in an SiO_2 matrix. The spectrum of the laser pulse used in the experiment is also depicted (*dotted curve*)

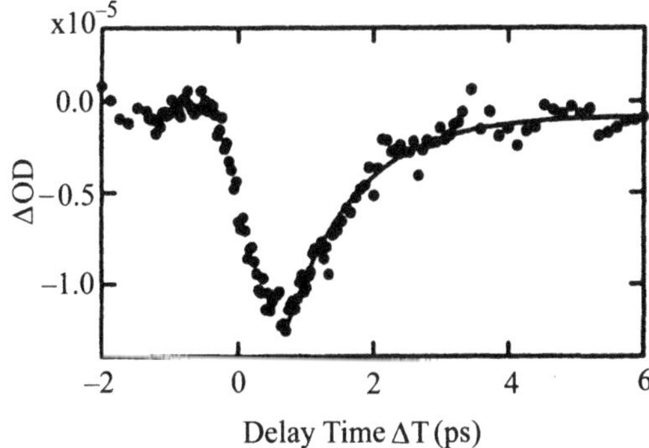

Fig. 7.9. Time evolution of bleaching signal measured at the absorption peak of the surface-plasmon band. The fitting result is also shown

rise component and two decay components, as was described in Sect. 1.4. Decay time constants are obtained by fitting. The best-fit curve is shown in the figure. The fast decay constant is 0.95 ps, and the slow decay constant is more than 100 ps. These time constants have been considered to be nonlinear response times in the gold nanoparticle system. It has already been pointed out that the fast decay component is mainly governed by the thermal equilibrium process between the electron and the lattice systems in the metallic nanoparticle, while the slow decay component originates from a thermal diffusion process from the metal nanoparticle to the host matrix [24]. The time constant of the rise component is also estimated to be 0.6 ps. Taking the FWHM of the incident pulse into account, the rise component is understood to be an integral of the incident pulse.

Figure 7.10 shows the pump power dependence of the observed Kerr signal at $\Delta T = 0$. The intensity of the Kerr signal is proportional to the square of the pump power. This result suggests that the signal is generated through the third-order nonlinear process.

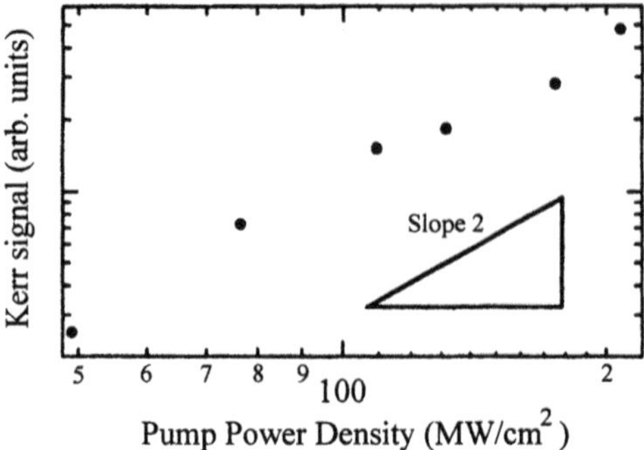

Fig. 7.10. The pump power dependence of the Kerr signal

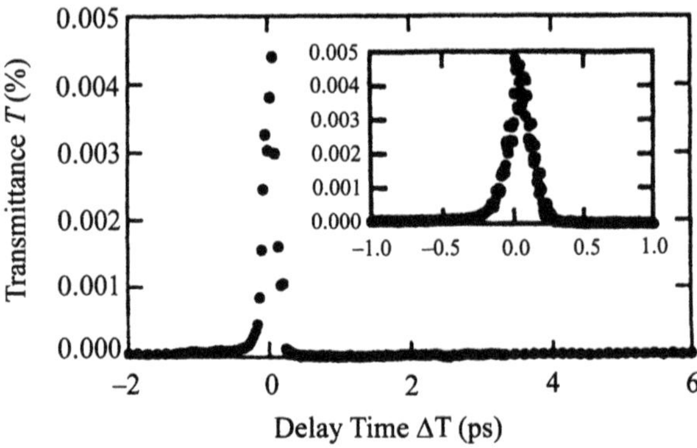

Fig. 7.11. Temporal behavior of the Kerr signal. Inset shows this on a short time scale

The temporal behavior of the observed Kerr signal is shown in Fig. 7.11. The inset shows this on a short time scale. The signal rises and falls suddenly at around $\Delta T = 0$. The FWHM of the Kerr signal is 240 fs. Such a fast response of the Kerr signal seems to be amazing, because the response time is about half the pulse width of the incident pulse, 500 fs. This response time is faster than any other one reported up to now for the gold nanoparticle system.

In order to understand this ultrafast response, a simple model was considered where two laser pulses strike the nonlinear material. When the time separation of the two pulses is within the field correlation time, the pulses interfere with each other. Bleaching of the absorption, due to gold nanoparticles, is induced at the bright part of the interference pattern, which causes a transient grating. The transient grating lasts as long as the bleaching remains, which is shown in Fig. 7.9. The transient grating generated by the interference between two incident beams whose wave vectors are $\boldsymbol{k}_1$ and $\boldsymbol{k}_2$ has the wave number k ($k = k_1 - k_2$). The transient grating diffracts the incident pulse itself to yield a Kerr signal. The incident beam with the wave vector of $\boldsymbol{k}_1$ is diffracted, by the transient grating, in the directions $k_1 \pm k$, k_2 and $2k_1 - k_2$. Since the pump beam has the wave vector $\boldsymbol{k}_1$, part of the pump beam is diffracted in the direction of the wave vector $\boldsymbol{k}_2$. Because the polarization plane of the pump beam is rotated by $\pi/4$ from that of the probe beam, half of the diffracted pump beam can pass through the analyzer and is observed as a Kerr signal.

In this model, the Kerr signal is observed when the time separation ΔT is within the field correlation time. An attempt was made to measure the field correlation time of the incident laser pulses. The FWHM of the field correlation was found to be 230 ± 20 fs. This time constant is equal to the response time of the observed Kerr signal. This result means that our model gives a good account of the ultrafast response of the Kerr signal.

From the diffraction efficiencies of the Kerr signal, the nonlinear susceptibility, $\chi^{(3)}$, can be estimated through comparison with the efficiency of CS_2, to be as follows [52]:

$$\chi^{(3)} = \chi^{(3)}_{CS_2} \sqrt{\frac{I}{I_{CS_2}} \frac{n^2}{n^2_{CS_2}}} d_{CS_2} \frac{\alpha \exp(\alpha d/2)}{1 - \exp(-\alpha d)} , \tag{7.3}$$

where I and I_{CS_2} are the diffraction efficiencies, n and n_{CS_2} are the linear refractive indices, and d and d_{CS_2} are the thicknesses of the sample and the reference material CS_2. α is the absorption coefficient at the surface-plasmon peak of the gold nanoparticle system. A value of 2×10^{-12} esu was used for $\chi^{(3)}_{CS_2}$ [341]. The index of refraction n was taken to be the same as that of glass, 1.5, because the volume fraction of gold nanoparticles is small. From (7.3), a value of 2.0×10^{-8} esu was obtained $\chi^{(3)}$. This value is much smaller than the value obtained in the nanosecond region. As pointed out before [24], the nonlinearity in the nanosecond region is mainly governed by the thermal effect. It is suggested that the apparent nonlinearity is large in the nanosecond region because the thermal effect increases in proportion to the incident pulse area due to the accumulation effect inside the incident laser pulse. It is considered that the thermal effect is negligible in the femtosecond region. Therefore, the value of the nonlinear susceptibility obtained should be more close to the real value.

References

1. Myers R. A., Mukherjee N., Brueck S. R. J., Opt. Lett. 16, 1732 (1991).
2. Snitzer E., Phys. Rev. Lett. 7, 444 (1961).
3. Hirao K., Ceramics 30, 689 (1996) in Japanese.
4. Davis K. M., Miura K., Sugimoto N., Hirao K., Opt. Lett. 21, 1729 (1996).
5. Miura K., Qiu J., Inouye H., Mitsuyu T., Hirao K., Appl. Phys. Lett. 71, 3329 (1997).
6. Qiu J., Miura K., Inouye H., Kondo Y., Mitsuyu T., and Hirao K., Appl. Phys. Lett. 73, 1763 (1998).
7. Kondo Y., Suzuki T., Inouye H., Miura K., Mitsuyu T., Hirao K., Jpn. J. Appl. Phys. 37, L94 (1998).
8. Qiu J., Miura K., Hirao K., Jpn. J. Appl. Phys. 37, 2263 (1998).
9. Qiu J., Kojima K., Miura K., Mitsuyu T., Hirao K, Opt. Lett. 24, 786 (1999).
10. Qiu J., Miura K., Suzuki T., Mitsuyu T., and Hirao K., Appl. Phys. Lett. 74, 10 (1999).
11. Si J., Kitaoka K., Qiu J., Mitsuyu T., Hirao K., Opt. Lett. 24, 911 (1999).
12. Kondo Y., Qiu J., Mitsuyu T., Hirao K., Jpn. J. Appl. Phys. 38, 212 (1999).
13. Miura K., Qiu J., Mitsuyu T., Hirao K., Opt. Lett. 25, 408 (2000).
14. Hill K. O., Fujii Y., Johnson D. C., and Kawasaki B. S., Appl. Phys. Lett. 32, 647 (1978).
15. Partovi A., Erdogan T., Mizrahi V., Lemaire P. L., Glass A. M., and Fleming J. W., Appl. Phys. Lett. 64, 821 (1994).
16. Österberg U. and Margulis W., Opt. Lett. 11, 516 (1986).
17. Fujiwara T., Wong D., Zhao Y., Fleming S., Pool S., and Sceats M., Electron. Lett. 31, 573 (1995).
18. Kitaoka K., Si J., Mitsuyu T., Hirao K., J. Ceram. Soc. Jpn. 107, 522 (1999).
19. Sugimoto N., Kanbara H., Fujiwara S., Tanaka K., Hirao K., Opt. Lett. 21, 1637 (1996).
20. Hirao K., Todoroki S., Cho D. H., and Soga N., Opt. Lett. 18, 1586 (1993).
21. Qiu J., Shimizukawa Y., Iwabuchi Y., and Hirao K., Appl. Phys. Lett. 71, 43 (1997).
22. Hirao K., Todoroki S., Soga N., J. Non-Cryst. Solids 143, 40 (1992).
23. Kanbara H., Fujiwara S., Tanaka K., Nasu H., Hirao K., Appl. Phys. Lett. 70, 925 (1997).
24. Inouye H., Tanaka K., Tanahashi I., Hirao K., Phys. Rev. B 57, 11334 (1998).
25. Kanbara H., Fujiwara S., Tanaka K., Hirao K., J. Phys. Chem. A 102, 674 (1998).
26. Kazansky Peter G., Inouye H., Mitsuyu T., Miura K., Qiu J., Hirao K., Phys. Rev. Lett. 82, 2199 (1999).
27. Hall D. W., Newhouse M. A., Borrelli N. F., Dumbaugh W. H., Weildman D. L., Appl. Phys. Lett. 54,1293 (1989).
28. Nasu H., Ibara Y., Kubodera K., J. Non-Cryst. Solids 110, 229 (1989).

29. Nasu H., Uchigaki T., Kamiya K., Kanmara H., Kubodera K., Jpn. Appl. Phys. 31, 3899 (1992).
30. Nasu H., Matsuoka J., Kamiya K., J. Non-Cryst. Solids 178, 23 (1994).
31. Miyaji F., Tadanaga K., Sakka S., Appl. Phys. Lett. 60, 2060 (1992).
32. Asobe M., Kanamori T., Kubodera K., IEEE Photon. Technol. Lett. 4, 362 (1992).
33. Meredith G. R., Buchalter B., Hanzlik C. J., Chem. Phys. 78, 1533 (1983).
34. Nasu H., Kubodera K., Kobayashi M., Nakamura M., Kamiya K., J. Am. Ceram. Soc. 73, 1794 (1990).
35. Kobayashi H., Kanbara H., Koga M., Kubodera K., J. Appl. Phys. 74, 3683 (1993).
36. Miyaji F., Yoko T., Jin J., Sakka S., Fukunaga T., Misawa M., J. Non-Cryst. Solids 175, 211 (1994).
37. Ippen E. P., Shank C. V., Appl. Phys. Lett. 26, 92 (1975).
38. Kubodera K., Kobayashi H., Mol. Cryst. Liq. Cryst. A 182, 103 (1990).
39. Chang T. Y., Opt. Eng. 20, 220 (1981).
40. Agrawal G. P., Cojan C., Flytzanis C., Phys. Rev. B 17, 776 (1978).
41. Close D. H., Giuliano C. R., Hellwarth R. W., Hess L. D., McClung F. J., Wagner W. G., IEEE J. Quantum Electron. QE-2, 553 (1966).
42. Kanbara H., Kobayashi H., Kaino T., Kurihana T., Ooba N., Kubodera K., J. Opt. Soc. Am. B 11, 2216 (1994).
43. Heflin J. R., Cai Y. M., Garito A. F., J. Opt. Soc. Am. B 8, 2132 (1991).
44. Mito A., Hagimoto K., Takahashi C., Nonlinear Opt. 13, 3 (1995).
45. Van de Hulst H. C.: *Light Scattering by Small Particles* (Dover Publications Inc., New York, 1981).
46. Tanahashi I., Manabe Y., Tohda T., Sasaki S., Nakamura A., J. Appl. Phys. 79, 1244 (1996).
47. Hache F., Ricard D., Flytzanis C., Kreibig U., Appl. Phys. A 47, 347 (1988).
48. Ruppin R., J. Appl. Phys. 59, 1355 (1986).
49. Tokizaki T., Nakamura A., Kaneko S., Uchida K., Omi S., Tanji H., Asahara Y., Appl. Phys. Lett. 65, 941 (1994).
50. Schoenlein R. W., Lin W. Z., Fujimoto J. G., Eesley G. L., Phys. Rev. Lett. 58, 1680 (1987).
51. Anisimov S. I., Kapeliovich B. L., Perel'man T. L., Sov. Phys. JETP 39, 375 (1975).
52. Puech K., Blau W., Grund A., Bubeck C., Cardenas G., Opt. Lett. 20, 1613 (1995).
53. Perner M., Bost P., Lemmer U., von Plessen G., Feldmann J., Becker U., Mennig M., Schmitt M., Schmidt H., Phys. Rev. Lett. 78, 2192 (1997).
54. Bloemer M. J., Haus J. W., Ashley P. R., J. Opt. Soc. Am. B 7, 790 (1990).
55. Bigot J.-Y., Merle J.-C., Cregut O., Daunois A., Phys. Rev. Lett. 75, 4702 (1995).
56. Fann W. S., Storz R., Tom H. W. K., Bokor J., Phys. Rev. Lett. 68, 2834 (1992).
57. Bansal Narottam P., Doremus R. H., *Handbook of Glass Properties* (Academic, New York, 1986) Chap. 2.
58. Nisoli M., Silvestri S. De, Cavalleri A., Malvezzi A. M., Stella A., Lanzani G., Cheyssac P., Kofman R., Phys. Rev. B 55, R13, 424 (1997).
59. Pines D., Nozieres P., *The Theory of Quantum Liquid* (Benjamin, New York, 1966) Vol. 1.
60. Zhou H. S., Honma I., Komiyama H., Haus J. W., Phys. Rev. B 50, 12052 (1994).

61. Yang L., Osborne D. H., Haglund R. F., Jr., Magruder R. H., White C. W., Zuhr R. A., Hosono H., Appl. Phys. A: Mater. Sci. Process. 62, 403 (1996).
62. Townsend P. D., Jackel J. L., Baker G. L., Shelburne J. A., III, Etemad, S. Appl. Phys. Lett. 55, 1829 (1989).
63. Prasad P. N., Williams D. J., *Introduction to Nonlinear Optical Effects in Molecules and Polymers* (Wiley: New York, 1991).
64. Kim D. Y., Sundheimer M., Otomo A., Stegeman G., Horsthuis W. H. G., Mohlmann G. R., Appl. Phys. Lett. 63, 290 (1993).
65. Kanbara H., Kobayashi H., Kaino T., Ooba N., Kurihara T., J. Phys. Chem. 98, 12270 (1994).
66. Gomes A. S. L., Demenicis L., Petrov D. V., Araujo C. B., Melo C. P., Souto-Maior R., Appl. Phys. Lett. 69, 2166 (1996).
67. Hattori T., Kobayashi T. J., Chem. Phys. 94, 3332 (1991).
68. Greene B. I., Farrow R. C., Chem. Phys. Lett. 98, 273 (1983).
69. Lotshaw W. T., McMorrow D., Kalpouzos C., Kenney-Wallace G. A., Chem. Phys. Lett. 136, 323 (1987).
70. Wegner P. J., Auerbach J. M., Barker C. E., Brading K. R., Britten J. A., Burkhart S. C., Caird J. A., Dixit S. N., Feru P., Henesian M. A., Hibbard R. L., Kozlowski M. R., Milam D., Murray J. E., Norton M. A., Rothenberg J. E., Weiland T. L., Williams W. H., Winters S. E., Van Wonterghem B. M., Zacharias R. A., in *Proceedings of the Conference on Lasers and Electro-Optics* (Optical Society of America, Washington, DC, 1998) No. CThE1.
71. Optical Fiber Communications III, ed. by Kaminov I., Koch T. (Academic Press, Boston, MA, 1997).
72. Snitzer E., J. Appl. Phys. 32, 36 (1961).
73. Friebele E. J., Griscom D. L., in *Defect in Glasses*, ed. by Galeener F. L., Griscom D. L., Weber M. L. (Material Research Society, Pittsburgh, PA, 1985) Vol. 61, pp. 319.
74. Hill K. O., et al., Annu. Rev. Mater. Sci. 23, 125 (1993).
75. Hosono H., Abe Y., Kinser D. L., Weeks R. A., Muta K., Kawazoe H., Phys. Rev. B 46, 11445 (1992).
76. Kohketsu M., Awazu K., Kawazoe H., Yamane M., Jpn. J. Appl. Phys. 28, 622 (1989).
77. Skuja L. N., Trukhin A. N., Plaudis A. E., Phys. Status Solidi A 84, K153 (1984).
78. Duval Y., Kashyap R., Fleming S., Ouellette F., Appl. Phys. Lett. 61, 2955 (1992).
79. Mizrahi V., Atkins R. M., Electron. Lett. 28, 2210 (1992).
80. Russell P. St. J., Archambault J.-L., Reekie L., Phys. World 6, 41 (1993).
81. Stolen R. H. and Tom H. W. K., Opt. Lett. 12, 585 (1987).
82. Margulis W., Laurell F., Lesche B., Nature (Lond.) 378, 699 (1995).
83. Dianov E. M., Kazansky P. G., and Stepanov D. Yu., Sov. J. Quantum Electron. 19, 575 (1989).
84. Yin Y. Y., Chen C., Elliot D. S., Smith A. V., Phys. Rev. Lett. 69, 2353 (1992).
85. Dupont E., Corkum P. B., Liu H. C., Buchanan M., Wasilevski Z. R., Phys. Rev. Lett. 74, 3596 (1995).
86. Atanasov R., Hache H., Hughes J. L. P., van Dreil H. M., Sipe J. E., Phys. Rev. Lett. 76, 1703 (1996).
87. Kazansky P. G., Pruneri V., Phys. Rev. Lett. 78, 2956 (1997).
88. Awazu K., Kawazoe H., Yamane M., J. Appl. Phys. 68, 2713 (1990).
89. Yang B., Schafer K. J., Walker B., Kulander K. C., Agostini P., DiMauro L. F., Phys. Rev. Lett. 71, 3770 (1993).

90. Helm H., Bjerre N., Dyer M. J., Huestis D. L., Saeed M., Phys. Rev. Lett. 70, 3221 (1993).
91. Si J., Kondo Y., Qiu J., Kitaoka K., Sugimoto N., Mitsuyu T., Hirao K., Opt. Commun. 180, 179 (2000).
92. Kitaoka K., Si J., Mitsuyu T., Hirao K., Appl. Phys. Lett. 75, 157 (1999).
93. Griscom D. L., in *Glass Science and Technology*, Vo1. 4B of *Advances in Structural Analysis*, ed. by D. R. Uhlmann and N. J. Kreidl (Academic, New York, 1990) pp. 197–223.
94. Weeks R. A., Sonder E., in *Proceedings of the Symposium on Paramagnetic Resonance* (Academic, New York, 1963) Vol. 2, p. 869.
95. Nelson C. M., Weeks R. A., J. Am. Ceram. Soc. 43, 396 (1960).
96. Devine R. A. B., Fiori C., Robertson J., in *Defects in Glasses*, ed. by Galeener F. L., Griscom D. L., and Weber M. J. (Materials Research Society, Pittsburgh, PA., 1986) pp. 177.
97. Tohmon R., Mizuno H., Ohki Y., Sasagane K., Nagawawa K., Hama Y., Phys. Rev. B 39, 1337 (1989).
98. Hand D. P., Russell P. St. J., Opt. Lett. 15, 102 (1990).
99. Williams D. L., Davey S. T., Kashyap R., Armitage J. R., Ainslie B. J., Appl. Phys. Lett. 59, 762 (1991).
100. Poumellec B., Niay P., Douay M., Bayon J. F., in *Photosensitivity and Quadratic Nonlinearity in Glass Waveguides: Fundamentals and Applications*, Vol. 22 of *1995 OSA Technical Digest Series* (Optical Society of America, Washington, DC, 1995) pp. 112.
101. Paillard E., *Proc. EFOC/LAN '87* (1987) Vol. 108.
102. Kawachi M., Workshop Digest '94 *Asia-Pacific Microwave Conference* (1994), Vol. 39.
103. Stookey S. D., Ind. Eng. Chem. 45, 115 (1953).
104. Maurer R. D., J. Appl. Phys. 29, 1 (1958).
105. Stookey S. D., Ind. Eng. Chem. 41, 856 (1949).
106. Stookey S. D., Schuler F. W., *IV Int. Congress on Glass* (Imprimerie Chaix, Paris, 1957) pp. 390.
107. Tantaka K., Hirao K., Tanaka H., Soga N., Jpn. J. Appl. Phys. 35, 2170 (1996).
108. Qiu J., Sugimoto N., Iwabuchi Y., Hirao K., J. Non-Cryst. Solids 209, 200 (1997).
109. Kingery W. D., Bowen H. K., Uhlmann D. R., *Introduction to Ceramics* (John Wiley & Sons, New York, 1976) pp. 320.
110. Ohtaka K., Phys. Rev. B 19, 5057 (1979).
111. Yablonovitch E., Phys. Rev. Lett. 58, 2059 (1987).
112. Peter F. M. and Zewail A. H., Phys. Rev. Lett. 53, 501 (1984).
113. Felker M. P., and Zewail A. H., Phys. Chem. 91, 754 (1987).
114. Rischel C. et al., Nature 390, 490 (1997).
115. Glezer E.N., Milosavljevic M., Huang L., Finalay R. J., Her T.-H., Callan J. P., and Mazur E., Opt. Lett. 21, 2023 (1996)
116. Hirao K. and Miura K., J. Non-Cryst. Solids 239, 91 (1998).
117. Qiu J., Miura K., Inouye H., Nishii J., Hirao K., Nucl. Instrum. Meth. Phys. Res. B 141, 699 (1998).
118. Stuart B. C., Feit M. D., Rubenchik A. M., Shore B. W., Perry M. D., Phys. Rev. Lett. 74, 2248 (1995).
119. Anderson D. Z., Mizrahi V., and Sipe J. E., Opt. Lett. 16, 796 (1991).
120. Charra F., Kajzar F., Nunzi J. M., Paimond P., and Idiart E., Opt. Lett. 18, 941 (1993).
121. Dominic V. and Feinberg J., Phys. Rev. Lett. 71, 3446 (1993).
122. Kyung J. H. and Lawandy N. M., Opt. Lett. 21, 186 (1996).

123. Kyung J. H. and Lawandy N. M., Opt. Lett. 21, 632 (1996).
124. Tsai T. E., Saifi M. A., Friebele E. J., Griscom D. L., and Österberg U., Opt. Lett. 14, 1023 (1989).
125. Krol D. M., DiGiovanni D. J., Pleibel W., and Stolen R. H., Opt. Lett. 18, 1220 (1993).
126. Krol D. M. and Stepanov D. Yu., CLEO '94, Summ. Papers Present. Conf. Lasers Electro-Opt. 18, 397 (1994).
127. Nageno Y., Kyung J. H., and Lawandy N. M., Opt. Lett. 20, 2180 (1995).
128. Hosono H., Mizuguchi M., Kawazoe H., and Nishii J., Jpn. J. Appl. Phys. 35, Part 2, 234 (1996).
129. Hibino Y., Mizrahi V., Stegeman G. I., Sudo S., Appl. Phys. Lett. 57, 656 (1990).
130. Nishii J., Fukumi K., Yamanaka H., Kawamura K., Hosono H., and Kawazoe H., Phys. Rev. B 52, 1661 (1995).
131. Hosono H., Kawazoe H., and Nishii J., Phys. Rev. B 53, 11921 (1996).
132. Sugimoto N., Kanbara H., Fujiwara S., Tanaka K., Shimizugawa Y., and Hirao K., J. Opt. Soc. Am. B 16, 1904 (1999).
133. Rodenberger D. C., Heflin J. R., and Garito A. F., Phys. Rev. A 51, 3234 (1995).
134. Si J., Kitaoka K., Mitsuyu T., and Hirao K., Appl. Phys. Lett. 75, 307 (1999).
135. Shuto Y., Tanaka H., Amano M., Kaino T., Jpn. J. Appl. Phys. 28, 2508 (1989).
136. Girton D. G., Kwiatkowski S. L., LipScomb G. F., Lytel R. S., Appl. Phys. Lett. 58, 1730 (1991).
137. Mortazavi M. A., Knoesen A., Kowel S. T., Higgins B. G., and Dienes A., J. Opt. Soc. Am. B 6, 733 (1989).
138. Ore. F. R. Jr., Hayden L. M., Sauter C. F., Pasillas P. L., Hoover J. M., Henry R. A., Lindsay G. A., in *Proceedings of SPIE-Int. Soc. Opt. Eng., Nonlinear Optical Properties of Organic Materials, II, Vol. 1147, San Diego, CA,* August 10–11, 1989 (SPIE, San Diego, 1990) pp. 26–35.
139. Singer K. D., Sohn J. E., Lalama S. J., Appl. Phys. Lett. 49, 248 (1986).
140. Sugihara O., Furukubo M., Hayashi H., Okamoto N., Nonlinear Opt. 14, 251 (1995).
141. Nakayama H., Sugihara O., Fujimura H., Mastushima R., Okamoto N., Opt. Rev. 2, 236 (1995).
142. Dominic V., Lambelet P., Feinberg J., Opt. Lett. 20, 444 (1995).
143. Chalupczak W., Fiorini C., Charra F., Nunzi J-M., and Raimond P., Opt. Commum. 126, 103 (1996).
144. Charra F., Devaux F., Nunzi J.-M., and Raimond P., Phys. Rev. Lett. 68, 2440 (1992).
145. Fiorini C., Charra F., Raimond P., Lorin A., and Nunzi J. M., Opt. Lett. 22, 1846 (1997).
146. Si J., Xu G., Liu X., Yang Q., Ye P., Li Z., Ma H., Shen Y., Zhang J., Zhai J., Opt. Commun. 142, 71 (1997).
147. Si J., Mitsuyu T., Ye P., Shen Y., Hirao K., Appl. Phys. Lett. 7.2, 762 (1998).
148. Izawa K., Okamoto N., Sugihara O., Jpn. J. Appl. Phys., 32, Part 1, 807 (1993).
149. Kurtz S. K., in *Quantum Electronics*, ed. by H. Rabin and C. L. Tang, (Academic, New York, 1975) pp. 209–81.
150. Palik E. D., *Handbook of Optical Constants*, (Academic Press, Orlando, FL, 1985).
151. Nakanishi M., Sugihara O., Okamoto N., Hirota K., Appl. Opt. 37, 1068 (1998).

152. Si J., Kitaoka K., Mitsuyu T., Ye P., Hirao K., J. Appl. Phys. 85, 8018 (1999).
153. Nouchi K., Watanabe H., Muta K., Mitsuyu T., Hirao K., Opt. Commun. 168, 233 (1999).
154. Qiu J., Shimizugawa Y., Iwabuchi Y., Hirao K., Appl. Phys. Lett. 71, 759 (1997).
155. Qiu J., Shimizugawa Y., Sugimoto N., Hirao K., J. Non-Cryst. Solids 222, 290 (1997).
156. Qiu J., Hirao K., Solid State Commun. 106, 795 (1998).
157. Qiu J., Kawasaki M., Tanaka K., Shimizugawa Y., Hirao K., J. Phys. Chem. Solids 59, 1521 (1998).
158. Qiu J., Miura K., Nouchi K., Suzuki T., Kondo Y., Mitsuyu T., Hirao K., Solid State Commun. 113, 341 (2000).
159. Jaaniso R., Bill H., Europhys. Lett. 16, 569 (1991).
160. Kodama N., Takahashi T., Hirao K., Appl. Phys. Lett. 72, 1548 (1998).
161. Kurita A., Kushida T., Izumitani T., Matsukawa M., Opt. Lett. 19, 314 (1994).
162. Nogami M., Abe Y., Hirao K., Cho D. H., Appl. Phys. Lett. 66, 2952 (1995).
163. Cho D. H., Hirao K., Fujita K., Soga N., J. Am. Ceram. Soc. 79, 327 (1996).
164. Arai K., Namikawa H., Kumata K., Honda T., J. Appl. Phys. 59, 3430 (1986).
165. Miyahara J., Kotaibutsuri (Phys. Solid State) 30, 674 (1995) in Japanese.
166. Amemiya Y., Miyahara J., Nature (London) 336, 89 (1988).
167. Qiu J., Miura K., Sugimoto N., Hirao K., J. Non-Cryst. Solids 213–214, 266 (1997).
168. Iwabuchi Y., Mori N., Takahashi K., Matsuda T., Shionoya S., Jpn. J. Appl. Phys. Part 1 33, 178 (1994).
169. Lakshamanan A. R., Phys. Status Solidi A 3, 153 (1996).
170. Takahashi K., Miyahara J., Shibahara Y., J. Electrochem. Soc. 132, 1492 (1985).
171. Hangleiter T., Koschnick F. K., Spaeth J. M., Eachus R. S., Radiat. Eff. 119, 615 (1991).
172. Seggern H. V., Voigt T., Knupfer W., Lange G., J. Appl. Phys. 64, 1405 (1988).
173. Harrison A., Harrison M. T., Keogh G. P., Templer R. H., Wills A. S., Phys. Rev. B 53, 5039 (1996).
174. Miyahara J., Kato H., OoyoButsuri (Appl. Phys.) 53, 884 (1984) in Japanese.
175. Galimov P. G., Karapetyan G. O., Detrovskii G. T., Tsurikova G. A., Yudin D. M., Izv. Akad. NaJuk. SSSR Neorg. Mat. 5, 1807 (1969).
176. Levin K. H., Tran D. C., Ginther R. J., Sigel G. H., Jr., Glass Technol. 24, 143 (1983).
177. Yokota R., in *Glass Handbook*, ed. by Sakka S., Sakaino T., Takahashi K., (Asakura Press, Tokyo, 1975) pp. 826, in Japanese.
178. Qiu J., Hirao K., O Plus E 203, 118 (1996) in Japanese.
179. Ohishi Y., Kanamori T., Kitayama T. , Takahashi S., Opt. Lett. 16, 1747 (1991).
180. Mitsunaga M., Yano R., Uesugi N., Opt. Lett. 16, 1890 (1991).
181. Shafer M. W. and Suit J. C., J. Am. Ceram. Soc. 49, 261 (1966).
182. Qiu J., Tanaka K., and Hirao K., J. Am. Ceram. Soc. 80, 2696 (1997).
183. Cohen A. J., Smith H. L., Science 336, 89 (1962).
184. Matsuzawa T., Aoki Y., Takeuchi N., Murayama Y., J. Electrochem. Soc. 143, 2670 (1996).
185. Nakazawa E., in *Handbook of Phosphors*, ed. by Keikoutai Dougakukai (Ohm Press, Tokyo, 1987) pp. 138, in Japanese.
186. Yamamoto A., in *Handbook of Phosphors*, ed. by Keikoutai Dougakukai (Ohm Press, Tokyo, 1987) pp. 138, in Japanese.
187. Hosono H., Yamazaki Y., Abe Y., J. Am. Ceram. Soc. 70, 867 (1987).

188. Nakata R., Hashimoto N., Kawano K., Jpn. J. Appl. Phys. 35, L90 (1996).
189. Kanou T., in *Handbook of Phosphors*, ed. by Keikoutai Dougakkai (Ohm Press, Tokyo 1987) pp. 117, in Japanese.
190. Feit M. D., Rubenchik A. M., Shore B. W., Perry M. D., Phys. Rev. Lett. 74, 2248 (1995).
191. Kushida T., in *Optical Physics* (Asakura Press, Tokyo, 1992) pp. 176, in Japanese.
192. Parthenopoulos D. A., Rentepis P. M., Science 245, 843 (1990).
193. Tamai N., Masuhara H., Chem. Phys. Lett. 191, 189 (1992).
194. Yanagimachi M., Tamai N., Masuhara H., Chem. Phys. Lett. 201, 115 (1993).
195. Herek J. L., Pedersen S., Banares L., Zewail A. H., J. Chem. Phys. 97, 353 (1992).
196. Pedersen S., Banares L., Zewail A. H., J. Chem. Phys. 97, 8801 (1992).
197. Fhundkar L. R., Zewail A. H., J. Chem. Phys. 92, 231 (1990).
198. Kanou T., in *Handbook of Phosphors*, ed. by Keikoutaidogakukai (Ohm Press, Tokyo, 1987) pp. 110, in Japanese.
199. MacFarlane D. R., Newman P. J., Cashion J. D., Edgar A., in *Extended Abstracts of the 11th International Symposium on Now-Oxide and New Optical Glasses* (Sheffield University, Sheffield, UK, 1998) pp. 33.
200. Griscom D. L., Friebele E. J., in *Fluoride Glass*, ed. by Comyns A. E. (Wiley, New York, 1989) pp. 307.
201. Efimov O. M., Gabel K., Garnov S. V., Glebov L. B., Grantham S., Richardson M., Soileau M. J., J. Opt. Soc. Am. B 15, 193 (1998).
202. Hirao K., J. Non-Cryst. Solids 196, 16 (1995).
203. Nakagawa K., in *Glass Dictionary*, ed. by Sakka S. (Asakura, Tokyo, 1985) pp. 362, in Japanese.
204. Kishimoto S., Hirao K., J. Non-Cryst. Solids 213–214, 393 (1997).
205. Shimizugawa Y, Qiu J., Hirao K., J. Non-Cryst. Solids, 222, 310 (1997).
206. Hirao K., Kishimoto S., Tanaka K., Tanabe S., Soga N., J. Non-Cryst. Solids 139, 151 (1992).
207. Tanabe S., Hirao K., Soga N., J. Non-Cryst. Solids 122, 79 (1990).
208. Allain J. Y., Monerie M., Poignant H., Electron. Lett. 26. 166 (1990).
209. Oomen E. W. J. L., J. Non-Cryst. Solids 140, 150 (1992).
210. Hirao K., Tanabe S., Kishimoto S., Tamai K., Soga N., J. Non-Cryst. Solids 135, 90 (1991).
211. Kishimoto S., Hirao K., J. Appl. Phys. 80, 1965 (1996).
212. Zemon S., et al., SPIE Fiber Laser Sources Amplifiers II 1373, 21 (1990).
213. Cho D. H., Hirao K., Soga N., J. Non-Cryst. Solids 189, 181 (1995).
214. Teo B. K., Lee P. A., J. Am. Chem. Soc. 101, 2815 (1979).
215. Cho D. H., Hirao K., Tanaka K., Soga N., J. Lumin. 68, 171 (1996).
216. Hill K. O., Malo B., Bilodeau F., Johnson D. C., Albert J., Appl. Phys. Lett. 62, 1035 (1993).
217. Galeenar F. L. and Geissberger A. E., Phys. Rev. B 27, 6199 (1983).
218. Devine R. A. B., J. Vac. Sci. Technol. A 6, 3154 (1988)
219. Born M. and Wolf E., in *Principles of Optics*, 6th edn. (Pergamon, New York, 1983) pp. 88.
220. Uchino T. and Yoko T., Science 273, 480 (1996).
221. Wyckoff R. W. G., *Crystal Structures*, Vol. 1 (Interscience, New York, 1963).
222. DiStefano T. H., Eastman D.E., Phys. Rev. Lett. 27 (1971) 1560;
223. Fischer B., Pollak R.A., DiStefano T.H., Grobman W.D., Phys. Rev. B 15, 3193 (1977).
224. Stephenson D.A., Binkowski N.J., J. Non-Cryst. Solids 22, 399 (1976).
225. Wiech G., Solid State Commun. 52, 803 (1984).

226. Wiech G., Kurmaev E. Z., J. Phys. C 18, 4393 (1985).
227. Tossell J.A., Vaughan D.J., Johnson K.H., Chem. Phys. Lett. 20, 329 (1973).
228. Pantelides S.T., W.A. W.A., Phys. Rev. B 13, 2667 (1976).
229. Ciraci S., Batra I.P., Phys. Rev. B 15, 1923 (1977).
230. Chelikowsky J.R., Schluter M., Phys. Rev. B 15, 4020 (1977).
231. Chelikowsky J.R., Schluter M., Solid State Commun. 21, 381 (1977).
232. Schneider P.M., Fowler W.B., Phys. Rev. Lett. 36, 425 (1976).
233. Schneider P.M., Fowler W.B., Phys. Rev. B 18, 7122 (1978).
234. Calabrese E., Fowler W.B., Phys. Rev. B 18, 2888 (1978).
235. Nucho R.N., Madhukar A., Phys. Rev. B 21, 1576 (1980).
236. O'Reilly E.P., Robertson J., Phys. Rev. B 27, 3780 (1983).
237. Rudra J.K., Fowler W.B., Phys. Rev. B 28, 1061 (1983).
238. Gupta R.P., Phys. Rev. B 32, 8278 (1985).
239. Li Y.P., Ching W.Y., Phys. Rev. B 31, 2172 (1985).
240. Cherlov G.B., Friedman S.P., Kurmaev E.Z., Viech G., Gubanov V.A., J. Non-Cryst. Solids 94, 276 (1987).
241. Xu Y.N., Ching W.Y., Phys. Rev. B 44, 11048 (1991).
242. Simunek A., Vackar J., Wiech G., J. Phys.: Condens. Matter 5, 867 (1993).
243. Tanaka I., Kawai J., Adachi H., Phys. Rev. B 52, 11733 (1995).
244. Laughlin R.B., Joannopoulos J.B., Chadi D.J., Phys. Rev. B 20, 5228 (1979).
245. Laughlin R.B., Joannopoulos J.B., Chadi D.J., Phys. Rev. B 21, 5733 (1980).
246. Martinez E., Yndurain F., Phys. Rev, B 24, 5718 (1981).
247. Ching W.Y., Phys. Rev. Lett. 46, 607 (1981).
248. Ching W.Y., Phys. Rev. B 26, 6610 (1982).
249. Ching W.Y., Phys. Rev. B 26, 6622 (1982).
250. Makino Y., Hirao K., Kawamura K., Tanaka I., Adachi H., J. Non-Cryst. Solids 259, 121 (1999).
251. Kawamura K., JCPE, P029.
252. Nosé S., J. Chem. Phys. 81, 511 (1984).
253. Nosé S., M.L. Klein, Molec. Phys. 52, 255 (1984).
254. Anderson H.C., J. Chem. Phys. 72, 2384 (1980).
255. Matsui M., J. Chem. Phys. 91, 489 (1989).
256. Kittel C., *Introduction to Solid State Physics*, 5th edn. (Wiley, New York, 1976).
257. Adachi H., Tsukada M., Satoko C., J. Phys. Soc. Jpn. 45, 875 (1978).
258. Ellis D.E. and Painter G.S., Phys. Rev. B 2, 2887 (1970).
259. *Advances in Quantum Chemistry (Proceedings of the First International Workshop on DV-Xα Method)*, Vol. 29 (Academic, New York, 1997).
260. Marcelli A., Davoli I., Bianconi A., Garcia J., Gargano A., Natoli C. R., Benfatto M., Chiaradia P., Fantoni M., Fritsch E., Calas G., Petiau J., J. Phys. (Paris) Collq. 46 (C-8), 107 (1985).
261. Li D., Bancroft G.M., Kasrai M., Fleet M.E., Feng X.H., Tan K.H., Yang B.X., Solid State Commun. 87, 613 (1993).
262. John S., Phys. Rev. Lett. 58, 2486 (1987).
263. Mekis A., Chen J. C., Kurland I., Fan S., Villeneuve P. R., and Joannopoulos J. D., Phys. Rev. Lett. 77, 3787 (1996).
264. Joannopoulos J. D., Meade R., and Winn J., *Photonic crystals* (Princeton Press, Princeton, NJ, 1995).
265. Inouye H., Hirao Active Glass Project News, No. 2, 23 (1997)
266. Wooten F., *Optical properties of solids* (Academic Press, New York, 1972).
267. Leung K. M., and Liu Y. F., Phys. Rev. Lett. 65, 2646 (1990).
268. Pendry J. B., and MacKinnon A., Phys. Rev. Lett. 69, 2772 (1992).
269. Miura K., Tanaka K., Hirao K., J. Non-Cryst. Solids, 213–214, 276 (1997).

270. Kishimoto S., Hirao K., J. Appl. Phys., 80, 10 (1997).
271. Hayashi M., Sugimoto N., Nasu H., Kamiya K., Fujiwara S., Hirao K., J. Mater. Sci., 33, 4829 (1998).
272. Qiu J., Kanbara H., Nasu H., Hirao K., J. Ceram. Soc. Jpn. 106, 228 (1998).
273. Qiu J., Hirao K., J. Ceram. Soc. Jpn. 106, 290 (1998).
274. Si J., Kitaoka K., Mitsuyu T., Hirao K., Jpn. J. Appl. Phys. 38, L390 (1998).
275. Kondo Y., Nouchi K., Watanabe S., Kazanski P. G., Mitsuyu T., Hirao K., Opt. Lett. 24, 646 (1999).
276. Richtmyer R.D., J. Appl. Phys. 10, 391 (1939).
277. Garrett C.G.B., W. Kaiser W., Bond W.L., Phys. Rev. 124, 1807 (1961).
278. Tzeng H.M., Wall K.F., Long M.B., R.K. Chang R.K., Opt. Lett. 9, 499 (1984).
279. Lin H.-B., Huston A.L., B.L. Justus B.L., Campillo A.J., Opt. Lett. 11, 614 (1986).
280. Kuwata-Gonokami M., K. Takeda K., H. Yasuda H., Ema K., Jpn. J. Appl. Phys. 31, L99 (1992).
281. Baer T., Opt. Lett. 12, 392 (1987).
282. Wetenkamp L., West G.F., Toebble H., *Ext. Abs. 7th Int. Symp. Halide Glasses* (1991).
283. Layne C. B. Weber M. J, Phys. Rev. B 16. 3259 (1977).
284. Kishimoto S. Fujii K., in *Proc. Ann. Meeting Ceram. Soc. Jpn* (1994) pp. 614.
285. Kishimoto S., Japanese patent, pending.
286. Hirao K., Tamai K., Tanabe S., Soga N., J. Non-Cryst. Solids 160, 261 (1993).
287. Weber M. J., Phys. Rev. 157, 262 (1967).
288. Miyagawa T., Dexter D. L., Phys. Rev. B 1, 2961 (1970).
289. Kido J., Polymer 43, 301 (1994).
290. Nakamura S., Mukai T., Senoh M., Appl. Phys. Lett. 64, 1687 (1994).
291. Yang X. H., Schmidt T. J., Shan W., Song J. J., Goldenburg B., Appl. Phys. Lett. 66, 1 (1995).
292. Colvin V. L., Schlamp M. C., Alivisatos A. P., Nature 370, 354 (1994).
293. Nasu H., Kaneko S., Tsunetomo K., Kamiya K., J. Ceram. Soc. Jpn. 99, 266 (1991).
294. Nasu H., Yamada H., Matsuoka J., Kamiya K., J. Non-Cryst. Solids 183, 290 (1995).
295. Hayashi M., Iwano T., Nasu H., Kamiya K., Sugimoto N., Hirao K., J. Mater. Res. 12, 2552 (1997).
296. Matsuoka J., Kawasaki Y., Nasu H., Kamiya K., Jpn. J. Appl. Phys. 35, 3928 (1996).
297. Nasu H., Tsunetomo K., Tokumitsu Y., Osaka Y., Jpn. J. Appl. Phys. 28, L862 (1989).
298. Hrostowski H. J., in *Semiconductor*, ed. by Hannay N. B. (Reinhold, New York, 1959) pp. 442.
299. Verbiest T., Burland D. M., Jurich M. C., Lee V. Y., Miller R. D., and Volksen W., Science, 268, 1604 (1995).
300. Mandal B. K., Chen Y. M., Lee J. Y., Kumar J., and Tripathy S., Appl. Phys. Lett. 58, 2459 (1991).
301. Eich M., Reck B., Willson C. G., Yoon D. Y., and Blorkland G. C., J. Appl. Phys. 66, 3241, (1989).
302. Shi Y., Steier W. H., Chen M., Yu L., and Dalton L. R., Appl. Phys. Lett. 60, 2577 (1992).
303. Si J., Mitsuyu T., Ye P., Li Z., Shen Y., and Hirao K., Opt. Commun. 147, 313 (1998).

304. Fiorini C., Charra F., Nunzi J. M., Raimond P., J. Opt, Soc. Am. B, 14, 1984 (1997).
305. Jerphagnon J. and Kurtz S. K., Phys. Rev. B 1, 1739 (1970).
306. Kohli J. T., in *Rare Elements in Glasses*, Vols. 94–95, ed. by Shelby J. E. (Trans Tech Pub., Aedermannsdorf, Switzerland, 1994) pp. 125.
307. Borrelli N. F., J. Chem. Phys. 41, 3289 (1964).
308. Berger S. B., Rubinstein C. B., Kurkjian C. R., and Treptow A. W., Phys. Rev. A 133, 723 (1964).
309. Qiu J., Qiu J. B., Higuchi H., Kawamoto Y., and Hirao K., J. Appl. Phys. 80, 5297 (1996).
310. Qiu J., Tanaka K., Sugimoto N., and Hirao K., J. Non-Cryst. Solids 213–214, 193 (1997).
311. Qiu J. and Hirao K., Jpn. J. Appl. Phys. 35, L1677 (1996).
312. Tanaka K., Fujita K., Soga N., Qiu J., and Hirao K., J. Appl. Phys. 28, 840 (1997).
313. Izumitani T., in *Glass Handbook*, ed. by Sakka S., Sakaino T., and Takahashi K. (Asakura Press, Tokyo, 1975) pp. 970–72.
314. Sakamoto K. and Yamashita T., New Glass 10, 34 (1995).
315. Fujino S., Takebe H., and Morinaga K., J. Am. Ceram. Soc. 78, 1179 (1995).
316. Shannon R. D., Acta Crystallogr. A 32, 751 (1976).
317. Meltz G., Morey W.W. and Glentl W.H., Opt. Lett. 14, 823 (1989).
318. Vengsarkar A.M., Pedrazzani J.R., Judkins J.B., Lemaire P.J., Bergano N.S. and Davidson C.R., Opt. Lett. 21, 336 (1996).
319. Johnson D.C., Hill K.O., Bilodeau F. and Faucher S., Electron. Lett. 23, 668 (1987).
320. Bilodeau F., Johnson D.C., Theriault S., Malo B., Albert J. and Hill K.O., IEEE Photonics Technol. Lett. 7, 388 (1995).
321. Hill K.O., Bilodeau F., Malo B., Kitagawa T., Theriault S., Johnson D.C., Albert J. and Takiguchi K., Opt. Lett. 19, 1314 (1994).
322. Bhatia V. and Vengsarkar A.M., Opt. Lett. 21, 692 (1996).
323. Vengsarkar A.M., Lemaire P.J., Judkins J.B., Bhatia V., Erdogan T. and Sipe J.E., J. Lightwave Technol. 14, 58 (1996).
324. Baker S.R., Rourke H.N., Baker V. and Goodchild D., J. Lightwave Technol. 15. 1470 (1997).
325. Akiyama M, Nishide K., Shima K., Wada A. and Yamauchi R., in *Optical Fiber Communication Conference and Exhibit*, Vol. 2 of *1998 OSA Technical Digest Series* (Optical Society of America, Washington, DC, 1998) paper ThG1.
326. Enomoto T., Shigehara M., Ishikawa S., Danzuka T. and Kanamori H., in *Optical Fiber Communication Conference and Exhibit*, Vol. 2 of *1998 OSA Technical Digest Series* (Optical Society of America, Washington, DC, 1998) paper ThG2.
327. Davis D.D., Gaylord T.K.. Glytsis E.N., Kosinski S.G., Mettler S.C. and Vengsarkar A.M., Electron. Lett. 34, 302 (1998).
328. Karpov V.I., Grekov M.V., Dianov E.M., Golant K.M., Vasiliev S.A., Medvedkov O.I. and Khrapko R.R., in *Optical Fiber Communication Conference and Exhibit*, Vol. 2 of *1998 OSA Technical Digest Series* (Optical Society of America, Washington, DC, 1998) paper ThG4.
329. Erdogan T.. Mizrahi V., Lemaire P.J. and Monroe D., J. Appl. Phys. 76, 73 (1994).
330. Tsai T.E., Williams G.M. and Friebele E.J., Opt. Lett. 22. 224 (1997).
331. Bloembergen N., IEEE J. Quantum Electron. QE-10, 375 (1974).
332. Glezer E.N. and Mazur E., Appl. Phys. Lett. 71, 882 (1997).
333. Roy R. and Cohen H.M., Nature (Lond.) 190. 798 (1961).

334. Shima K., Himeno K., Sakai T., Okude S., Wada A. and Yamauchi R., in *Optical Fiber Communication Conference*, Vol. 6 of *1997 OSA Technical Digest Series* (Optical Society of America, Washington, DC, 1997) paper FB2.
335. Fujiwara S., Suzuki T., Sugimoto N., Kanbara H., Hirao K. J. Non-Cryst. Solids 259, 116 (1999).
336. Inouye H., Tanaka K., Tanahashi I., Hirao K., Jpn. J. Appl. Phys. 37, 1520 (1998).
337. Kanbara H., Sugimoto N., Fujiwara S., Hirao K., Opt. Commun. 148, 101 (1998).
338. Sugimoto N., Fujiwara S., Ito S., Suzuki T., Kanbara H., Hirao K., SPIE 3491, 24 (1998).
339. Weiner A.M., Leairird D.E., Patel J.S., Wullert J.R., J. Quantum Electron. 28, 920 (1992).
340. Weiner A.M., Leairird D.E., Wiederrecht G.P., Nelson K.A., Science 247, 1317 (1990).
341. Hellwarth R. W., Pros. Quantum Electron. 5, 1 (1977).

Index

GPSR Compliance
The European Union's (EU) General Product Safety Regulation (GPSR) is a set of rules that requires consumer products to be safe and our obligations to ensure this.

If you have any concerns about our products, you can contact us on

ProductSafety@springernature.com

In case Publisher is established outside the EU, the EU authorized representative is:

Springer Nature Customer Service Center GmbH
Europaplatz 3
69115 Heidelberg, Germany

www.ingramcontent.com/pod-product-compliance
Ingram Content Group UK Ltd.
Pitfield, Milton Keynes, MK11 3LW, UK
UKHW021333070726
13610UKWH00011B/57

* 9 7 8 3 6 6 2 0 4 6 0 4 3 *